GCSE SCIENCE DOUBLE AWARD

PHYSICS

K Foulds

JOHN MURRAY

Other titles in this series:
GCSE Science Double Award Biology ISBN 0 7195 7157 X
GCSE Science Double Award Chemistry ISBN 0 7195 7158 8

First published in 1996 by
John Murray (Publishers) Ltd
50 Albemarle Street
London W1X 4BD

Artwork by Peter Bull Art Studio, Tom Cross, David Farris, Philip Ford, Mike Humphries, Jon Owen/Seacourt Illustration, Tim Smith.
Layouts by Ann Samuel.
Typeset in Rockwell Light and News Gothic by Servis Filmsetting Ltd, Manchester.
Printed and bound in Great Britain by Butler & Tanner Limited, Frome and London.

A CIP catalogue record for this book is available from the British Library.

ISBN 0 7195 7159 6

Contents

1 ENERGY

2 ELECTRICITY

3 FORCES

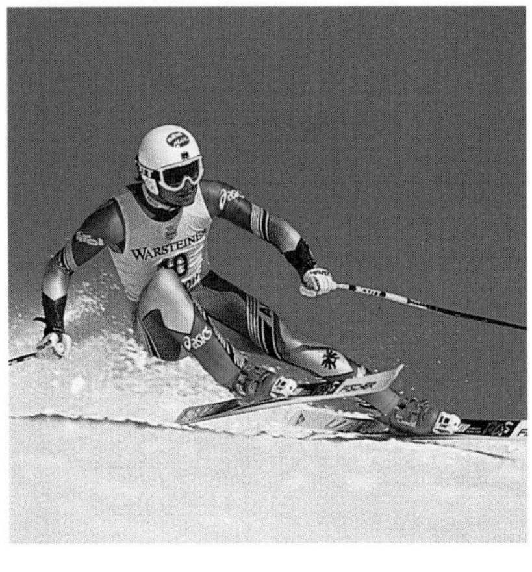

4 RADIATION AND WAVES

To the student

This textbook has been written to help you study physics as part of a science course towards GCSE assessment. It includes details to cover the GCSE syllabus of many examination boards and may provide more detail than you will need for your examination. So you should check carefully with your teacher whether there are any parts that are less relevant to your studies.

The book is divided into four sections, each covering a major theme of physics. Within each section most topics are written at foundation level. You should read these topics fully. The remaining topics are written at a higher level; you may not need to study all of these.

Each topic provides background information and explanation set in different contexts, allowing you to think through the main ideas fully. Exercises draw upon information provided in a topic, so you may answer questions to show an understanding, follow instructions to carry out practical work and investigate your own ideas.

Any book can give only a certain amount of information, so you should try to develop confidence in searching for information from a variety of sources both in and out of school. This textbook provides a stimulus to find out more about physics – use your curiosity to seek out further data, to increase your understanding and to inform your investigations.

Examination questions are given at the end of each section, so you can test your knowledge and understanding on a regular basis. Higher level questions are denoted by a solid bar. The glossary could also be used as a self-test or as a simple reference. Try to read and re-read the relevant topics often so you become familiar with the ideas and learn effectively. Frequent revision will improve your understanding and recall of facts – and this will make further learning easier!

Finally, enjoy your studies. Take time to look around you, think about what you see and how the knowledge and understanding you have gained can help explain what is going on around you. By doing so you will reinforce what you have learnt and begin to appreciate the enormous part that science plays in everyday life.

Acknowledgements

The author wishes to thank his family and friends for their encouragement and support, and the staff at John Murray and Jane Roth for their hard work, during the production of this book.

The authors and publishers are grateful to Mr Vernon Hudson, Senior Teacher and Head of Science at Radcliffe High School, for his advice on the texts of GCSE Science Double Award Physics, Chemistry and Biology.

Exam questions are reproduced by kind permission of:
the Midland Examining Group (MEG);
Northern Examinations and Assessment Board (NEAB);
Southern Examining Group (SEG);
University of London Examinations and Assessment Council (ULEAC);
Welsh Joint Education Committee (WJEC).

The Publishers have made every effort to trace copyright holders, but if they have inadvertently overlooked any they will be pleased to make the necessary arrangements at the earliest opportunity.

Photo credits

Cover: *(centre)* Sand ripples in Monument Valley, Utah, USA; *(left)* Waterfall, Blue Mountains, New South Wales, Australia; *(right)* Antarctic ice formations. All courtesy of ZEFA. **p.iii** *t* Martin Bond/Science Photo Library, *b* Peter Menzel/ Science Photo Library; **p.iv** *t* Shaun Botterill/Allsport, *b* Popperfoto/Reuter; **p.1** Martin Bond/Science Photo Library; **p.2** SmithKline Beecham; **p.4** *t* Rex Features, *c* Allsport, *b* John Cleare/Mountain Camera; **p.8** The Automobile Association; **p.10** Trans World International; **p.12** Last Resort; **p.20** Barnaby's Picture Library; **p.23** Last Resort; **p.24** © Peter Gould; **p.26** Ken Foulds; **p.27** *tl* ETSU/Department of Trade & Industry, *tr* John Hoffmann/Allsport, *b* Stevie Grand/ Science Photo Library, **p.29** Peter Scoones/BBC Natural History Unit; **p.30** Carol Shayle/ICCE; **p.34** *t* Rex Features, *c* Boutin/Robert Harding Picture Library, *b* Geoscience Features, **p.35** Ford Kristo/Planet Earth Pictures; **p.38** National Power plc; **p.40** GEC Alsthom; **p.42** *t* Honda Motor Europe Ltd., *c* Peter Menzel/Science Photo Library, *b* Lowell Georgia/Science Photo Library; **p.44** Rex Features; **p.49** Peter Menzel/Science Photo Library; **p.50** *t* Peter Menzel/ Science Photo Library, *b* Shout Pictures; **p.52** Peter Menzel/ Science Photo Library; **p.53** © Dean and Chapter of York; **p.54** *t* Anglesey Aluminium Metal Ltd., *b* Last Resort; **p.56** John Townson/Creation; **p.58** John Townson/Creation; **p.60** Philip Harris Education; **p.61** Andrew Lambert; **p.63** *l* Popperfoto, *r* John Townson/Creation; **p.64** Barnaby's Picture Library; **p.68** *l* Ever Ready Ltd., *c* Russell Hobbs, *r* Belling Appliances Ltd.; **p.70** Last Resort; **p.71** RS Components; **p.74** *t* ZEFA-TM-Foto, *ct* Angus Fire, Sprinkler Division, *cb & b* RS Components; **p.78** Last Resort; **p.79** John Townson/Creation; **p.80** *t* Brian Lovell/Milepost 92 1/2, *b* Milepost 92 1/2; **p.82** Ford Motor Company Ltd; **p.84** *l* Flymo, *r* Jon Riley/Tony Stone; **p.90** *t* Rick Colls/Rex Features, *b* PowerGen; **p.92** *t* National Power plc, *b* Popperfoto; **p.94** Kudos/Rex Features; **p.99** Shaun Botterill/Allsport; **p.100** *t* Last Resort, *bl* European Space Agency/Science Photo Library, *br* Nathan Bilow/Allsport; **p.101** Ian Griffiths/Robert Harding Picture Library; **p.102** Alex Bartel/Science Photo Library; **p.104** *t & b* John Townson/Creation; **p.105** Barnaby's Picture Library; **p.106** Last Resort; **p.107** Jerome Yeats/Science Photo Library; **p.108** *t & b* Barnaby's Picture Library; **p.110** Allsport/Vandystadt; **p.111** Robert Harding Picture Library; **p.112** O. Comitti & Son, Ltd.; **p.113** *l* John Townson/Creation, *c* JCB, *r* NASA/Science Photo Library; **p.114** Andrew Lambert; **p.115** Last Resort; **p.116** Andrew Lambert; **p.118** ZEFA; **p.120** *t* The Times/Rex Features, *c* Mike Cooper/ Allsport, *b* Robert Harding Picture Library; **p.121** *l* ZEFA, *r* NASA/Science Photo Library; **p.122** *t* Georgette Douwma/ BBC Natural History Unit, *b* Didier Klein/Agence Vandystadt/ Allsport; **p.123** *tl* Ford Motor Company Ltd, *tr* Shaun Botterill/ Allsport, *b* Jan Halady/RSPB; **p.124** *tl* S. Wyman/ZEFA, *tc* Ross Kinnaird/Empics/Hulton © Empics Ltd., *tr* Topham Picture Point, *b* Alex Bartel/Science Photo Library; **p.128** *t* Mike Powell/Allsport, *b* Today/Rex Features; **p.133** Transport Research Laboratory; **p.135** *t* Topham Picture Point, *b* Barnaby's Picture Library; **p.136** Bob Martin/Allsport; **p.138** Rex Features; **p.139** *t* Paul Brown/Rex Features, *b* Robert Harding Picture Library; **p.140** John Frassanito, NASA/ Science Photo Library; **p.141** Science Photo Library; **p.144** *t* NASA/Science Photo Library, *c* NRSC Ltd/Science Photo Library, *b* US Geological Survey/Science Photo Library; **p.145** Richard J. Wainscoat, Peter Arnold Inc./Science Photo Library; **p.146** David Nunuk/Science Photo Library; **p.147** Jerry Schad/Science Photo Library; **p.149** Royal Observatory, Edinburgh/AATB/Science Photo Library; **p.152** *t* Dr Seth Shostak/Science Photo Library, *b* NOAO/Science Photo Library; **p.157** Popperfoto/Reuter; **p.158** *t* Alain Compost/Still Pictures, *bl & br* Andrew Lambert; **p.159** Ken Foulds; **p.161** David Hughes/Robert Harding Picture Library; **p.162** Richard Megna/Fundamental/Science Photo Library; **p.164** ZEFA; **p.166** Birmingham Symphony Hall; **p.167** ZEFA; **p.168** Yves Baulieu, Publiphoto Diffusion/Science Photo Library; **p.169** DENTSPLY UK; **p.171** Alastair Shay/Oxford Scientific Films; **p.172** *t* Bernard Castelein/BBC Natural History Unit, *c & b* Last Resort; **p.173** Shout Pictures; **p.176** Robin Scagell/ Science Photo Library; **p.178** *tl* Dr. P. Marazzi/Science Photo Library, *tr* John Greim/Science Photo Library, *b* Barnaby's Picture Library; **p.180** David A. Ponton/Planet Earth Pictures; **p.181** *l & r* Andrew Lambert; **p.182** *t & bl (3 photos)* Last Resort, *br (2 photos)* Ken Foulds; **p.183** *t* Last Resort, *b* John Townson/Creation; **p.188** *tl* Cambridge University Collection of Air Photographs: copyright reserved, *tr* Barnaby's Picture Library, *b* Markitwise International; **p.189** *t* Philippe Plailly /Science Photo Library, *b* Clinical Radiology Dept., Salisbury District Hospital/Science Photo Library; **p.190** *l* HR Wallingford, *c & r* from Llowarch, 'Ripple Tank Studies of Wave Motion' (Clarendon Press, Oxford) reproduced by permission of Oxford University Press; **p.192** *l* Popperfoto/ Reuter, *r* James Prince/Science Photo Library; **p.196** CNRI/ Science Photo Library; **p.198** U.S. Navy/Science Photo Library; **p.200** Popperfoto/Reuter.

(*t* = top, *b* = bottom, *r* = right, *l* = left, *c* = centre)

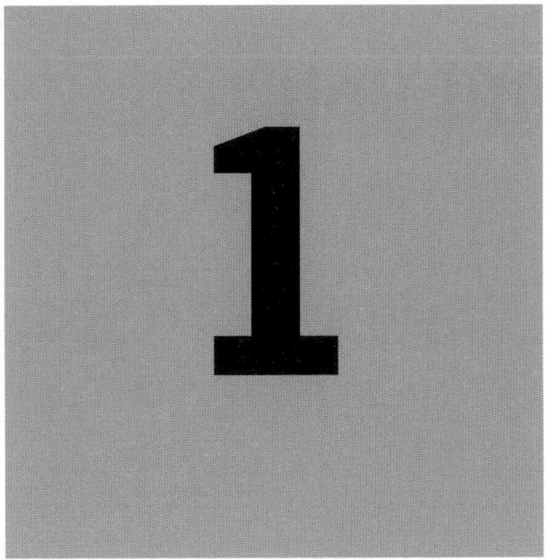

ENERGY

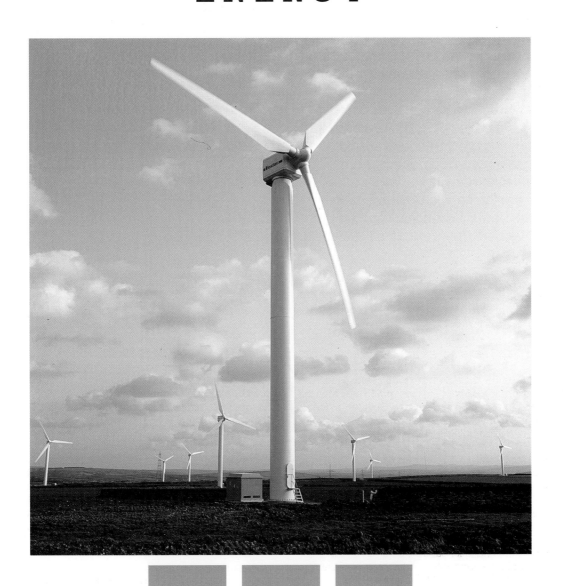

1.1 Energy and you

The word 'energy' is used in many different ways. We talk about 'high energy' foods and drinks. We sometimes describe people as 'energetic', or as 'bundles of energy', because they are always on the move, doing something. When we are tired, we might say we have 'run out of energy'. When we are off-colour, we might say 'I haven't got the energy to do anything'. These everyday examples provide us with one way of thinking about energy – that it is needed for everything we do.

'High energy' drink

The energy you need is released from food during respiration (see *GCSE Science Double Award Biology*, topic 1.9) and is used for everything that your body does – from keeping warm to growing.

Some of the things you do need more energy than others. When you exercise, for example, the body must release more energy than 'normal'.

Activity	Energy released by the body every ten minutes
Lying in bed	60 000 J (60 kJ)
Walking slowly	135 000 J (135 kJ)
Walking quickly	210 000 J (210 kJ)
Running	250 000 J (250 kJ)
Swimming	330 000 J (330 kJ)

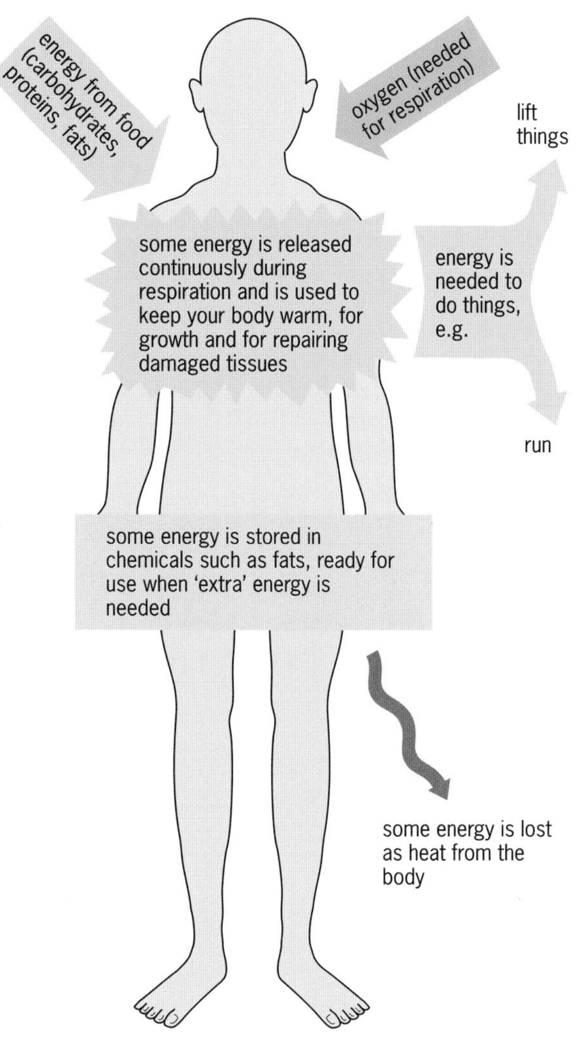

Your body needs energy

Energy is measured in units called **joules** (J). Larger amounts of energy are measured in **kilojoules** (kJ). One kilojoule is equivalent to 1000 joules.

Where do you get the energy from?

Energy is stored (as chemical energy) in the molecules of foods such as carbohydrates, proteins and fats. During respiration some of these molecules are 'broken down' in the cells of the body. Energy is released as the reaction takes place (see *GCSE Science Double Award Chemistry*, topic 4.7). In this sense food can be thought of as a concentrated source of energy for the body.

Energy is transferred from one living thing to another through food chains.

In the first stage of any food chain, plants absorb energy from the sun. During photosynthesis, some of this energy becomes stored in the chemicals made by the plant. When animals eat the plants some of the energy is passed to them. At each stage of the food chain, stored energy is transferred.

Some foods release more energy than others when they are broken down during respiration. That is why active people, such as athletes, eat a carefully planned diet which provides them with the energy they need.

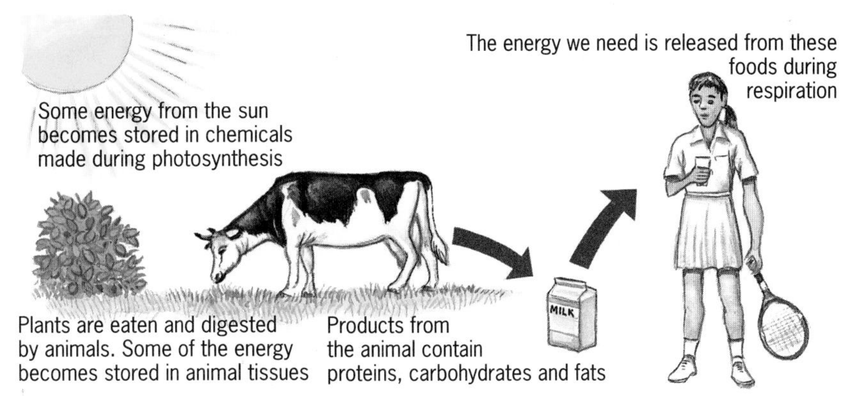

Some energy from the sun becomes stored in chemicals made during photosynthesis
The energy we need is released from these foods during respiration
MILK
Plants are eaten and digested by animals. Some of the energy becomes stored in animal tissues
Products from the animal contain proteins, carbohydrates and fats

Energy transfer in a food chain

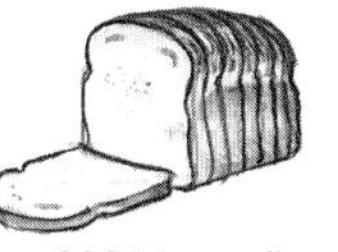

Some foods contain more stored energy than others

★ THINGS TO DO

1 Collect ten food labels which show how much carbohydrate, protein, fat and stored energy the food contains. Complete the table below with the information.

Type of food	Amount of carbohydrate	Amount of protein	Amount of fat	Energy content

Does one constituent of the food – protein, carbohydrate or fat – seem to contribute more of the energy value of the food than the others?

2 Use a strip thermometer to measure the temperature of your arm or leg muscle before and after exercise. Explain any difference which you observe.

3 Snakes are cold-blooded. They feed only once every three or four months. How can they survive on so little food?

4 The graph shows the amount of energy needed when walking and climbing.

a) How much energy is needed for a 6 km walk?

b) How much extra energy is needed for a 6 km walk which involves climbing 500 m?

c) Why is extra energy needed for walking uphill compared with walking on flat ground?

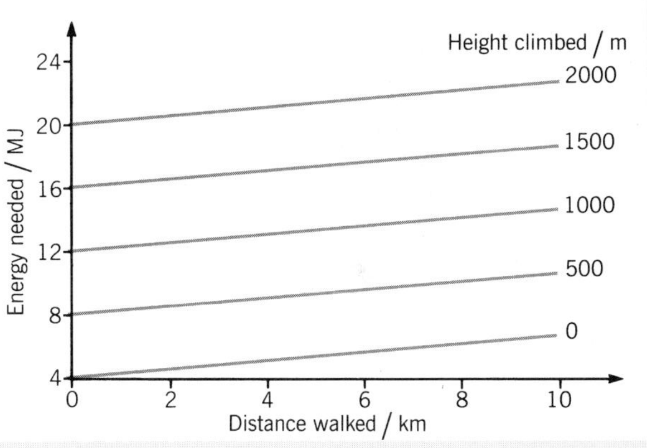

1.2 Energy transfer

Many people are rescued from the mountains and hills each year suffering from hypothermia. Some die before they can be helped

Most of the energy released from food is used to keep your body warm. The reactions which take place in the body work best at 37 °C. The cells in the body must release energy continuously to maintain this temperature. In cold weather energy can be transferred quickly from the body to the surrounding air. If energy is 'lost' faster than it can be supplied, then your body temperature falls. You may not be able to think clearly and may feel very tired. Eventually you will slump to the ground exhausted. At that point you are in severe danger of dying from hypothermia – extreme loss of body energy.

To reduce the risk of hypothermia, climbers and walkers wear special clothing which reduces the rate at which energy is transferred from their bodies. The materials used are thermal insulators

What happens to your energy?

Some muscles in the body, such as the heart and those which control the lungs, are working all the time. The cells in these muscles release energy continuously. During exercise, the cells release energy faster and you begin to feel hot. To prevent your body overheating, energy is 'lost' in several different ways (see *GCSE Science Double Award Biology*, topics 1.19 and 1.20).

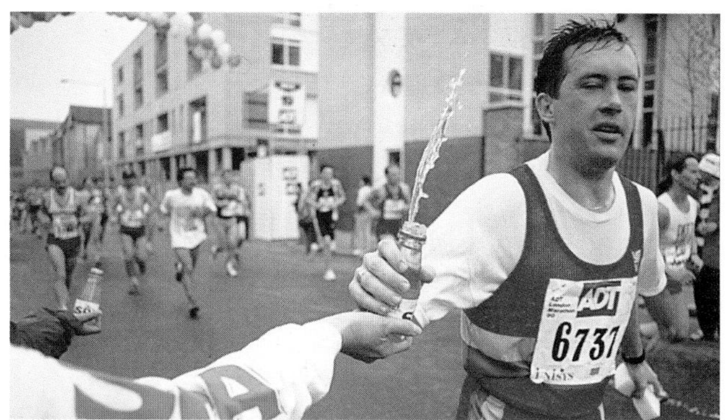

Sweating helps to remove heat from the body

The energy which is 'lost' from the body does not disappear – it is transferred to the air around you. You may have noticed that a cold classroom warms up quickly when a class enters. That is because the air absorbs the energy 'lost' from the people in the room and its temperature rises. Outdoors, the energy spreads quickly through the air, so any temperature change is not noticed.

The energy absorbed by the air is the same energy that was released by the cells in the body. We can think of the chemical energy released by the cells as having been transferred to the air where it exists in a different form – heat, or 'internal energy' (see page 20).

This provides another way of thinking about energy – that *it is needed to do anything that involves a change* of some kind. Here, the temperature change of the air only takes place because energy has been transferred to it.

The energy released by our muscles can be transferred in other ways, depending on what we do.

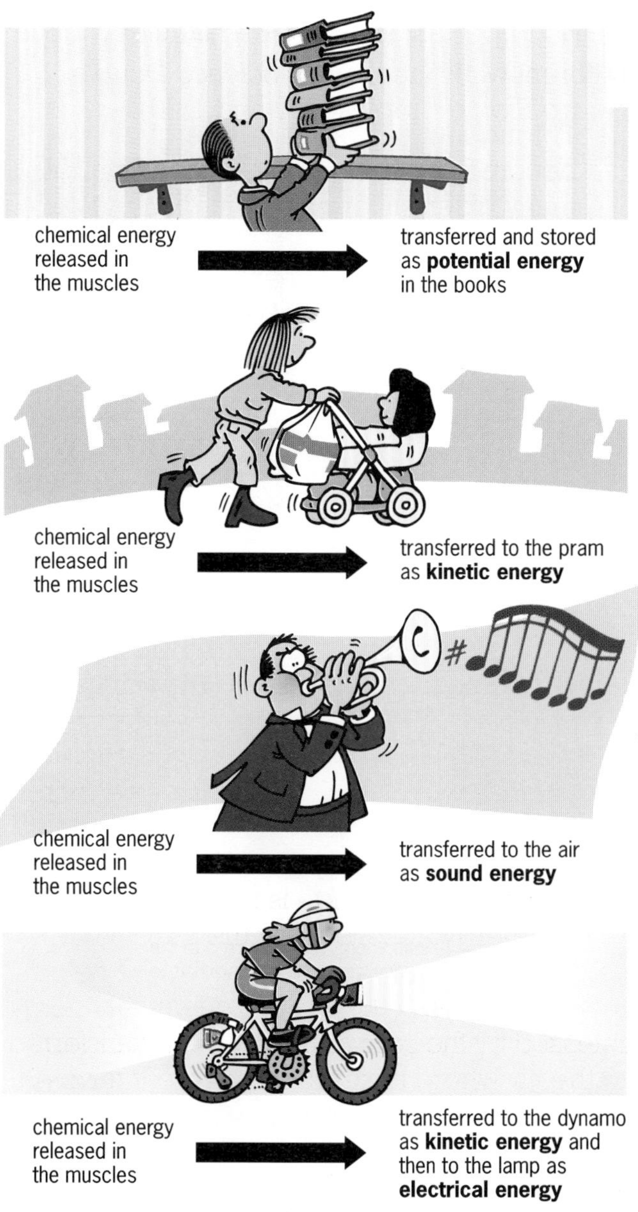

During each of these transfers, some of the energy released by the muscles is transferred directly to the air as heat. Eventually all of the energy released by the muscles will end up spread throughout the air as heat.

Everything else needs energy too

Many of the things we use every day are designed to transfer energy in a particular way. A loudspeaker connected to a hi-fi, for example, is specially designed to transfer the electrical energy from the amplifier to the air as sound energy.

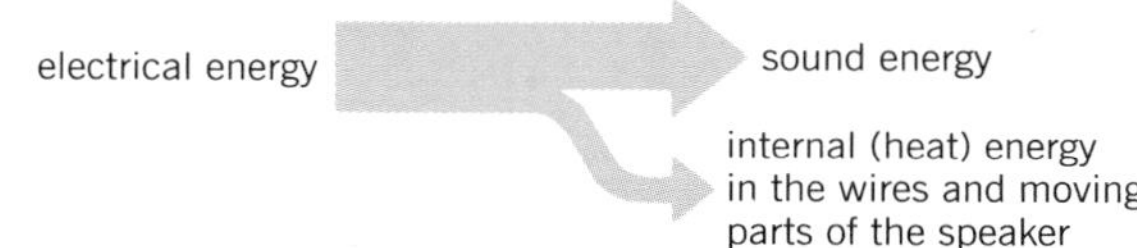

When the chemicals inside the batteries of a torch react, they release the energy needed to heat the filament and light the bulb.

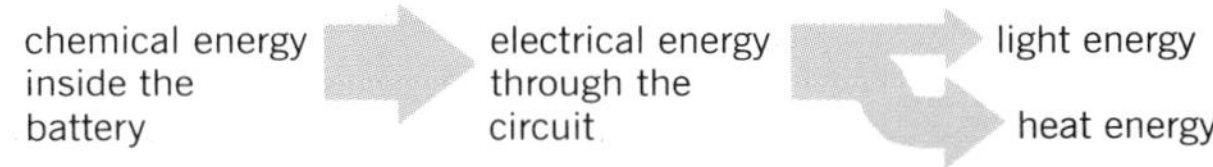

Some milk floats use batteries to supply the energy they need. During the process of energy transfer a force is exerted which makes the milk float move. The energy released by the chemicals in the batteries is transferred to the motor as electrical energy. The motor then transfers the energy to the milk float as kinetic energy.

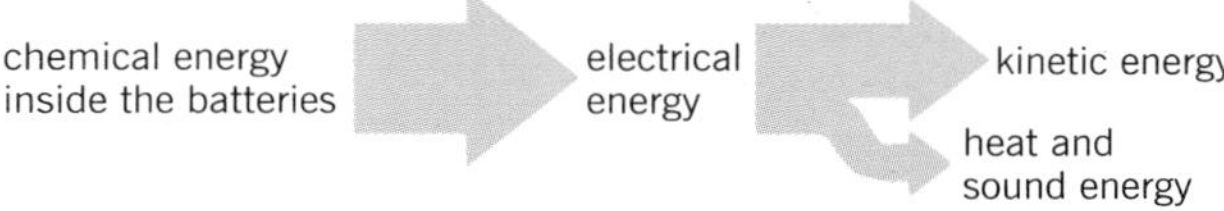

Energy is also released when fuels such as natural gas burn in oxygen. The energy is transferred to the pan and the food as heat energy, so their temperature rises.

These cases show two important ideas:

- that energy is needed to make something happen, and
- that energy does not 'disappear' but is transferred to another place, or *transformed* (changed) into some other form.

Energy is never lost

Consider the energy changes which take place when electricity lights a lamp.

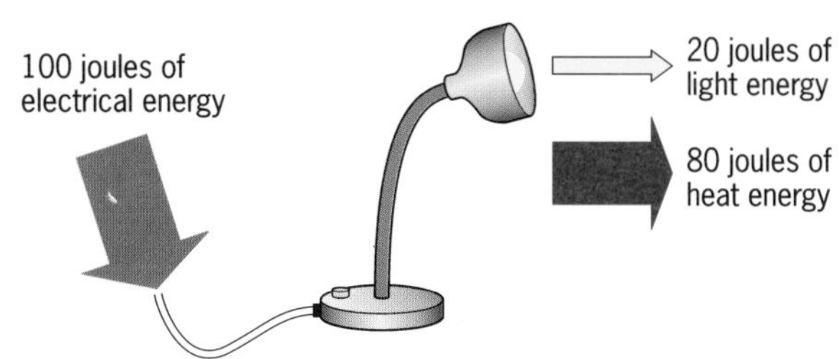

The energy output is the same as the energy input

You can see that the amount of energy released by the lamp (as heat and light) is the same as the amount of energy transferred to the lamp by the electric current. Energy has not been lost – the same amount of energy still exists, but in different forms.

The same principle applies to the much more complicated series of energy transfers, shown in the illustration below, which eventually provide the energy needed to light the bulb.

The amount of energy transferred at each stage (including all the energy apparently 'lost'), in all its different forms, is the same throughout the whole process. The original solar energy absorbed by the plants has become spread out in many different forms, and in many different places.

Two important laws summarise these ideas about energy:

1. Throughout any process, energy becomes more and more spread out, in many different forms and in many different places.
2. The total amount of energy (in all different forms) which exists at the end of any process is the same as the amount of energy at the beginning.

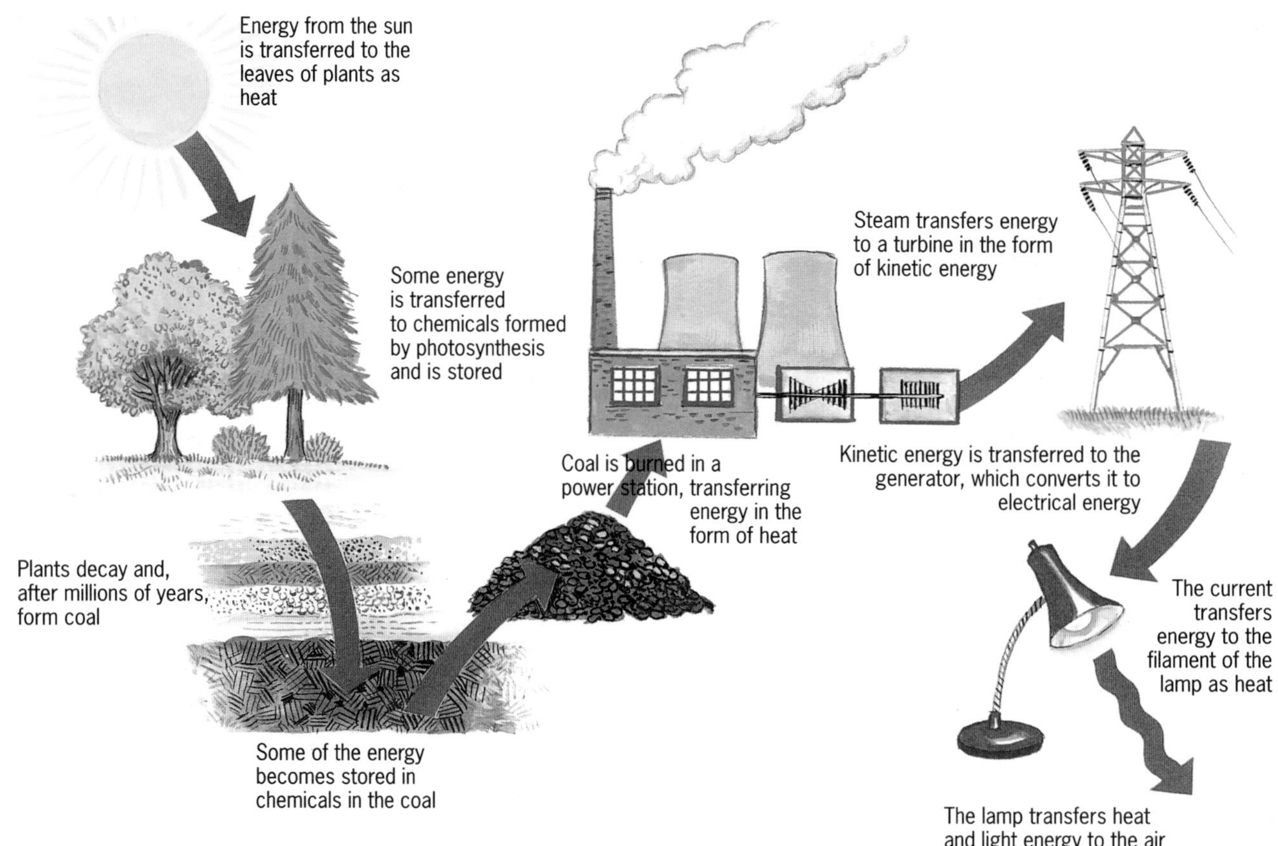

Energy transfers involved in lighting an electric lamp

★ THINGS TO DO

1 For years scientists have tried unsuccessfully to design 'perpetual motion' machines – machines which would work forever without an external energy supply. A pupil produced this design for a car, believing that it would provide the energy to go forever.

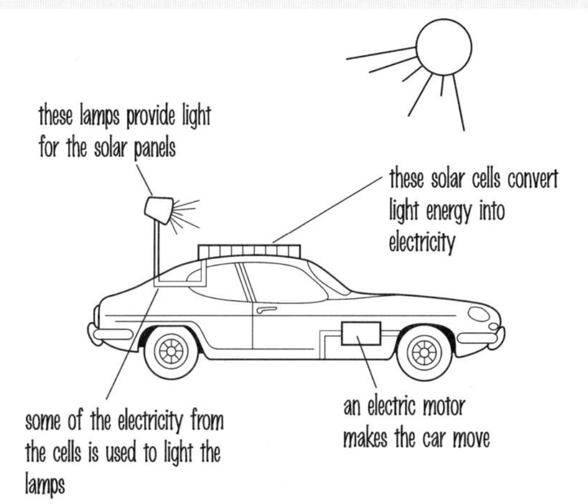
these lamps provide light for the solar panels
these solar cells convert light energy into electricity
some of the electricity from the cells is used to light the lamps
an electric motor makes the car move

a) Would the design work? Explain your answer.
b) Try to design your own perpetual motion machine. Add a note describing how you think it will work.
c) Discuss your design with a friend. Does he or she think it will work? If not, make a note explaining why.

2 Make a list of as many things as you can which transfer, or transform, energy in some way.
For each one describe the energy change which takes place and say what eventually happens to the energy.

3 Paper and wood can be burned to release energy. Where did that energy originally come from?

4 A group of pupils tested different fuels to find out which released most energy when burned. This is part of their account.

We put each fuel in a small crucible and burned it so that the heat warmed some water in a beaker above the crucible. We measured the temperature rise of the water for each fuel

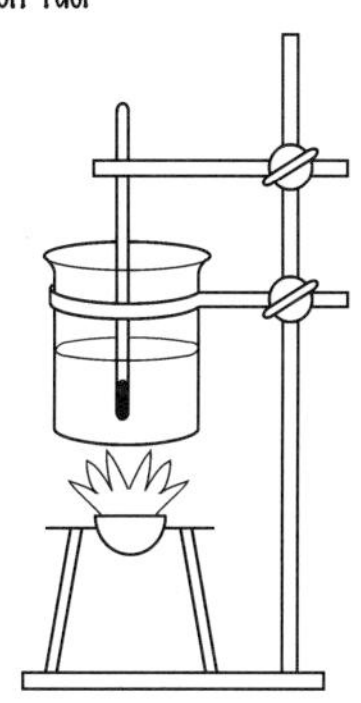

Fuel	Starting temperature of water/°C	Temperature after heating/°C	Rise in temperature/°C
meths	16	57	41
paraffin	17	46	29
meta (solid fuel)	15	57	42

a) What steps should the pupils have taken to make their test 'fair'?
b) Assuming their test was fair, which fuel released most energy? Explain your answer using their results.
c) One pupil said that 'all of the energy released by the fuel was transferred to the water'. Do you agree? If not, say what you think could have happened to some of the energy released by the fuel, and how their investigation could have been improved.

1.3 Hard at work

chemical energy released in the muscles → potential energy in the weights

When the man lifts the weights they gain potential energy. Chemical energy released in the muscles is transferred to the weights as potential energy. The force is exerted during the process of energy transfer

chemical energy released in the muscles → kinetic energy in the trolley

A stationary trolley has no kinetic energy. When it is pushed it begins to move and its kinetic energy increases. The energy gained by the trolley is transferred from the muscles of the person pushing it. The force is exerted during the process of energy transfer

You may use the word 'work' in many ways, such as 'I've been doing my homework' or 'Mum has been to work' or 'The television won't work', but in science **work** has a special meaning. *Work is done only when a force makes something move or tries to stop it moving.* When work is done, energy is transferred from one place to another, or is transformed.

In the examples illustrated alongside, work is done because a force is being exerted and is causing something to move. *The work done during the process is a measure of the amount of energy transferred.*

Machines also do work. Consider, for example, a winch.

Here a winch driven by the engine exerts the force which pulls the car up the ramp. Work is done on the car as it is raised, and it gains potential energy

The force which draws the car up the ramp is exerted during a complicated sequence of energy transfers.

chemical energy released as the fuel burns in the engine → kinetic energy in the moving engine → kinetic energy in the winch as it turns → potential energy as the car is pulled up the ramp

Note that:

- as the chemical energy in the fuel is released a force is exerted which turns the engine, and
- the force which raises the car is exerted as kinetic energy (from the winch) which is transferred to the car as potential energy.

If the winch is stopped and the car is held steady then no further energy is transferred – the potential energy of the car is not changing. Even though there is still a force acting on the car *no work is done because it is not moving.*

Calculating the amount of work done

The amount of work done depends on:

- the force which is exerted, measured in **newtons** (N), and
- the distance moved.

The work done can be calculated using the equation:

work done (joules)	=	force (newtons)	×	distance moved (metres)

Imagine, for example, someone pushing a trolley through 200 metres using a force of 150 newtons.

The work done on the trolley = force × distance
= 150 N × 200 m
= 30 000 J (or 30 kJ)

Notice that the work done has the same units as energy – joules.

Work and energy

When the weights shown opposite are lifted, work is done and energy is transferred to them as potential energy. The potential energy gained is equal to the work done.

Similarly, work is done when the trolley is given a push to get it moving. Energy is transferred to the trolley as kinetic energy. The kinetic energy gained is equal to the work done, ignoring energy 'losses' due to friction between the wheels and the floor.

If the trolley is moving at a steady speed, then its kinetic energy does not change. Under these circumstances all of the work done on the trolley is used to overcome friction.

★ THINGS TO DO

1 Do your own tests to calculate the work done when you:
a) open a drawer,
b) open the classroom door,
c) lift your school bag from the floor onto the desk,
d) step from the floor onto a chair or stool.
Put your results into a table.

2 Calculate the work done when:
a) someone pushes a pram through 1000 m using a force of 50 N,
b) a crane lifts a beam weighing 2000 N through 10 m,
c) a person weighing 500 N climbs a flight of stairs which have a vertical height of 4 m,
d) the winch on the relay lorry shown opposite raises a car weighing 10 000 N through a vertical height of 3 m.

3 An electric motor is used to pull skiers up a dry-ski slope, as shown below.
a) Draw a flow chart showing the energy changes which take place from the time a skier leaves the bottom of the slope to the time he or she returns to the same place after skiing down.
b) Why do the skiers slow down when they reach the uphill section at the bottom?

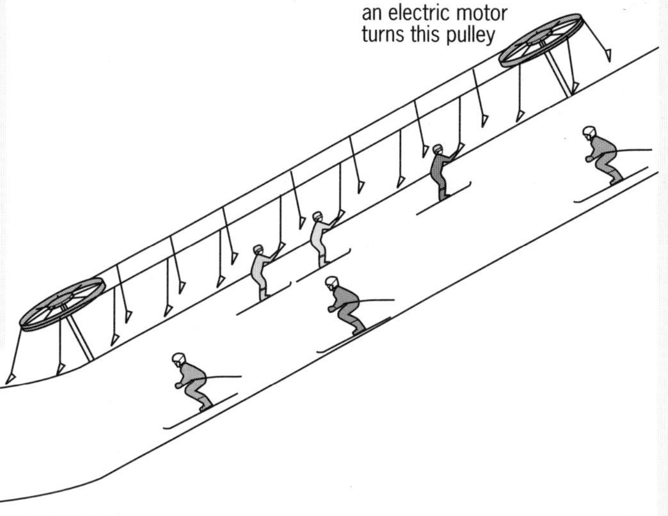

1.4 Power

'Power' is often confused with 'strength' in everyday language. It may appear, for example, that the strongest person must be the most powerful, but this is not necessarily the case. The most powerful is the one who can do work fastest. **Power** is the rate at which work is done – the faster work is done, the greater the power.

Think about this truck-pulling contest.

The world's strongest man?

Each contestant must pull the same truck over the same distance – 100 metres. If they keep the truck moving at the same steady speed, each man will have to exert the same force. They will, therefore, have to do the same amount of work:

$$\text{work done} = \text{force} \times \text{distance}$$

But suppose they took different times.

The first past the finishing post has exerted a greater force in a shorter time

The first one past the finishing post will have done more work and in a shorter time. That person is not necessarily the strongest, but he is the *most powerful*.

Calculating power

Imagine someone doing 40 joules of work in 2 seconds – they would be doing work at the rate of 20 joules per second (or transferring energy at the rate of 20 joules per second). Their power would be written as 20 watts (20 W). The **watt** (W) is one of the units used for power. A larger unit is the **kilowatt** (kW), equal to 1000 watts. A power of one kilowatt means work is done at the rate of 1000 joules per second.

The equation:

$$\text{power (watts)} = \frac{\text{work done (joules)}}{\text{time taken to do the work (seconds)}}$$

can be used to calculate power. The work done is equal to the amount of energy transferred (assuming no energy is wasted), so another way of writing this equation is:

$$\text{power (watts)} = \frac{\text{amount of energy transferred (joules)}}{\text{time taken (seconds)}}$$

It follows that you must calculate the work done (or energy transferred) before the power can be calculated. Suppose, for example, that the strongman in the photograph exerted an average force of 50 000 N to pull the truck, and that he took 50 seconds to pull it through 100 metres. Then:

$$\begin{aligned} \text{work done} &= \text{force} \times \text{distance} \\ &= 50\,000\,\text{N} \times 100\,\text{m} \\ &= 5\,000\,000 \text{ joules (or 5000 kJ)} \end{aligned}$$

$$\begin{aligned} \text{power developed} &= \frac{\text{work done}}{\text{time taken}} \\ &= \frac{5\,000\,000\,\text{J}}{50\,\text{s}} \\ &= 100\,000 \text{ watts (or 100 kW)} \end{aligned}$$

This is the equivalent of his body transferring (on average) 100 000 joules of energy to the truck each second while he pulls it – no wonder the contestants get tired!

★ THINGS TO DO

1 Plan and carry out an experiment to find the power you develop whilst climbing a flight of stairs.

2 Calculate the power developed by:
a) a weight-lifter who raises a load of 2500 N through 2 m in 2 seconds,
b) a lift which raises people through 30 m in a shop in 15 seconds, if the lift and the people weigh 40 000 N.

3 Complete this table by calculating the missing values.

Force /N	**Distance moved** /m	**Work done** /J	**Time taken** /s	**Power developed** /W
100	2		5	
	5	1000	20	
500		2000		400

4 The illustration shows a Victorian lift in Saltburn, Cleveland, which lifts people from the beach to the clifftop. The lift is water-powered. The two cars are joined by a steel cable which passes around a large wheel at the top of the slope. When the cars are stationary, passengers enter. Water is then added to the tank on the upper car until it just begins to fall. As it falls, it pulls the lower car up the slope.

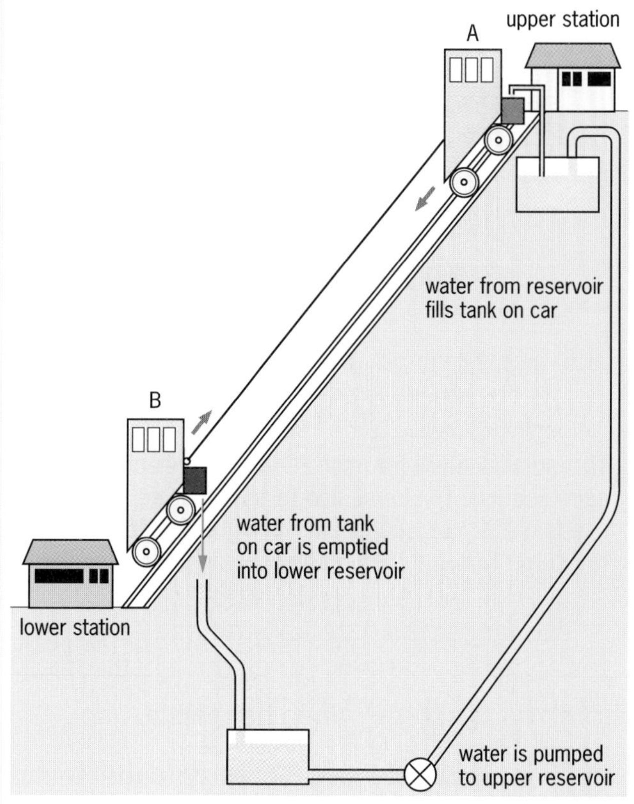
A
upper station
water from reservoir fills tank on car
B
water from tank on car is emptied into lower reservoir
lower station
water is pumped to upper reservoir

a) The average force exerted on car B is 15 000 N and the length of the track is 40 m. Calculate the amount of work done in raising car B and the passengers to the top of the cliff.
b) Assuming car B is raised from the bottom of the system to the top in 40 s, calculate the power developed by the system.
c) The amount of potential energy transferred from car A as it falls is given by:

$$\underset{(\text{J})}{\text{change in potential energy}} = \underset{(\text{N})}{\text{weight}} \times \underset{(\text{m})}{\text{vertical height moved}}$$

The weight of car A, including passengers and water, is 30 000 N. The vertical height of the cliff is 30 m.
i) Calculate the amount of potential energy transferred from car A as it falls.
ii) One pupil said 'Energy cannot disappear, so the potential energy lost by car A should all be transferred to car B as it rises'. Explain why this does not happen in practice.

1.5

Electricity around your home

Many of the things we use in our homes need electrical energy to work. Electrical energy is one of the most useful forms of energy, because:

- it is easily transferred from place to place by an electric current flowing through a circuit, and
- it is readily transformed (changed) into other forms of energy.

Most electrical appliances are energy 'changers' – they have been designed and built to transform electrical energy into some other (often more useful) form.

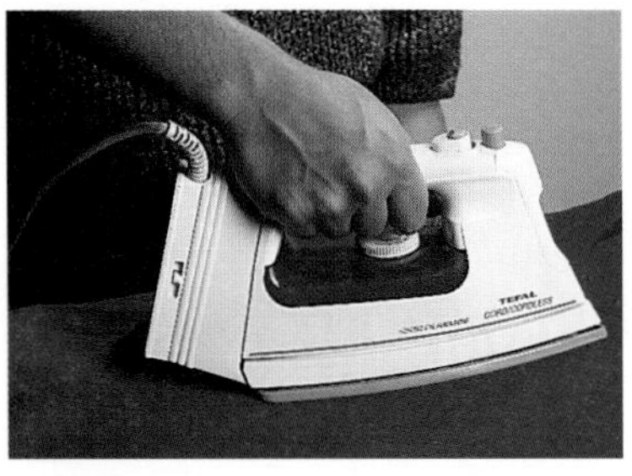

An iron is an energy changer

An electric iron, for example, contains a heating element. As an electric current flows through the element, energy is transferred to the atoms in the metal as heat energy and its temperature rises.

electrical energy ⟶ heat energy

The element then transfers heat to the base of the iron, raising its temperature. The temperature can be adjusted by increasing or decreasing the rate at which energy is transferred.

A food mixer, on the other hand, is designed to convert electrical energy into kinetic energy (of the blades).

electrical energy ⟶ kinetic energy

During the process a small amount of energy is transformed into sound.

Electrical power

When you buy a light bulb you might ask for a '60 watt bulb' or a '100 watt bulb'. The 'wattage' is a measure of the amount of energy transferred each second, or the **power** of the bulb. A power of 60 watts (60 W), for example, means that 60 joules of electrical energy are transferred to the filament, and then to the air as heat and light, each second.

This 100 W bulb transforms 100 joules of electrical energy into heat and light energy each second. The bulb is therefore brighter than the 60 W bulb

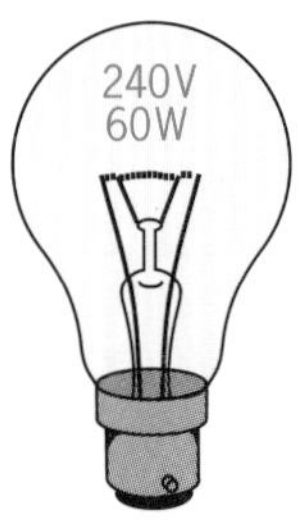

This 60 W bulb transforms 60 joules of electrical energy into heat and light energy each second

The power rating of an appliance can often be found on a small label such as the one shown.

230 V~	50 Hz
20 W	

This appliance will transfer 20 joules of electrical energy each second. The label also tells us that the appliance needs a 230 volt supply alternating at 50 Hz (this means the current changes direction 50 times each second)

The larger unit, the kilowatt, may be used for some appliances. An electric kettle, for example, may have a power rating of 2 kilowatts (2 kW). This means that it transfers 2000 joules of electrical energy to the heating element each second when it is switched on.

Calculating the amount of energy used by an appliance

The amount of energy which an appliance transfers will depend on:

- its power – the more powerful it is, the faster it transfers energy, and
- the time for which it is used – the longer it is used, the more energy it transfers.

The total amount of energy transferred can be calculated using the equation:

$$\underset{\text{(joules)}}{\text{total energy transferred}} = \underset{\text{(watts)}}{\text{power}} \times \underset{\text{(seconds)}}{\text{time}}$$

So, for example, the amount of energy needed to operate the toaster shown for 5 minutes is:

$$\begin{aligned} \text{power} \times \text{time} &= 800\,\text{W} \times 300\,\text{s} \\ &= 240\,000\,\text{J} \\ &\text{or } 240\,\text{kJ} \end{aligned}$$

Notice that the time must be converted into seconds.

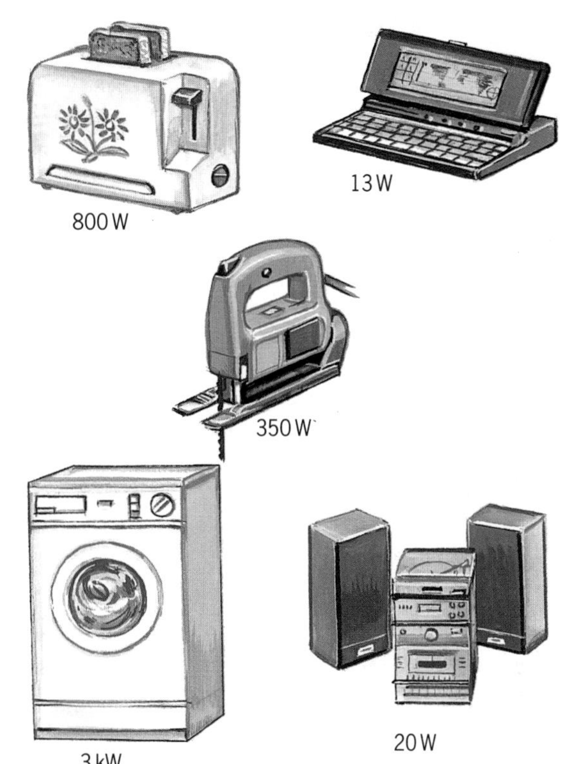

Some household appliances and typical power ratings

★ THINGS TO DO

1 These labels were found on four household appliances. The appliances were a television, a lap-top computer, a hairdrier and a tumble-drier. Copy the labels. Under each label add a sentence saying which device it belongs to and giving a reason for your answer.

230 V~ 50–60 Hz 2200 W	230 V~ 50 Hz 104 W
230 V~ 50 Hz 1200 W	8–14 V d.c. 12 W

2 Complete the spaces in this table (being careful with the units!)

Appliance	Power/W	Time for which it is on	Amount of energy transferred/J
Car headlamp	25	4 minutes	
Hi-fi		10 minutes	12 000
Kettle	1000	4 minutes	
Bedside lamp	60		3 600

3 Choose four electrical appliances in your home. Think about what eventually happens to the electrical energy transferred to them. Draw a flow chart for each one showing the energy transfers which take place. For example, for a toaster you could write:

electrical energy → heat energy in element → heat energy in the air

1.6 Paying the price

Generating electricity and maintaining supply is a costly business. We must pay for the energy we use.

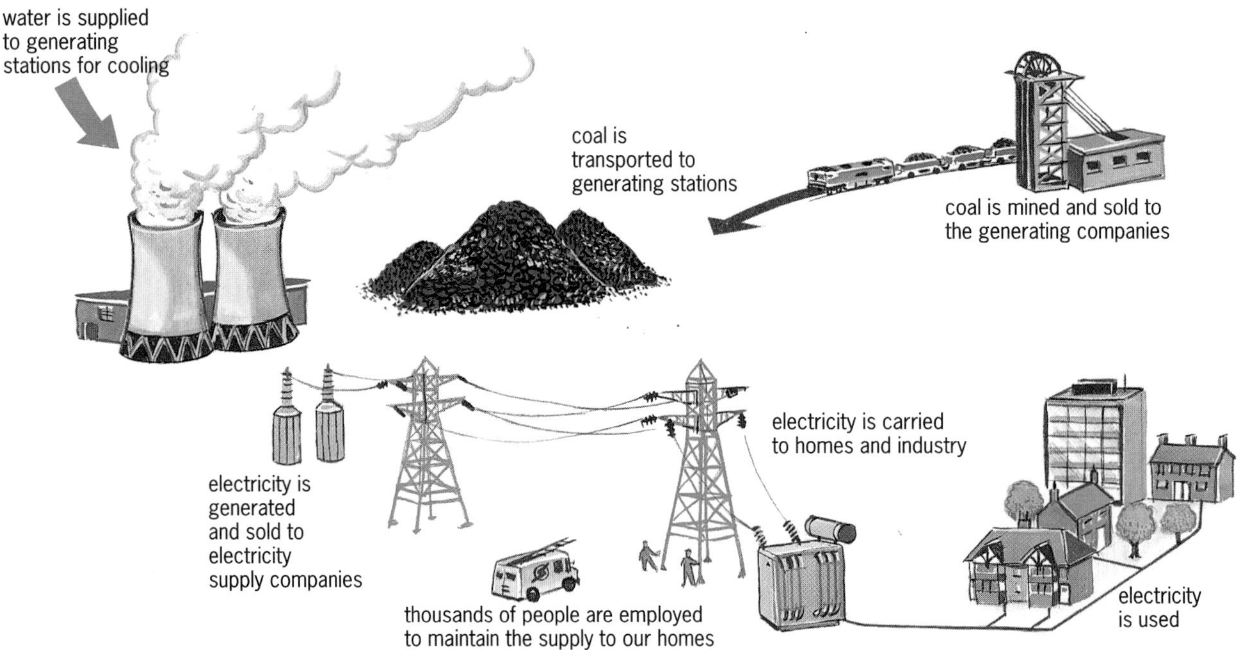
water is supplied to generating stations for cooling
coal is transported to generating stations
coal is mined and sold to the generating companies
electricity is generated and sold to electricity supply companies
electricity is carried to homes and industry
thousands of people are employed to maintain the supply to our homes
electricity is used

The electricity supply business

Electricity meters measure how much energy is used in our homes, schools, offices and factories.

Every three months the meter is checked. The electricity supply company then sends out a bill showing how much energy has been used, and how much we must pay

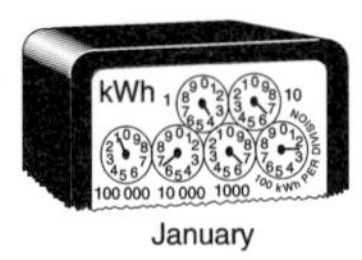
kWh
January

kWh
April

This is the cost per unit

The standing charge is made to cover the cost of supplying cables to new homes and maintaining those which are already used

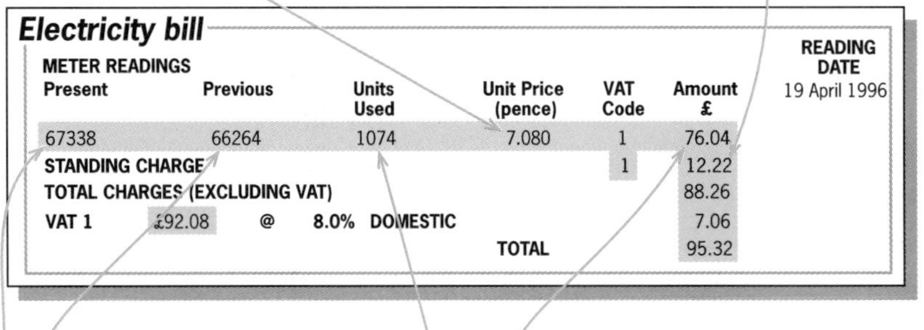

Electricity bill

READING DATE 19 April 1996

METER READINGS

Present	Previous	Units Used	Unit Price (pence)	VAT Code	Amount £
67338	66264	1074	7.080	1	76.04
STANDING CHARGE				1	12.22
TOTAL CHARGES (EXCLUDING VAT)					88.26
VAT 1 £92.08 @ **8.0% DOMESTIC**					7.06
			TOTAL		95.32

This was the meter reading when the meter was read in January

This is the amount which must be paid for the electricity used

This was the meter reading when the meter was read in April

This is the number of units of electricity which have been used between January and April

What is one unit of electricity?

The amount of energy transferred to appliances in your home could be measured in joules. The problem is that the joule is such a small unit that we would have huge numbers on our bills (the bill shown here would state that 3866.4 million joules of electricity had been used in the three-month period).

The electricity supply companies use a unit which is much bigger than the joule – the **kilowatt-hour**. One kilowatt-hour (kWh) is the amount of energy transferred to a 1 kW appliance working for one hour. This is sometimes just called one 'unit' of electricity.

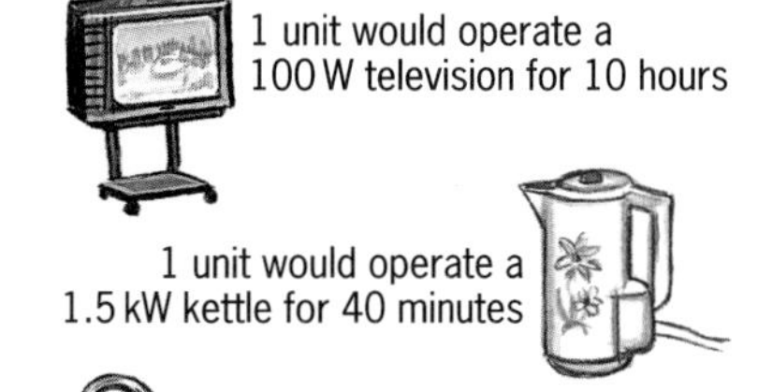
1 unit would operate a 100 W television for 10 hours
1 unit would operate a 1.5 kW kettle for 40 minutes
1 unit would operate a 60 W light bulb for 16 hours 40 minutes

One unit of electricity will operate different appliances for different times

The number of units of electricity transferred to any appliance can be calculated using:

number of kilowatt-hours = power of appliance (kW) × time for which it is working (hours)

Imagine, for example, a 1.5 kW kettle used for a total of three hours per week.

The number of units used (kWh) = power (kW) × time (h)
= 1.5 × 3 = 4.5

Notice that in this equation the power must be expressed in kilowatts.

If we know the cost of each unit, we can then calculate the cost of the electricity used:

cost of electricity = number of units used × cost per unit

Assume the cost is 7p per unit.

Cost of using kettle = number of units × cost per unit
= 4.5 × 7p = 31.5p

★ THINGS TO DO

1 For each of the appliances in the table calculate how many units would be used each week, and the weekly cost of each one, assuming electricity costs 7p per unit.

Appliance	Power	Time used in a week
Washing machine	3 kW	4 hours
Toaster	1300 W	30 minutes
Television	60 W	40 hours
Video recorder	20 W	6 hours
Hairdrier	800 W	30 minutes
Lights (all)	250 W	18 hours

2 An ordinary light bulb and an 'energy-efficient' bulb were connected through two electricity meters. The bulbs were connected in such a way that they were both 'on' for the same time each week. The table below shows the readings obtained each week for ten weeks.

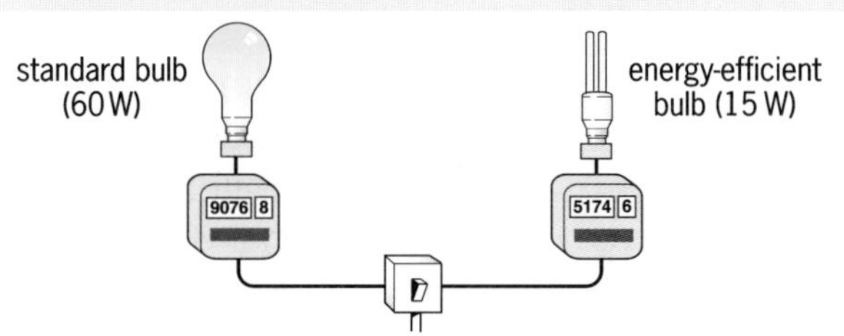
standard bulb (60 W)
energy-efficient bulb (15 W)
9076 8
5174 6

a) Draw two graphs (on the same axes) showing the meter readings for each bulb over the ten weeks. Explain any similarities and differences between the two graphs.

b) Calculate the number of units of electricity used by each bulb over the ten weeks. Then calculate the cost of using each bulb over the ten weeks if electricity costs 7p per unit.

How much money would be saved if the energy-efficient bulb were used instead of the ordinary bulb?

c) The energy-efficient bulb had a power rating of 15 W. The light from it was brighter than that from the ordinary 60 W bulb. Suggest a reason why the lower power bulb was brighter.

Type of bulb	Meter reading at end of week 0	1	2	3	4	5	6	7	8	9	10
Ordinary bulb	0	2.5	4.9	7.5	9.8	12.4	14.9	17.6	20.1	22.6	25.1
Energy-efficient bulb	0	0.6	1.3	1.9	2.5	3.1	3.7	4.4	5.0	5.7	6.4

1.7 What a waste!

We must try to make sure that we waste as little energy as possible. Reducing waste keeps our energy bills low, and could help to make fossil fuels last longer (see page 35).

Machines are designed to transfer energy in a particular way. A car engine, for example, is designed to transfer chemical energy (released from burning fuel) to the car as kinetic energy. A perfect engine would transfer all of the energy in this way. Unfortunately, car engines, like other machines, are far from perfect. Some of the energy released by the fuel is transformed into non-useful forms. This means that some of the fuel (and the money we spent on it) is wasted.

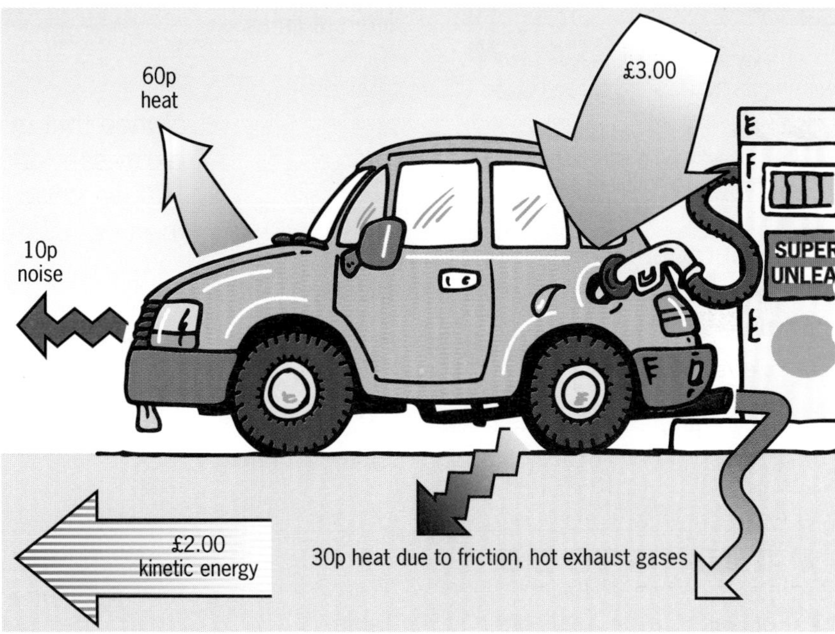

For every tankful of petrol put into a car, only about ⅔ is used usefully – the other ⅓ is wasted

The energy transferred to the car as kinetic energy is the 'useful' part of the energy transferred from the fuel. The other forms of energy are not useful in this sense. The heat and sound are effectively 'wasted' energy – they are not used to do the job for which the engine was designed. The more energy an engine wastes, the less 'efficient' it is.

Other devices have similar problems. A gas cooker is designed to heat food placed inside the oven. Some of the energy released by the burning gas is, however, transferred to the surroundings. This energy is wasted. Only the energy which is transferred to the food is usefully used. An 'efficient' oven is one which traps most of the energy inside – less fuel is then needed to raise the inside of the oven to a particular temperature.

Efficiency

The **efficiency** of a device is a measure of how much energy it transfers in a useful way (doing the job for which it was designed). If a lot of energy is wasted then the efficiency is low. If most of the energy is transferred in a useful form, the efficiency is high.

If, for example, only half of the energy released by the burning gas in a cooker was used to heat the food then its efficiency would be 50%.

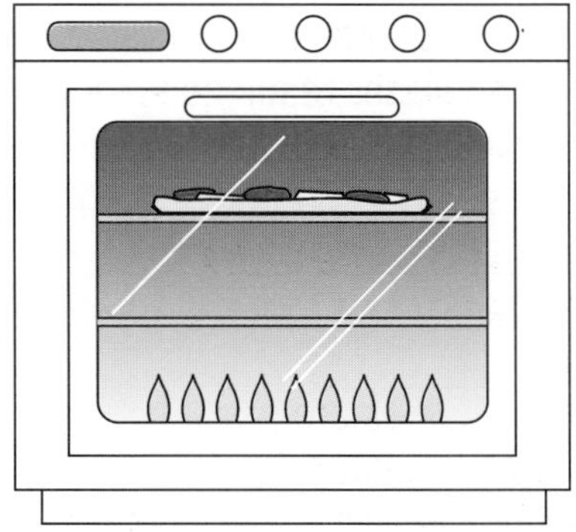

A gas cooker wastes energy in warming the air outside

Filament bulbs

Light bulbs are designed to convert electrical energy into light energy. In an ordinary filament light bulb energy is transferred to the filament as current flows through it. The temperature of the filament rises and it emits light. Some of the energy is, however, transferred to the bulb and the air as heat. This is wasted energy.

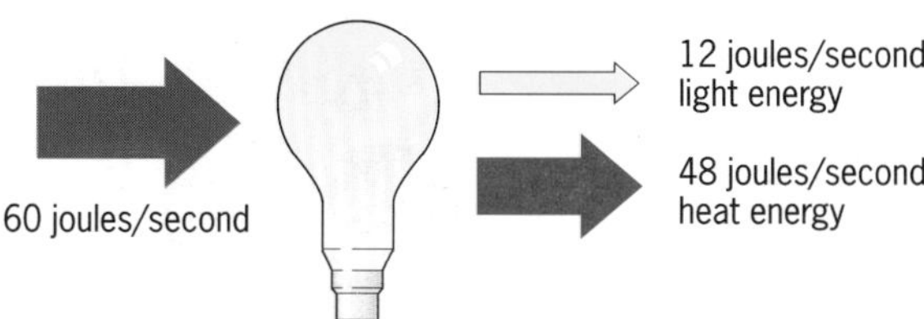

Only 12 joules of the energy is transformed into light by this bulb. This is 20% of the energy transferred to the filament, so the efficiency of the bulb is only 20%. This means 80% of the energy transferred to the filament (and 80% of the money you spend) is wasted.

Energy-efficient bulbs

Energy-efficient or 'low-energy' bulbs, although more expensive to buy, are much cheaper to use.

In this bulb 12 joules of energy is transferred as useful light. This is $^{12}/_{15}$ or 80% of the energy transferred to the bulb by the current. The efficiency of the bulb is therefore 80% – only 20% of the energy is wasted as heat.

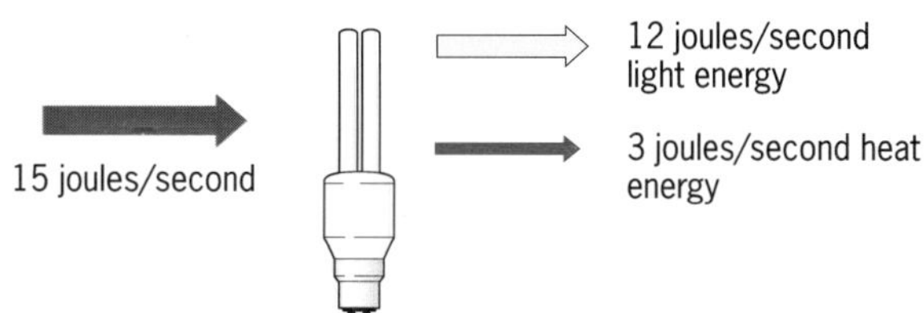

The 'low-energy' bulb can produce the same brightness using far less energy than the filament bulb. This is because more of the energy is transformed (usefully) into light, and less into heat. It is much more efficient.

★ THINGS TO DO

1 In what ways could energy be 'wasted'
a) when a gas burner is used to heat food in an uncovered pan,
b) when water is boiled in an electric kettle,
c) when a jack is used to raise a car's wheel?
For each one say how the amount of 'wasted' energy could be reduced.

2 Which do you think is most efficient – a microwave oven or a conventional gas cooker? Explain your answer.

3 Describe how each of the situations below has something to do with efficiency.
a) The hulls of ships used to become covered with large shellfish. Chemicals are now painted on the hulls to prevent shellfish sticking to them.
b) Modern cars are designed to be as aerodynamic as possible. This reduces 'drag' as they move through the air.
c) Modern kettles are made from plastic. Plastic is an insulator which reduces the rate at which energy is transferred from the water to the air.

4 The illustrations show two devices around the home with the amounts of energy they transfer.

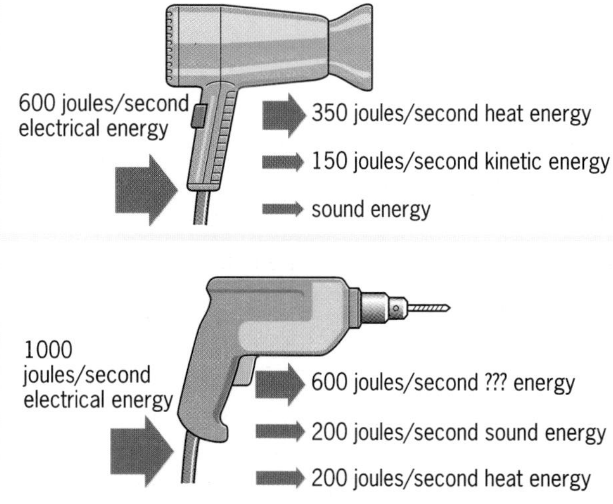

a) How much sound energy must the hairdrier produce? Explain your answer.
b) In what form is useful energy obtained from the drill?
c) Which device is most efficient? Explain your answer.

1.8 Machines and efficiency

None of us could lift a car far enough from the ground to change the wheel. We couldn't exert a large enough force. We can however do the job using a car jack.

The car jack is an example of a machine that changes the small force which we exert into a much larger force. It is a **force multiplier**.

When the car jack is used, a force is exerted which lifts the car. Work is therefore done on the car. Assuming the car is lifted at a steady speed:

The girl exerts a force of 40 newtons
The jack exerts a lifting force of 10 000 newtons

Machines help us to do jobs

Force needed to lift car = its weight (N)
= mass (kg) × gravitational field strength (N/kg) (see page 103)
= $m \times g$

Distance through which car is lifted = height above ground (m)
= h

So work done on car (J) = force exerted by jack (N) × distance through which car is lifted (m)
= mgh

Gravitational potential energy

As the car jack is used, some of the chemical energy released in the muscles is transferred to the car as potential energy. When objects are raised above the ground, against the force of gravity, the potential energy they gain can be described as **gravitational potential energy**.

chemical energy in muscles ⟶ gravitational potential energy of car

If the jack were 100% efficient, all the work done on the car would be transferred to the car as gravitational potential energy.

So the increase in gravitational potential energy (J)
= work done on car (J) = mgh

Any object at ground level is considered to have zero gravitational potential energy. So, we can say for any object raised to a height h above the ground:

gravitational potential energy (J) = mgh

or, because mass × gravitational field strength = weight,

gravitational potential energy (J) = weight (N) × height (m)

In practice, most car jacks are inefficient – much of the energy transferred by the person operating a jack is used in overcoming friction in the moving parts. This means that the energy put into the system must be much greater than the gravitational potential energy gained by the car.

Calculating efficiency

Machines should transfer energy as efficiently as possible. **Efficiency** is calculated using the equation:

$$\text{efficiency} = \frac{\text{useful energy transferred}}{\text{energy put into the system.}} \times 100\%$$

Imagine, for example, someone using the pulleys illustrated here to lift a car engine from the body.

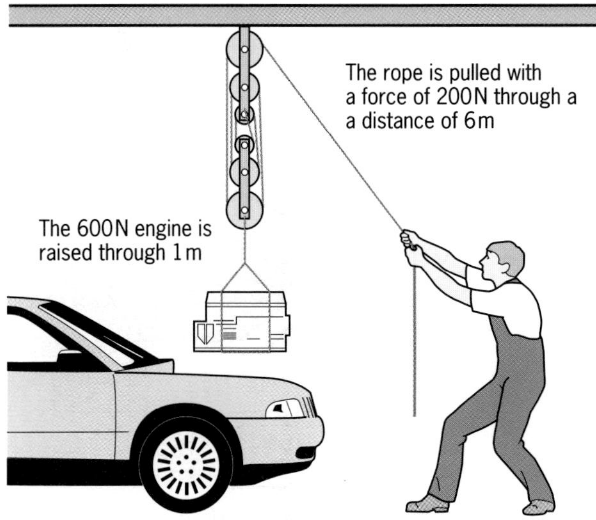
The rope is pulled with a force of 200N through a a distance of 6m
The 600N engine is raised through 1m

How much of the man's energy is used to lift the engine?

Work done by person pulling rope = force × distance
= 200 N × 6 m
= 1200 J

Increase in gravitational potential energy of engine =
weight × height = 600 N × 1 m
= 600 J

The efficiency of the pulley system is therefore:

$$\text{efficiency} = \frac{\text{energy transferred to engine}}{\text{energy put in to system}} \times 100\%$$

$$= \frac{600}{1200} \times 100\%$$

$$= 50\%$$

This means that only 50% of the energy transferred by the person pulling the rope is actually transferred to the engine. The other 50% is wasted in the system (as work done in overcoming friction) and will be transferred to the air as heat.

★ THINGS TO DO

1 Calculate (i) the change in gravitational potential energy and (ii) the work done in each of the following cases. (g = 10 N/kg)

a) A high jumper of mass 40 kg raising her body 2 m as she crosses the bar.

b) Someone lifting a 100 N baby 1 metre above its cot.

c) A crane lifting a 3000 N girder 15 metres.

d) A ski-tow pulling an 800 N skier up a vertical height of 150 m. The ski-tow exerts an average force of 500 N and pulls the skier through a distance of 300 m.

2 Look at some pulley systems set up by your teacher. What factors do you think affect the efficiency of a pulley system? Write down your predictions and give a reason for each one.

Carry out your own investigations to test your predictions. Try to give an explanation for your results.

3 A group of pupils tested three different types of car jack to find out which worked best. In the laboratory they used the jacks to lift a 200 N steel bar. Their results are shown in the table.

a) Calculate the work done by the person using the jack in each case.

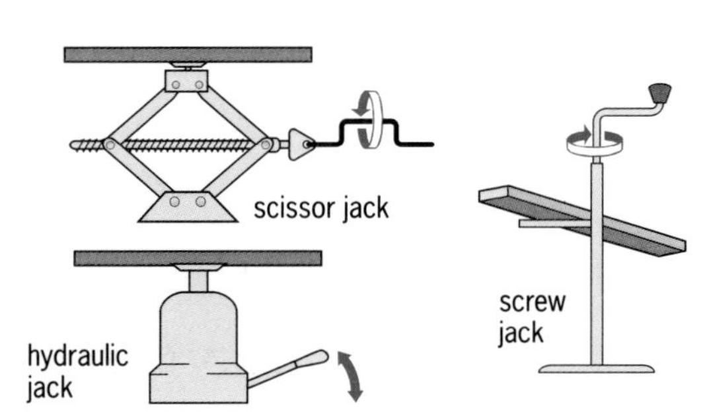
scissor jack
screw jack
hydraulic jack

b) Calculate the efficiency of each jack.

c) Suggest reasons why the efficiencies of the car jacks are so different.

Type of jack	Weight of bar /N	Height through which bar was lifted /m	Force needed to move jack handle /N	Total distance through which jack handle was moved to raise the bar through 0.1 m /m
hydraulic	200	0.1	9	3
scissor	200	0.1	4	9
screw	200	0.1	3	12

1.9 Warming up and cooling down

The icicles in this photograph are frozen water. As the ice absorbs energy from the sun it becomes warmer – its temperature will rise. At 0°C the ice will melt, turning back into water. The change in temperature is a result of energy transfer.

Temperature, heat and energy

Temperature, heat and energy are often confused. To understand the differences we need to think about what happens to the particles of a substance as it is heated or cooled.

Although you cannot see them, the particles of a substance are always moving – they have kinetic energy. The **temperature** of the substance is a measure of the average kinetic energy of the particles.

- When the substance is heated, energy is transferred to the particles. Their average kinetic energy increases so the temperature rises. The more energy they gain, the more the temperature rises.
- When the substance is cooled, energy is transferred from it – the particles lose kinetic energy and the temperature falls. The more energy the particles lose, the lower the temperature falls.

When hot the particles move quickly

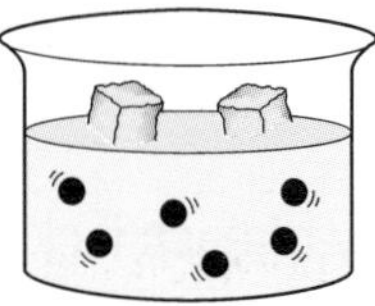

When cold the particles move more slowly

If energy continues to be transferred from the substance, the particles eventually reach a point where they have no kinetic energy – they stop moving. The temperature at which this occurs is **absolute zero** (–273 °C), the lowest temperature which anything can reach.

The total amount of energy stored in the particles of a substance is called the **internal energy**, or sometimes 'thermal energy' or simply 'heat'. A bathful of water at 30 °C has more internal energy than a cupful of water at 30 °C. The average kinetic energy of the water molecules is the same in each but because there are more molecules in the bath the total energy is greater. When we speak of something gaining or losing 'heat', we really mean that the internal energy is increasing or decreasing.

Well frozen

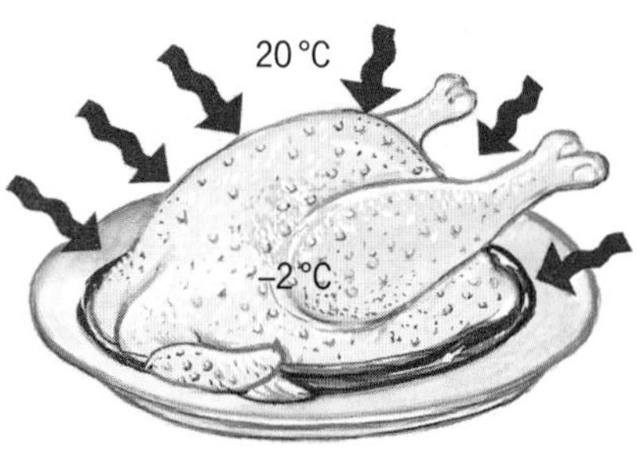

A chicken taken from your home freezer may have a temperature of about –8 °C. To completely defrost it, the temperature throughout the chicken must be raised above 0 °C – the temperature at which ice melts. The air in the house is warmer than the frozen chicken, so energy or 'heat' is transferred from the air to the chicken. The temperature of the chicken rises and it defrosts.

When you place fresh food in the freezer, the opposite happens. The inside of the freezer is colder than the food, and so energy passes from the food to the freezer interior. As a result, the temperature of the food falls and the water inside the food freezes.

These examples illustrate the principle that heat energy always spreads out – *warmer objects will always transfer energy to cooler objects around them*. As one object cools down, the other warms up. *Energy will be transferred until they both reach the same temperature*. The bigger the temperature difference, the faster energy will be transferred.

★ THINGS TO DO

1 Steve was camping in France during the summer holidays. He had difficulty keeping his drinks cool because the weather was so hot. Someone suggested filling a bucket with cold water and keeping the drinks in the water.

a) Do you think this method would help to keep the drinks cool? Explain your answer using ideas about energy transfer.
b) Make a list of things which could affect how well this method works. Then plan a series of tests to check your ideas. When your teacher approves your plan, carry out your tests and prepare a written report.
c) Write a short article for a camping magazine describing the best way to keep drinks cool. Use the results of your own tests to show how the method works.

2 This table shows the defrosting and cooking times for turkeys of different sizes. The defrosting time assumes the turkey is left in the kitchen.

Size of turkey	Defrosting time	Cooking time
2.3–3.6 kg	14–18 hours	2.5–3.25 hours
3.6–5 kg	18–24 hours	3.25–3.75 hours
5–6.8 kg	24–26 hours	3.75–4.5 hours
6.8–9 kg	26–28 hours	4.5–5 hours
9–11.3 kg	28–36 hours	5–5.5 hours

a) What is the connection between the defrosting time and the size of the turkey?
b) Why do smaller turkeys cook faster than larger turkeys?
c) Many people suffer upset stomachs at Christmas because the turkey is not cooked right through. Bacteria manage to survive in the flesh which is not cooked fully. If the turkey is not fully defrosted before cooking, which part of the turkey is most likely to be undercooked?
d) A turkey at –8 °C was taken from the freezer. It was placed in a refrigerator where the temperature was 4 °C. Would the turkey still defrost? If so, how would the defrosting time be affected? Explain your answer.

1.10 Conduction and convection

A cup of coffee which is left standing will cool down. Energy is transferred from the hot drink to the cooler surroundings by the following processes:

- **conduction**
- **convection**
- **radiation**, and
- **evaporation** (see *GCSE Science Double Award Chemistry*, topic 3.5).

In all situations where heat transfer is taking place, one or more of these processes will be at work.

At times we need to cool things down more rapidly than would normally take place. If, for example, a car engine overheats, the metal parts expand and the engine siezes. To prevent this the engine must be continually cooled. The cooling system is carefully designed to transfer heat from the engine. The diagram above right shows a typical cooling system.

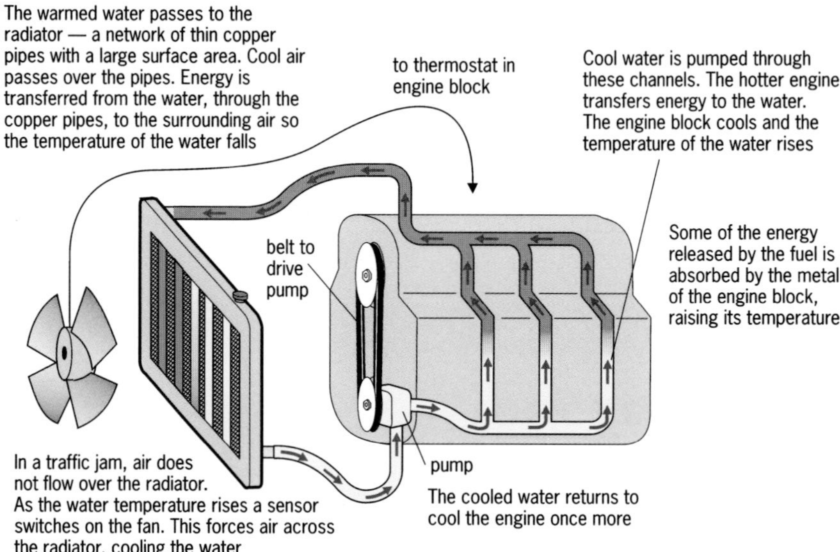
The warmed water passes to the radiator — a network of thin copper pipes with a large surface area. Cool air passes over the pipes. Energy is transferred from the water, through the copper pipes, to the surrounding air so the temperature of the water falls
to thermostat in engine block
Cool water is pumped through these channels. The hotter engine transfers energy to the water. The engine block cools and the temperature of the water rises
belt to drive pump
Some of the energy released by the fuel is absorbed by the metal of the engine block, raising its temperature
In a traffic jam, air does not flow over the radiator. As the water temperature rises a sensor switches on the fan. This forces air across the radiator, cooling the water
pump
The cooled water returns to cool the engine once more

Most car engines are cooled by water which flows through holes drilled in the engine block

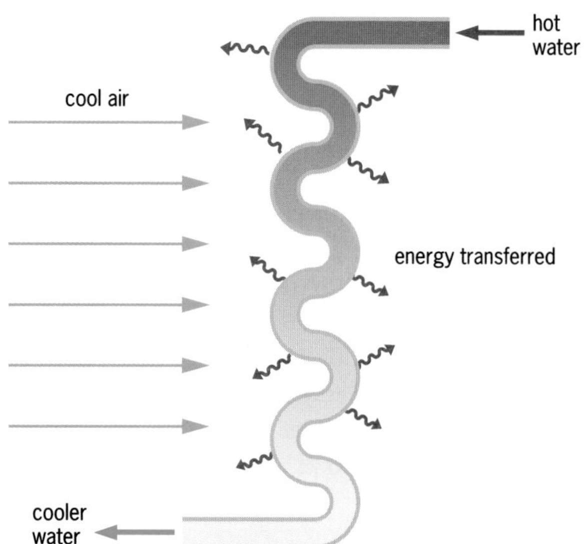
hot water
cool air
energy transferred
cooler water

Cross-section through a copper pipe in a car engine's radiator

Conduction

Imagine what happens as the hot water passes through the car radiator. Fast-moving molecules in the hot water collide with the nearest copper atoms and transfer energy to them, raising their temperature. They will then be hotter than their neighbours, so they transfer energy to them, raising their temperature. This process is repeated until the outside layer of atoms is warmed. Energy is then transferred to the cooler air as it flows across the surface of the hotter metal. The energy becomes so spread out in the air that any temperature rise is not noticeable.

The atoms of the copper do not move from place to place – they only serve to pass energy from one to another by vibration. The transfer of energy in this way is called **conduction**.

Conductors and insulators

Metals are good **conductors** – energy spreads through them quickly. In metals some of the electrons (normally held tightly by the atoms) are able to move freely through the material. These 'free electrons' help to transfer heat faster than if it were only passed from atom to atom .

Heat spreads more slowly through non-metals by conduction. These materials are described as poor conductors or **insulators**. Wood, rubber, plastics and polystyrene are examples of insulators. Gases are good insulators – that's why double glazing helps to keep a house warm – the panes of glass have a layer of air between them which slows down the transfer of heat.

Some materials are chosen specifically because they are conductors or insulators. Copper, for example, is chosen for the car radiator opposite because it is a very good conductor – energy spreads through it quickly, cooling the water rapidly.

The filling in a duvet traps air. Air is a poor conductor, so heat from the body spreads through very slowly, keeping you warm

Heat spreads quickly through the metal of a pan (a conductor), warming the food. Heat spreads more slowly through the wooden handle (an insulator) so it does not feel so hot when you hold it

Convection

Heat spreads through solids only by conduction because the particles are in fixed positions. In liquids and gases the particles are free to move about, carrying energy with them. The spreading of energy through liquids and gases takes place by **convection**.

When liquids and gases are heated they expand, becoming less dense. The warmed region rises away from the source of heat, carrying energy with it. As a result, heat is transferred from one place to another. The water in your home may be heated by convection.

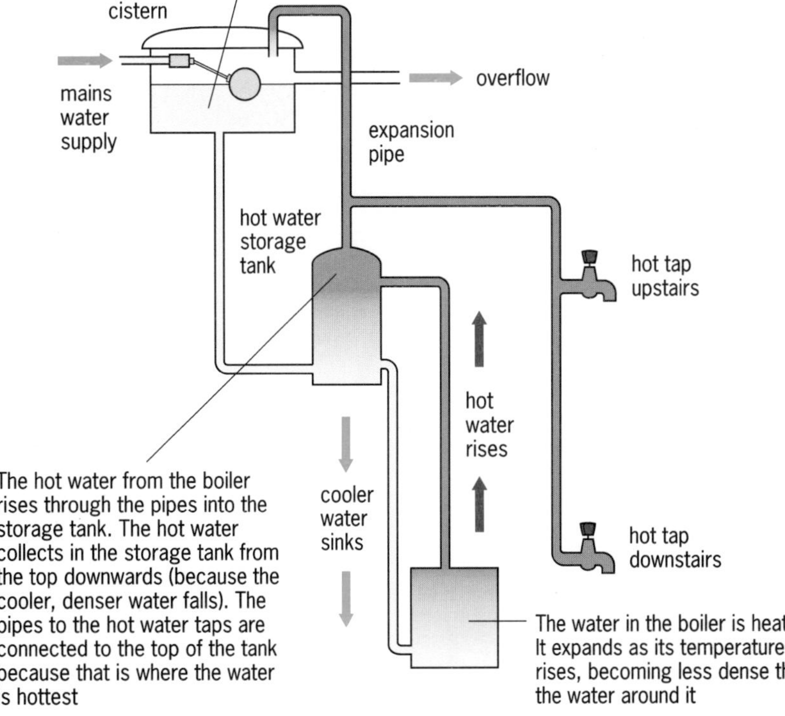
The cistern controls the flow of water into the tank. As water flows from the tank, through the taps, the level in the cistern drops and the ball falls, opening the valve. Fresh water flows from the mains supply into the cistern until it is at the right level again
cistern
mains water supply
overflow
expansion pipe
hot water storage tank
hot tap upstairs
hot water rises
cooler water sinks
hot tap downstairs
The hot water from the boiler rises through the pipes into the storage tank. The hot water collects in the storage tank from the top downwards (because the cooler, denser water falls). The pipes to the hot water taps are connected to the top of the tank because that is where the water is hottest
The water in the boiler is heated. It expands as its temperature rises, becoming less dense than the water around it

A type of hot water system found in many homes. The arrows show the movement of the water through the pipes, the boiler and the tank

Convection currents

The movement of water as it is heated can be seen if a small coloured crystal of, say, potassium permanganate is placed in one corner of a beaker containing water. When the water is heated just below the crystal, the warmed, coloured water rises to the surface. As it does, cooler water falls to take its place.

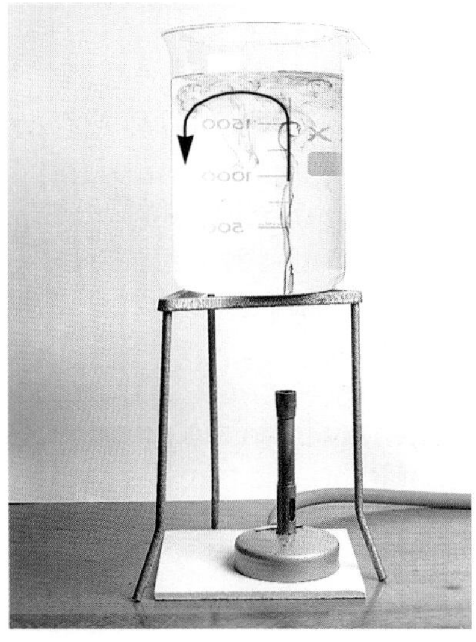

Demonstrating a convection current

The coloured water can be seen to slowly spread across the surface and fall down the opposite side of the beaker as it cools, forming a continuous flow or **convection current**.

Air which is heated by radiators in a closed room moves in a similar way. The air layer near a radiator is warmed by contact. It becomes less dense (more spread out) than the air which surrounds it. The warm, less dense air rises.

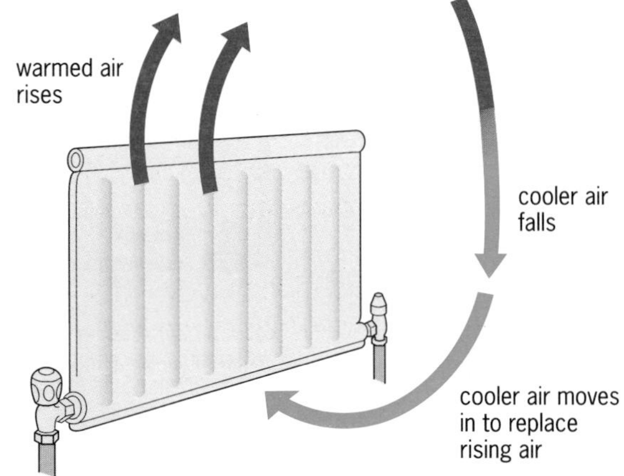
warmed air rises
cooler air falls
cooler air moves in to replace rising air

Formation of a convection current in your living room

Slowly this warmer air transfers energy to the cooler surroundings, such as the walls, windows and ceiling. The energy becomes more and more spread out. The air temperature falls and the air becomes denser. The cooled air then falls to be warmed by the radiator once again, and the whole process is repeated. A convection current (a continuous flow of warmed and cooled air) flows around the room.

Notice that the heat from the radiator is spread throughout the room by the *movement of the air particles*, unlike heat transfer by conduction where the particles do not move.

Reducing energy losses by conduction and convection

When you buy a hot drink outdoors, it may be served in a polystyrene cup with a lid covering it.

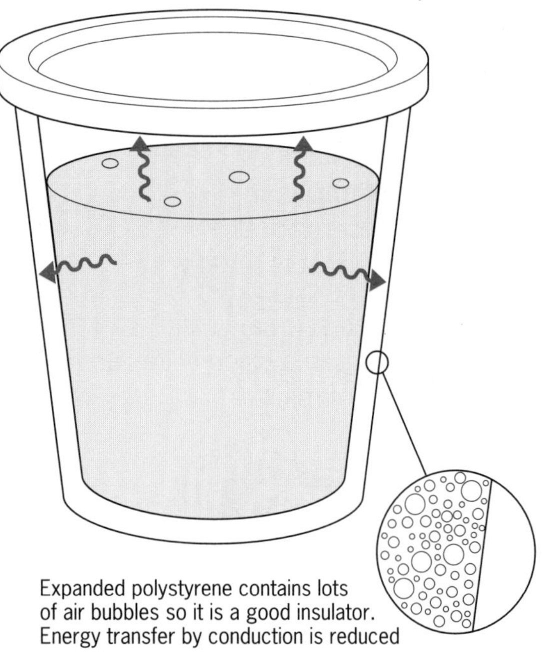
The lid reduces the transfer of energy by convection (and by evaporation)
The lid may be plastic – an insulator which reduces energy transfer by conduction
Expanded polystyrene contains lots of air bubbles so it is a good insulator. Energy transfer by conduction is reduced

A 'stay-warm' cup

The same type of cup can be used to keep drinks cool. The polystyrene reduces the transfer of heat from the hands and the surroundings to the drink.

★ THINGS TO DO

1 Make a list of situations where you have seen conductors and insulators at work. For each one say which of the materials is the conductor or insulator, and how they affect what happens.

2 Julie bought a hot drink at a hockey match. By the time she got back to her seat the drink had cooled down. It was too cold to drink! One of her friends said that the drink had cooled down because heat was conducted through the sides. Another said it had 'lost' most of its heat from the surface by convection and evaporation.

Who do you think was right? Which do you think will have most effect – the heat lost from the surface or the heat transferred through the sides of the cup? Suggest a reason for your prediction.

Plan how to test your ideas. When your teacher has checked your plan, carry out your investigation and write a clear report about what you find out.

3 Two pupils decided to do their own tests on loft insulation. They got six empty cans which were the same size. They wrapped a layer of loft insulation material around each of the cans, using the same material but different thicknesses on each can. They also put the same thickness of insulation onto the lids and the base of each can. They then put 100 cm^3 of warmed water into each can, measured the temperature, and measured it again after 15 minutes. Each can was standing on the same bench, in the same place in the laboratory. This is their table of results.

Thickness of insulation	Temperature at beginning	Temperature after 15 mins
2 cm	80°C	64°C
5 cm	80°C	67°C
8 cm	79°C	70°C
10 cm	80°C	73°C
15 cm	79°C	76°C
18 cm	80°C	76.5°C
21 cm	79°C	76°C

a) Copy the table, adding another column to show the fall in temperature of each can after 15 minutes.
b) What was the least thickness of insulation which they used in their investigation?
c) What was the fall in temperature after 15 minutes of the can with 10 cm of insulation wrapped around it?
d) Draw a graph showing how the fall in temperature depends on the thickness of the insulation used.
e) Write a sentence or two saying what these results tell you.

4 Water pipes sometimes burst during the winter months because the water in the pipes expands (swells) when it freezes. To prevent the pipes freezing up we can wrap insulating material around them.

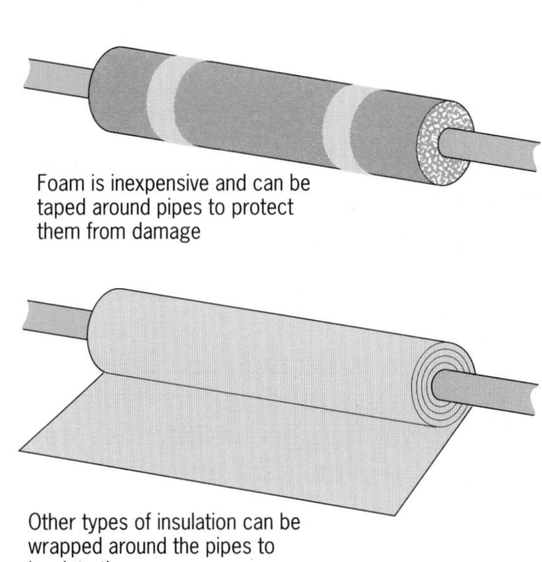

Foam is inexpensive and can be taped around pipes to protect them from damage

Other types of insulation can be wrapped around the pipes to insulate them

Carry out investigations to find out:
a) whether water in the pipes without insulation cools down faster than water in pipes which are lagged;
b) how the thickness of the insulation affects how fast the water in the pipes cools down. You could use test tubes to model the pipes.

1.11 Radiation

Radiation from the Sun is absorbed by plants, providing the energy for photosynthesis. Some of this energy is stored, eventually to be transferred through a food chain

The surface of the Earth (and everything on it) is warmed by energy from the Sun. This energy travels through space as **radiation** – energy transfer by electromagnetic waves (see topic 4.12).

Electromagnetic waves do not depend on the presence of particles – they can pass through a vacuum. Radiation from the Sun, for example, passes through 93 million miles of space to reach the Earth. The Sun has a surface temperature of 6000 °C and emits huge amounts of infra-red radiation, as well as light and ultra-violet radiation. It is the infra-red radiation that produces the heating effect.

We feel warm in the sun because we absorb some of the infra-red radiation (some is also reflected). The absorbed energy is converted into internal energy, or heat.

Everything emits infra-red radiation. In general, the hotter the object the more radiation it emits.

Emission of radiation

The colour of the surface of an object affects how much radiation it emits at a particular temperature. This can be tested using Leslie's Cube, a hollow steel cube which is filled with hot water. One side of the cube is painted gloss white, another dull (matt) black, another is dull white, whilst the fourth is a dark gloss (shiny) colour. To measure the radiation (energy) emitted from the sides, a thermopile (heat-sensing device) is used, connected to a galvanometer (a sensitive current detector).

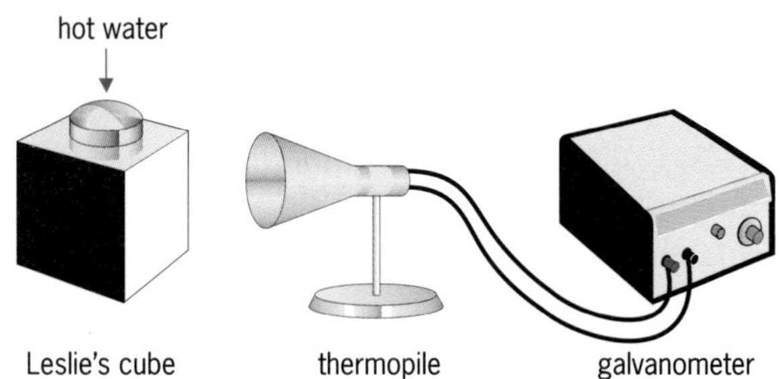

Comparing the radiation emitted from different surfaces

As the thermopile is moved from one side to another, it is found that the dull black surface is the best emitter, whilst the shiny white surface is the worst emitter.

Absorption of radiation

Similar experiments may be done to find out which colour is the best absorber of radiation. A simplified demonstration can be done using two conical flasks, one painted dull black and the other covered with aluminium foil (or shiny white paint). Both flasks contain the same amount of water, at the same temperature, and they are placed at equal distances from a radiant heater.

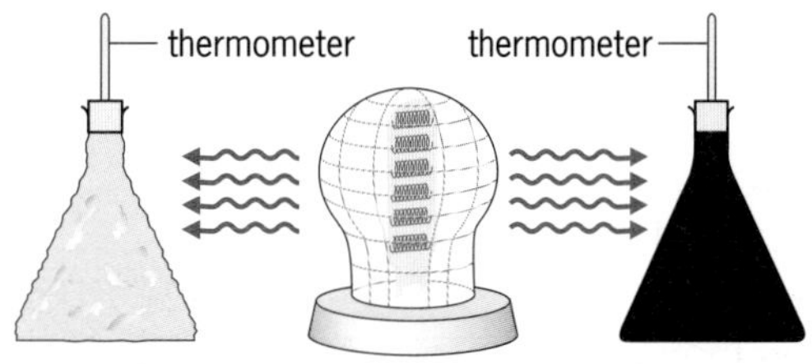

Comparing the radiation absorbed by different surfaces

The temperature of the water in the flask with the dull black surface is found to rise quicker, showing that dull dark surfaces are the best absorbers as well as the best emitters of radiation. Light shiny surfaces are good reflectors of radiation.

Microwave ovens

The food inside a microwave oven is heated by the microwave radiation it absorbs. When the oven is switched on, microwaves are produced at the top (or side) of the oven. These electromagnetic waves act as 'energy carriers', transferring energy to the food (see page 187).

The microwaves are absorbed by the water in the food. The extra energy gained by the water molecules raises the temperature of the water. Heat is then transferred from the water to the rest of the food by conduction.

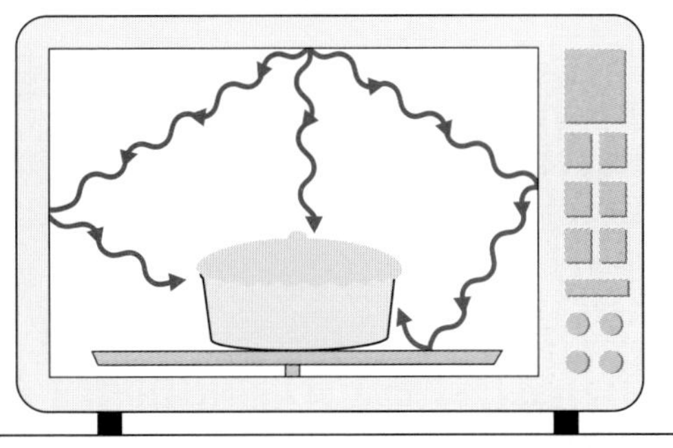

The highly polished sides of the microwave oven improve its efficiency by reflecting the microwaves, increasing the rate at which they strike the food

★ THINGS TO DO

1 Conduction, convection and radiation are all involved as solar energy is transferred to the water in a solar panel.

The solar panels on this roof absorb radiation from the Sun. The absorbed energy warms water which runs through pipes inside the panel

Explain how the efficiency of the panel depends on:
a) the materials which are used,
b) the colour of the materials,
c) the way the panel is designed.

A typical solar panel

2 Look at the photographs below. For each one write a paragraph about how heat transfer is affected by what is done.

Some marathon runners cover themselves in metal foil after a race

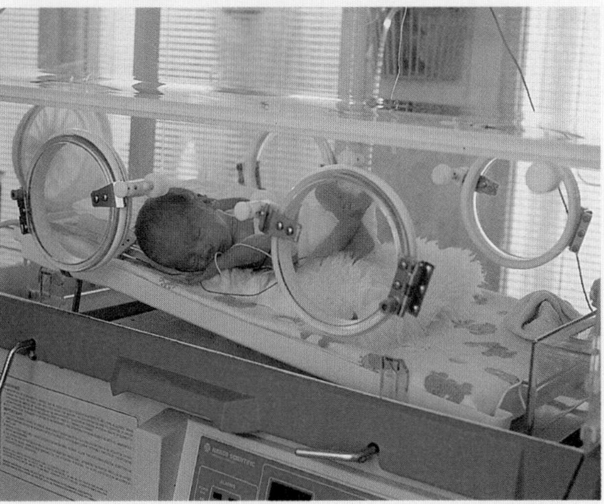

Premature babies need to be kept in incubators

1.12 Careful – it's hot!

Generally all four processes of heat transfer – conduction, convection, radiation and evaporation – are at work together. Consider, for example, what happens when water is heated in an electric kettle.

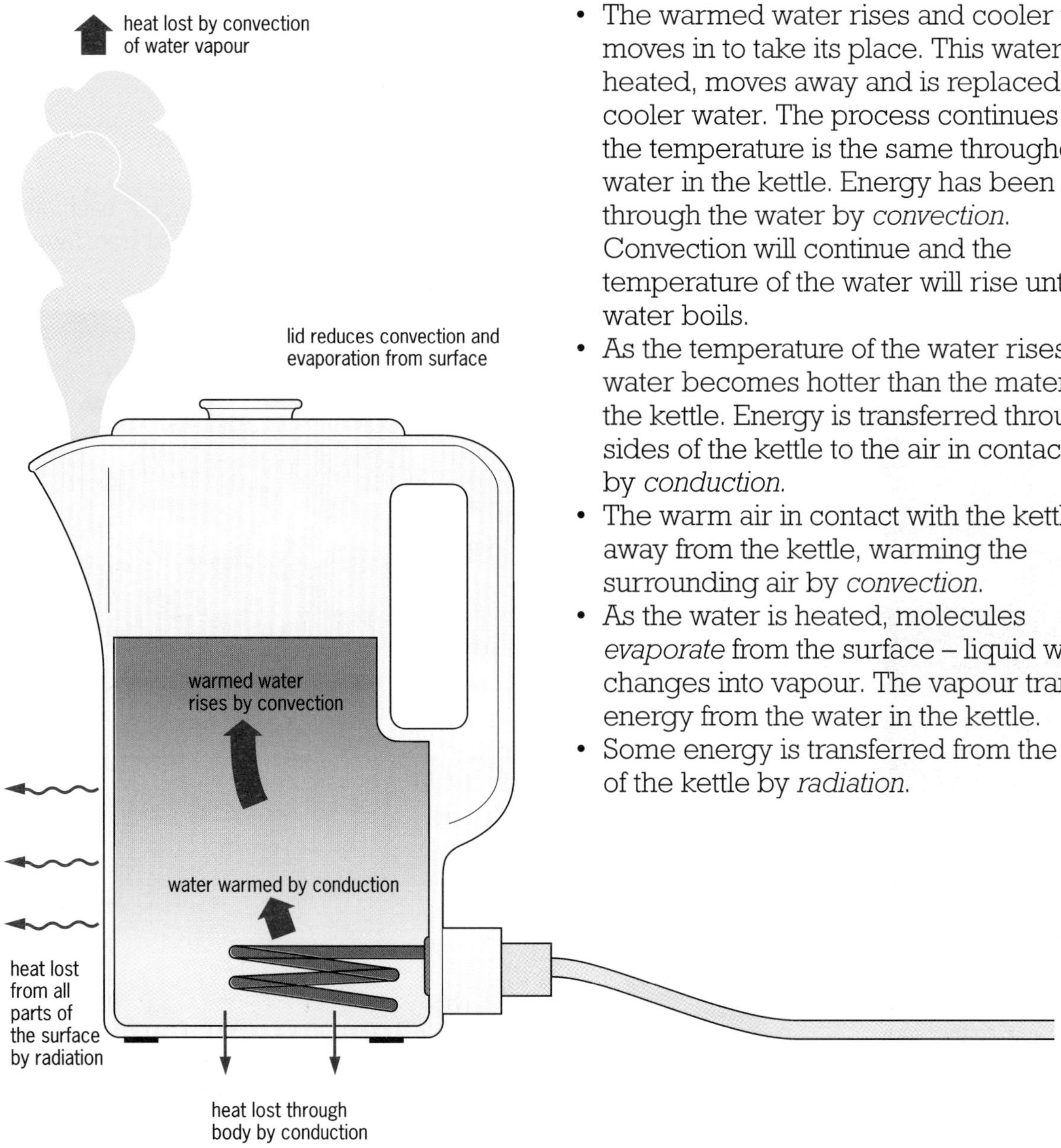

Heat transfer in an electric kettle

- As electricity flows through the element, the element gets red-hot. *Radiation* transfers energy to the metal tube which surrounds the element. The metal tube gets hot.
- Energy is transferred from the hot tube to the cooler water by *conduction*. The temperature of the water near the element rises.
- The warmed water rises and cooler water moves in to take its place. This water is heated, moves away and is replaced by cooler water. The process continues until the temperature is the same throughout the water in the kettle. Energy has been spread through the water by *convection*. Convection will continue and the temperature of the water will rise until the water boils.
- As the temperature of the water rises, the water becomes hotter than the material of the kettle. Energy is transferred through the sides of the kettle to the air in contact with it by *conduction*.
- The warm air in contact with the kettle rises away from the kettle, warming the surrounding air by *convection*.
- As the water is heated, molecules *evaporate* from the surface – liquid water changes into vapour. The vapour transfers energy from the water in the kettle.
- Some energy is transferred from the sides of the kettle by *radiation*.

★ THINGS TO DO

1 A company which designs and sells photographic equipment needs a design for a water bath in which the developing tanks can be placed while the films develop. The developer in the developing tank must stay at the same temperature (20 °C) for 20 minutes. Before designing the bath they need to know what effect different factors, such as the size of the bath or the material used, would have on the rate at which developer in the tank cools down.

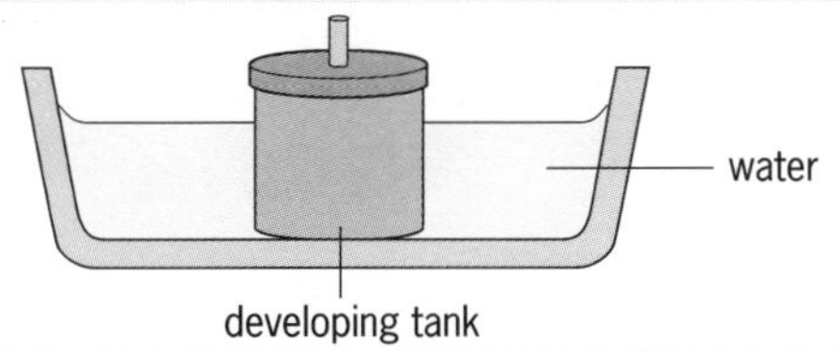

Carry out a series of investigations to help them solve their problem. If you have time, design your own water bath using the results of your tests.

2 Some animals are in constant danger due to heat transfer to and from their bodies. The information below appears in David Attenborough's book 'Life on Earth'.

a) Do you think iguanas are cold-blooded or warm-blooded? Explain your answer.

b) Make a table showing the ways in which iguanas (i) raise their temperature, (ii) cool down.

c) When humans are cold they tend to look very pale. When they are hot they look red. What information in the text below helps to explain why this happens?

d) What could happen if the iguanas went swimming at sunset? Explain your answer.

e) How do conduction, convection, radiation and evaporation help the iguanas to warm up or cool down?

Marine iguanas, Galapagos

Marine iguanas must keep their bodies at around 37 °C. At dawn they gather on the black lava ridges or climb onto east-facing boulders, lying with their sides facing the rising sun. Within an hour their bodies reach the optimum temperature so they turn to face the sun. Now their sides are in shadow and the rays strike only their chests. As the sun climbs higher, the risk of overheating grows.

They stiffen their legs and hold their bodies off the baking black rock, while the wind blows over their undersides as well as their back.

At some time in the middle of the day when their blood is almost as hot as they can stand, they plunge into the sea, swimming strongly.

Instead of dispersing heat, they must now retain as much as they can. They narrow the arteries near the surface of their bodies so that the blood, now retained near the centre, remains warm for longer. If they become too cold they will be unable to swim. After a few minutes their temperature has fallen by some 10 °C and they return to land.

Back on the rocks they prostrate themselves, all four legs outstretched. Not until their body temperature has risen again will they be able to digest any food in their stomachs.

As the sun starts to set in the afternoon, they gather on the crests or ridges to absorb as much sunlight as possible before the sun sets.

From *Life on Earth*, David Attenborough (HarperCollins Publishers Limited)

1.13 Warmer homes and smaller bills

You pay for the energy used to warm your home. If you have gas heating you pay for the gas. If you have solid fuel heating, you pay for the coal or the coke. The energy released by the fuel eventually ends up spread throughout the atmosphere – lost from your home forever.

This photograph was taken three hours after snow had fallen. One house owner had the loft insulated. The other did not. Can you tell which is which?

Every home loses heat. For every one hundred pounds spent on fuel, one hundred pounds is lost through the windows, walls, roof, floors and by draughts.

25% is lost through the roof
£100
10% is lost through the windows
35% is lost through the external walls
15% is lost through draughts
15% is lost through the floor

Where the heat escapes

Reducing energy losses

If we reduce the energy losses from our homes, then less fuel will be needed to keep the temperature at a comfortable level – and that means smaller bills, conservation of precious energy sources and less pollution.

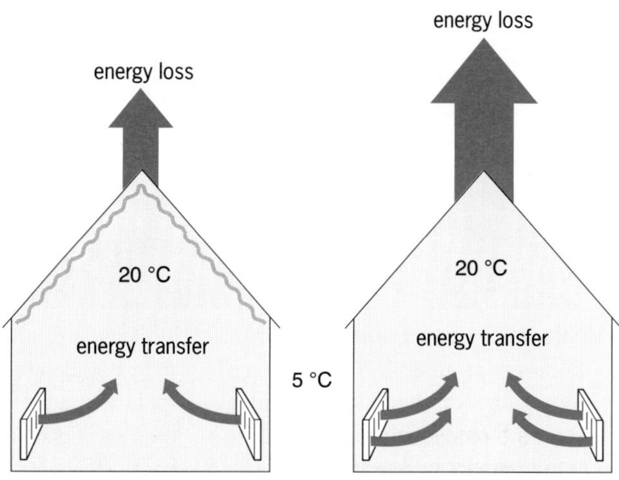
energy loss
energy loss
20 °C
20 °C
energy transfer
energy transfer
5 °C

To keep the temperature in a house constant, energy must be supplied at the same rate at which it is lost

Modern homes must have energy-saving materials included in their design but many older houses have no form of insulation. There are lots of ways in which the energy losses from such houses could be reduced.

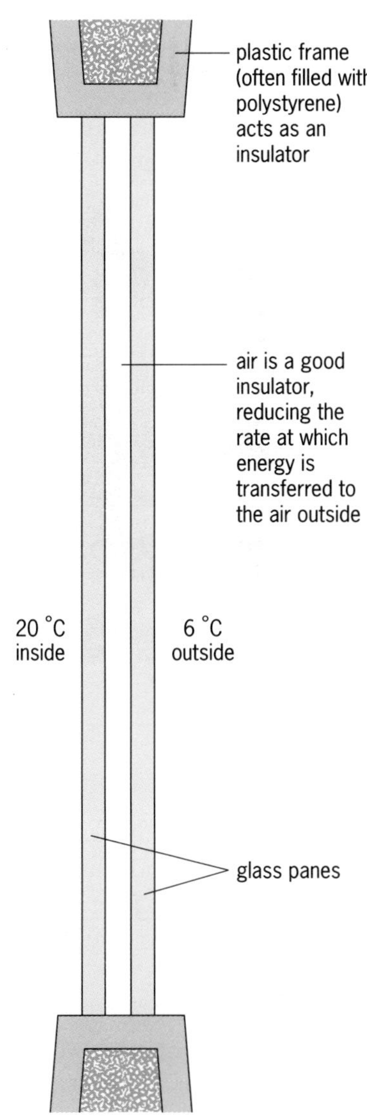

Double-glazed windows are designed to reduce energy loss

Double glazing

Windows in older housing consist of a single pane of glass. The greater the area of the window, the faster energy passes through it by conduction. Energy loss through the windows can be reduced by 50% by installing double glazing – two panes of glass with an air (or a vacuum) gap between them.

Some modern types of glass are also claimed to reduce energy losses by radiation.

Cavity wall insulation

Most house walls consist of a layer of bricks on the outside with a second layer of bricks or concrete blocks making up the inside wall. The gap between these two layers is known as the cavity.

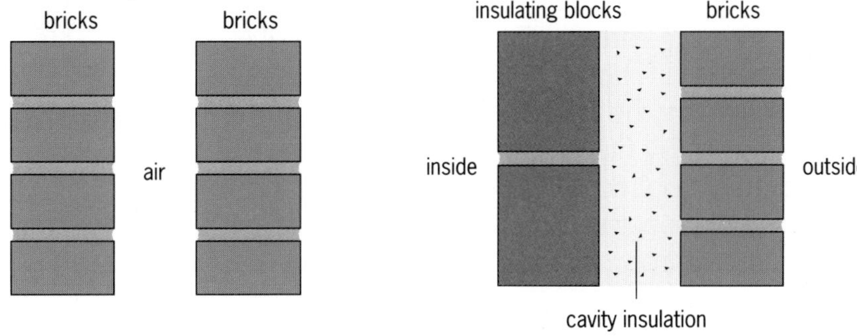

Older houses have a double brick wall with an air gap between

Modern houses have an inner layer of insulating blocks. The cavity is filled with an insulating material such as plastic fibre or polystyrene

Although air is a poor conductor, the air next to the inner wall is warmed and rises (by convection) carrying heat away with it. Heat loss can be reduced by filling this space with an insulating material. There are many types of cavity wall insulation but most consist of fine fibres which are blown into the cavity through holes drilled in the walls.

Energy loss through cavity walls can be reduced by 80% if cavity wall insulation is used.

Loft insulation

Heat escapes through the upstairs ceiling of a house by conduction. Loft insulation, placed directly above the ceiling, helps reduce the rate at which energy is transferred by conduction. Loft insulation is the cheapest form of insulation to include in your home, and government grants may be available to help with the cost. Energy loss through the roof can be reduced by 85% by putting down a layer of loft insulation 75 mm thick.

Heat loss through the roof is reduced greatly by laying down loft insulation

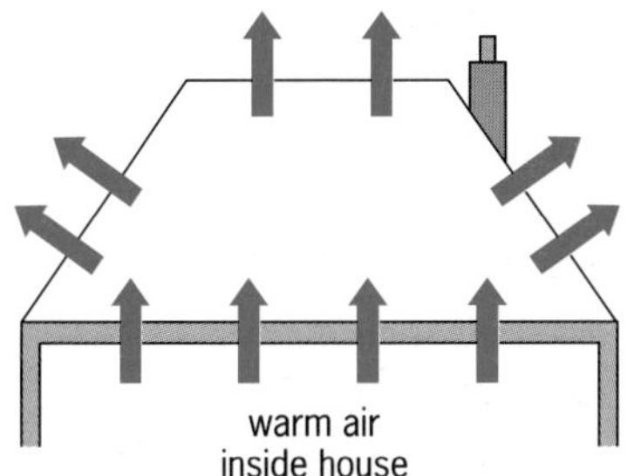

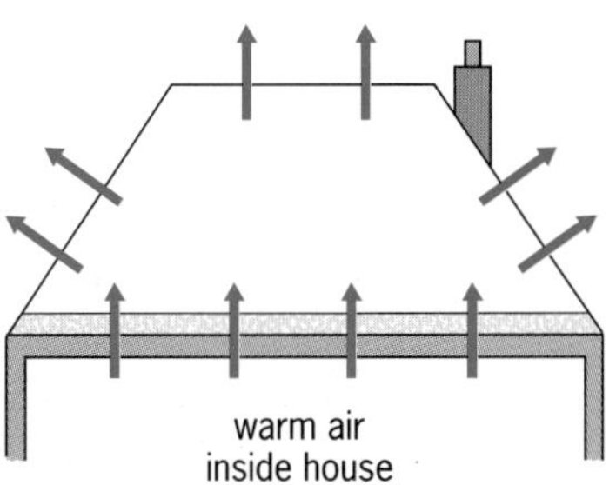

Draught exclusion

Draughts do not cause energy transfer from the house. Colder air which enters through badly fitting doors and windows mixes with the warmer air, reducing the temperature of the air inside the house. Extra energy must be supplied by the heating system to keep the air warm. By fitting draught excluders most of this 'cooling effect' can be eliminated. Some ventilation must be allowed, however, particularly in rooms where there is a gas fire.

Stop those draughts!

Draughts through door and window frames are usually easy and cheap to stop. You'll feel the benefit immediately and see the benefit next time your heating bill comes in. All sorts of draught excluders are available, ranging in price from about a pound for simple adhesive strip to £5 or so for a sophisticated 'threshold' sealer.

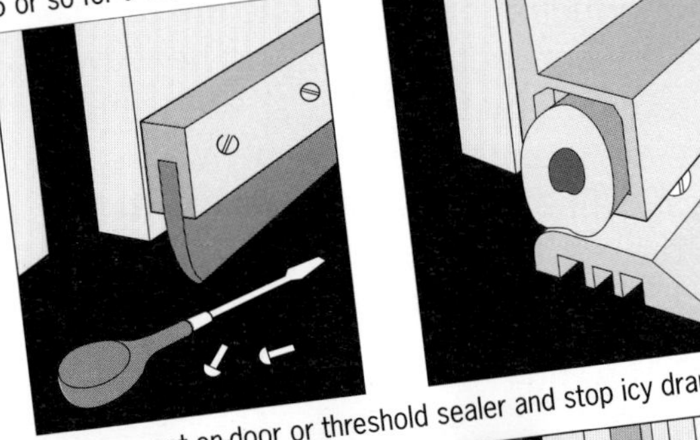

▶ Fit a neat on-door or threshold sealer and stop icy draughts.

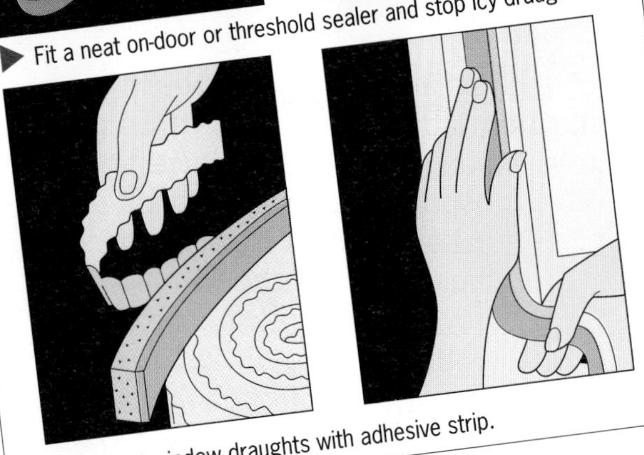

▶ Cut out window draughts with adhesive strip.

Carpeting

Thick carpets can reduce the heat lost through the floors – the carpet material acts as insulation, reducing heat transfer by conduction.

The cost of different types of insulation

The table shows the cost of installing different types of insulation in an average three-bedroom semi-detached house.

Type of insulation	Average cost
Double glazing	£7000
Cavity wall insulation	£900
Loft insulation	£80
Draught excluders	£40

U-values

Builders use *U*-values when considering how much energy will escape from a building with various forms of insulation. The higher the *U*-value, the more energy escapes in any given time. The amount of energy which can escape also depends on the temperature difference between the inside and outside surfaces and the surface area of, for example, the window or wall. The larger the temperature difference and the larger the area, the faster energy will be transferred from the building.

$$\underset{\text{(joules)}}{\text{heat transferred}} = \underset{(\text{W/m}^2\,^\circ\text{C})}{U\text{-value}} \times \underset{(\text{m}^2)}{\text{surface area}} \times \underset{\text{(s)}}{\text{time}} \times \underset{(^\circ\text{C})}{\text{temperature difference}}$$

Some typical *U*-values are shown below.

	U/W/m^2°C
Concrete wall 150 mm thick	3.5
Brick wall 220 mm thick	2.3
Cavity wall with no insulation	1.5
Cavity wall with insulation	0.7
Single-glazed window	5.6
Double-glazed window (12 mm gap)	3.0
Timber floor	0.5
Tiled roof with plaster ceiling	2.0
Roof as above with 50 mm insulation	0.4

Passive solar heating

Our homes are warmed by radiation from the Sun. To make the most of this source of energy, houses can be designed with large double- (or even triple-) glazed windows on the south side to capture as much sunlight as possible. This is called 'passive solar heating' (to distinguish from 'active solar heating' through the use of solar panels, page 27). With effective house insulation, heating bills can be reduced by over 50%.

★ THINGS TO DO

1 Where is most heat 'lost' from in our homes?

2 Using the information given on page 30, draw a pie chart showing how much heat escapes from different parts of a house.

3 Copy and complete this table showing ways of reducing heat transfer from a house.

Heat transfer through	**How this can be reduced**
Windows	

4 Work out how much it would cost to install double glazing, cavity wall insulation and loft insulation into the average three-bedroom semi-detached home. Then work out how much would be saved on the average yearly heating bill of £600 if this insulation work was done.

How long would it take to recoup (by savings on bills) the amount spent on the insulation?

5 The Department of Energy is concerned about the amount of energy which is being wasted in homes. They are to produce a brochure which is to be sent to every household in the country. The aim is to encourage people to consider the ways in which they can save energy and to show them how they will benefit from installing insulation.

The brochure is to be a double-page spread, including pictures, cartoons or whatever is thought will persuade people to read it. It should also include details of costs, and how much can be saved.

Your job is to design this brochure. Before starting, think carefully of the things which make brochures, adverts, etc., attractive to those who read them.

1.14

Fuels

On 6th July 1988, an explosion on the oil rig 'Piper Alpha' resulted in the death of 167 workers. Many others suffered severe burns or suffered from hypothermia after jumping into the sea to escape the fire. Piper Alpha was completely destroyed by the explosion and was sunk the same year

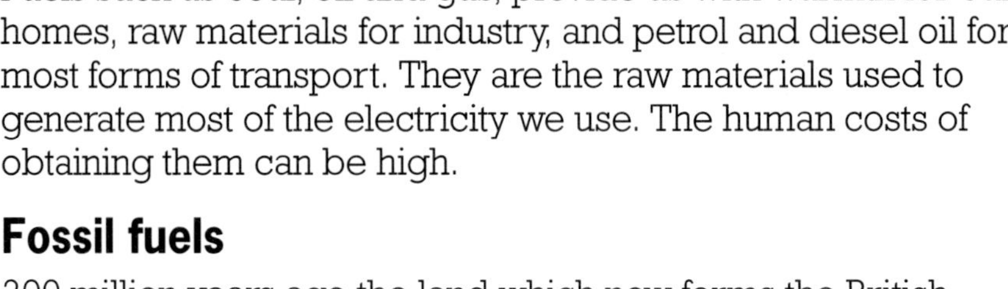

Fuels such as coal, oil and gas, provide us with warmth for our homes, raw materials for industry, and petrol and diesel oil for most forms of transport. They are the raw materials used to generate most of the electricity we use. The human costs of obtaining them can be high.

Fossil fuels

300 million years ago the land which now forms the British Isles was close to the equator. The climate was warm and damp, with bright sunshine. Plants and animals flourished. Low-lying land was covered in freshwater swamps.

300 million years ago much of Britain had a landscape similar to that in parts of Florida now

Trees and other plants grew quickly. When they died others quickly replaced them. The dead trees fell into stagnant water so in the absence of oxygen they only partially decayed. As more and more trees died a layer tens of metres thick formed. Layers of sand built up on top of the remains of the trees. Over thousands of years, alternating layers of trees and sediment were formed which became hundreds of metres thick.

Over millions of years, the weight of the sediments squashed the soft tree layers into thin strips. The layers of sediment formed rock. The chemicals in the decayed plants changed into coal.

Oil and gas were also formed over millions of years, from the partially decayed remains of animals and plants that lived in the tropical seas.

Coal, oil and gas are called **fossil fuels** because they are the fossilised remains of living things.

When fossil fuels are burned in the presence of oxygen, heat energy is released. The original source of the energy was the Sun – the plants from which the fossil fuel originated absorbed energy from sunlight and stored it in their tissues.

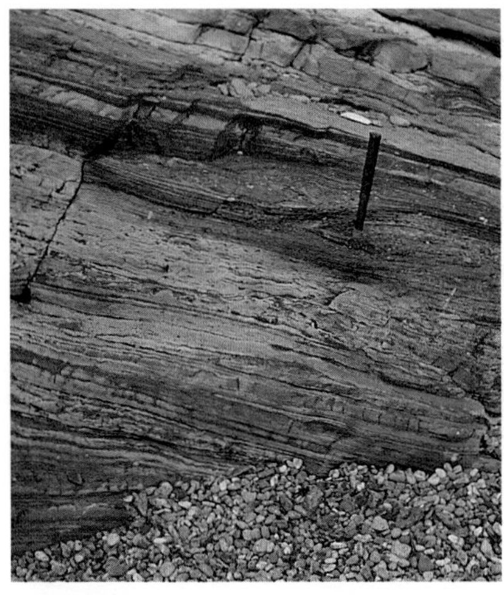

Cross-section through sedimentary rocks showing a coal seam

chemical energy ⟶ heat energy

A bucket of coal which took 300 million years to form will be burned in 40 minutes. One litre of petrol may be used in about 5 minutes. Once used, these fuels cannot be used again. They cannot be replaced fast enough to meet demand. They will eventually run out. They are called **non-renewable sources** of energy. This chart shows how long the world's known supplies of fossil fuels are expected to last if we continue using them at our present rate.

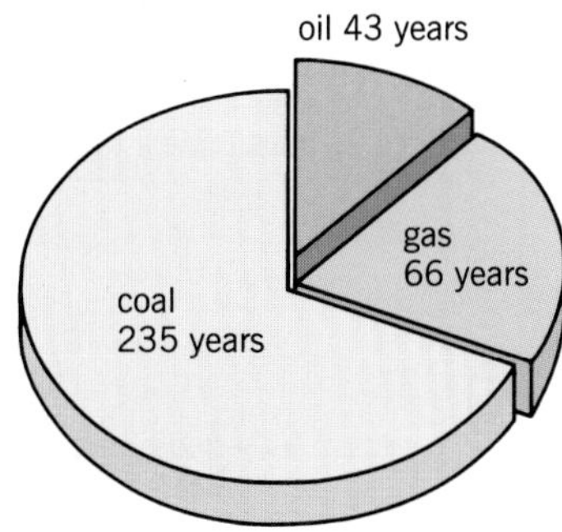

Fossil fuel reserves

Nuclear fuels

Some modern power stations use nuclear fuels such as uranium and plutonium. Nuclear fuels are also non-renewable. Eventually the sources of uranium and plutonium will run out, and we will not be able to supply the fuel needed by nuclear generating stations.

The ores from which we extract pure uranium are found in the Earth's crust, and are mined just like other minerals

Wood

The use of wood as a fuel has decreased considerably, but there are still millions of people for whom it is the only source of heat. New trees will grow, but wood burns much faster than it grows, so supplies could become increasingly difficult to obtain.

Today, when timber is cut commercially, the area is immediately replanted. With careful management there will be a continuous supply of wood in the future. Only if it can be grown as fast as it is used can it be thought of as a **renewable source** of energy.

★ THINGS TO DO

1 a) Eventually we will run out of oil and gas. Make a list of ways in which this would affect your life.
b) Make a list of ways in which we could make fuel reserves last longer.
c) Design a poster which would encourage people to save energy.

2 A test was done by a group of pupils to find out which fuel was best – paraffin or gas. The pupils measured the temperature of some water in a pan, heated it using paraffin for five minutes, then measured the temperature again. They repeated the test using gas.
a) What would they need to keep the same to make their test 'fair'?
b) Another pupil said that the temperature rise was not an accurate measure of how much energy was released as the fuel burned. What do you think she meant?

3 Plan your own investigation to find out whether a sugar-coated breakfast cereal releases more energy when burned than the packet in which it is sold. If possible, after checking your plans with your teacher, carry out your investigation.

1.15

Electrical energy

The electrical energy we need is made or 'generated' in power stations and transferred to our homes by an electric current through overhead or underground cables. The big advantage of electrical energy is that it is clean when used, producing no polluting gases or waste materials (see topic 2.18 and 2.19).

In the UK, 77% of electricity is generated from coal, oil or gas (fossil fuels) and 21% from nuclear fuels. Regardless of which fuel is used, fuel-burning power stations all make electricity in the same way.

A fuel-burning power station

to National Grid
The electricity is passed into the National Grid
step-up transformer
The turbines turn a generator, producing electricity
generator
cooling water from nearby river
Waste gases, mainly carbon dioxide and sulphur dioxide, pass into the atmosphere. Sulphur dioxide causes acid rain. Some power stations are using flue-gas 'desulphurisation' processes to reduce the output
turbines
to cooling tower
The high-pressure steam is directed onto turbines, making them turn
The excess steam is cooled and the water is used again
Coal, oil or gas are burned in the furnace, releasing energy which is used to heat water. The water changes into high-pressure steam
steam outlets
condensed steam
Nuclear fuels release energy as their atoms undergo 'fission' in the reactor. The energy changes water into high-pressure steam
high-pressure steam
pump
coal, oil or gas furnace or nuclear reactor
boiler
The ash waste from coal-fired power stations is removed and used to make thermal insulating blocks for the inside walls of modern homes

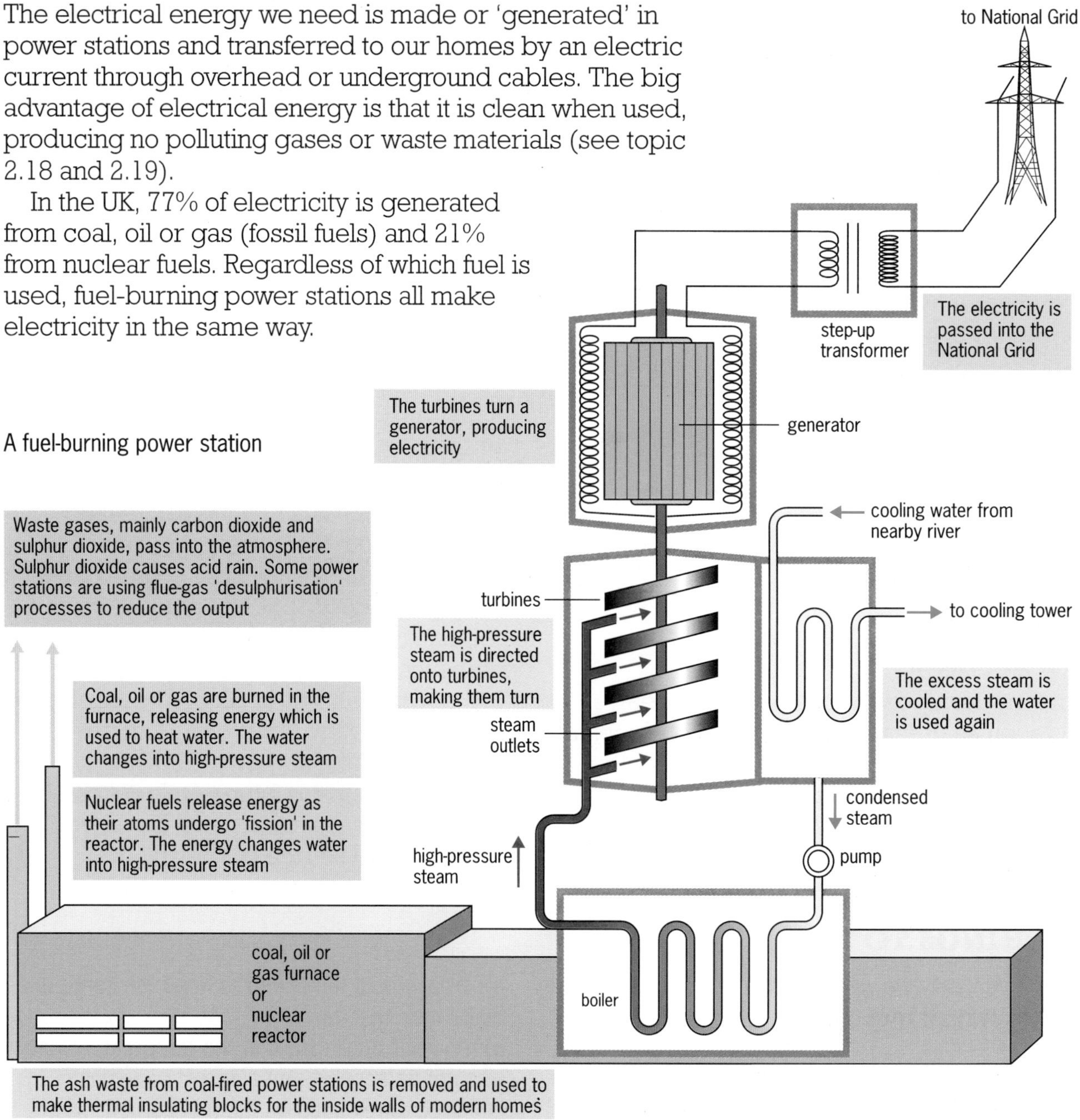

The processes in a power station involve a series of energy transformations:

chemical energy stored in the atoms and molecules of the fuel → heat energy released as the fuel burns or the nuclear material changes → kinetic energy in the turbines and generator → electrical energy from the generator

Meeting our needs

The electricity generating companies must try to supply enough energy to meet our demands. In this way it is rather like food in a shop – if the shop runs out then you cannot get the food you need. If the generating companies could not make enough electricity to meet demand, then some people would have to do without at times.

The graph shows how the demand for electricity changes throughout the day.

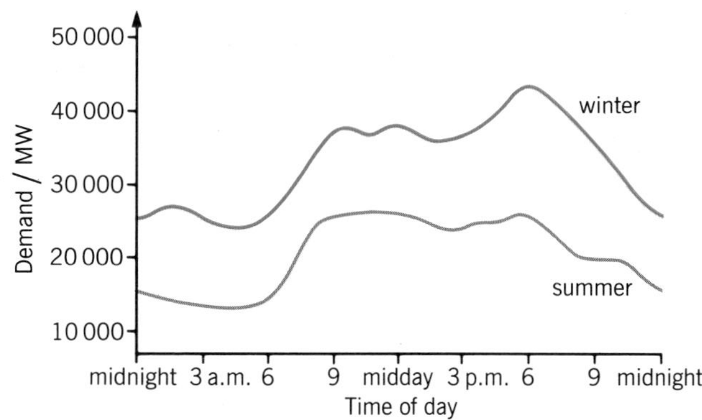

Electricity demand in the UK over a 24-hour period

Sometimes the demand is bigger than the rate at which the power stations can generate electricity. The generating companies have 'stand-by' systems which are used to generate extra electricity when it is needed. One such system, at Cruachan in Scotland, is illustrated here.

Although the system is not efficient financially (the money obtained from selling the electricity is less than it costs to pump the water back into the upper reservoir), systems such as these are the only way to provide the energy which is needed to meet the extra demand at certain times.

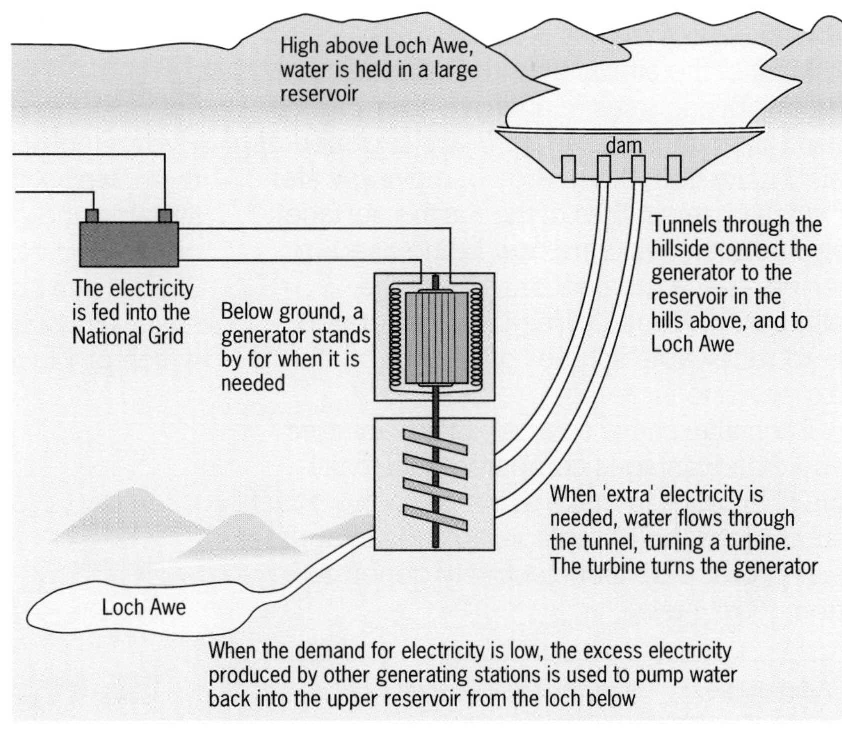

Pumped storage at Cruachan

★ THINGS TO DO

1 The generating companies have to predict what the demand for electricity will be hour by hour each day. When a popular series is on television, extra electricity is needed to cope with the demand of millions of people switching on their televisions. Make a list of other events which could suddenly increase the demand for electricity.

2 Copy the graphs showing how the demand for electricity changes during the day in summer and winter.

a) Add brief notes explaining why the demand increases or decreases at different times.

b) Explain how the demand for electricity on a winter day differs from that on a typical summer day.

3 Draw a flow chart showing the energy transfers which take place at Cruachan,

a) when water is flowing downhill,

b) when the water is being pumped back uphill.

1.16 Thinking ahead

Use of fossil fuels

If we are to make sure that we can produce sufficient electricity in the future, then we must make plans before fossil fuels run out. By reducing our use of fossil fuels we will also reduce the effect of problems such as global warming (see *GCSE Science Double Award Biology*, topic 3.20), acid rain (see *GCSE Science Double Award Chemistry*, topic 2.16) and air pollution (see *GCSE Science Double Award Biology*, topics 3.18 and 3.20).

Most of the alternatives to fossil fuels are renewable sources of energy – they can be used over and over again. Ways of generating electricity from the energy of moving water (which covers 4/5ths of the Earth's surface) and from the wind are now being used or tested. At the moment only 2% of the electricity needed in the UK is generated from renewable sources of energy, but this is expected to increase.

Each alternative source has advantages and disadvantages compared with fossil fuels. In order to make a comparison we first summarise the advantages, disadvantages and power output of electricity generated from fossil fuels.

Advantages: Generally available source of energy currently in plentiful supply.
Continued use would keep people in existing jobs.
Power stations are relatively cheap to build and to operate compared with nuclear power stations.

Disadvantages: Releases atmospheric pollutants which increase the greenhouse effect, produce acid rain, and cause health problems.
Non-renewable, so will eventually run out.

Power output: Fairly high.

Burning fossil fuels causes pollution

Hydroelectricity

Hydroelectricity is electricity generated from the power of falling water. Rain runs into streams and rivers which run into a large lake created by damming a valley. As the water flows down large pipes through the dam it turns a turbine. The turbine turns a generator which produces the electricity.

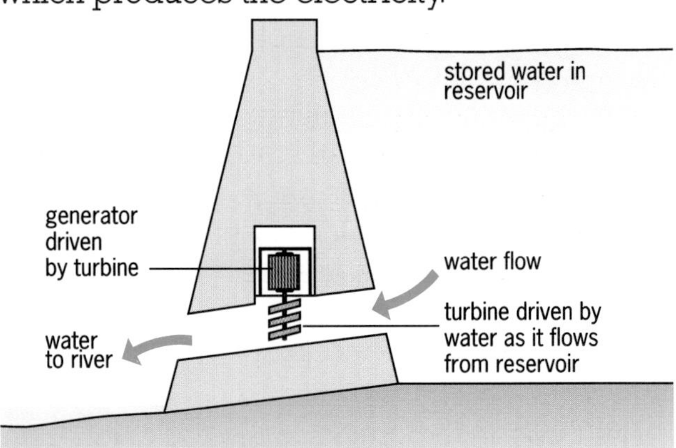

Generating electricity from water

Advantages: Clean, renewable source of energy.
Can create leisure facilities – boating, fishing.
Can provide alternative habitats for animals.

Disadvantages: Depends on rainfall.
Environmental effect – large areas of countryside must be covered with water, displacing people from homes and animals from natural habitats.

Power output: Can be fairly high, as the same water often flows through several power stations in any one system.
About 9000 large hydroelectric power stations would be needed to meet current demand.

Wind energy

Winds (moving air) blow across the surface of the Earth every day. Sometimes the winds are strong; at other times there may be very little, if any, wind. Wind turbines are turned by the force of the wind. The photograph on page 1 shows a modern wind turbine. The blades of the turbine are connected directly to a generator. As the generator turns, electricity is produced.

Advantages: Clean source of renewable energy.

Disadvantages: High costs involved in implementing and maintaining.
Environmental effects – may visually spoil countryside.
Unpredictable – wind may not be strong enough to turn turbines when electricity is needed.

Power output: Fairly low – about 80 million wind generators would be needed to supply all the electricity we need at peak times.

Geothermal energy

In some parts of the world the rocks close to the surface are hot. They are heated by the energy released by radioactive elements as they decay within the Earth's crust. This 'geothermal' energy can be extracted. Two boreholes are drilled and the rock between them fractured by an explosive charge. Cold water is then forced, under pressure, down one of the holes. The water is heated as it flows through the cracks in the rock, and then rises through the second borehole.

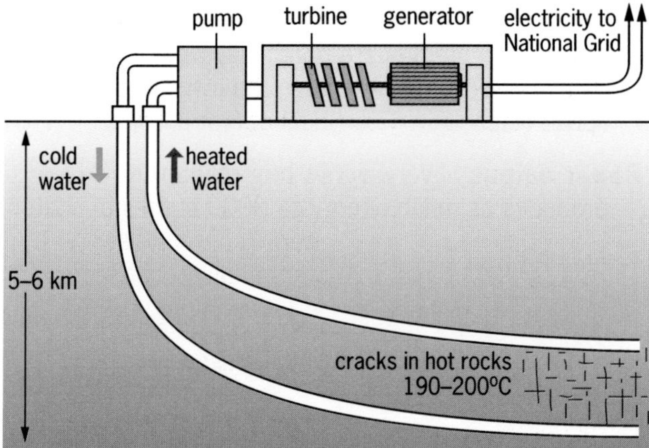

Extracting energy from hot rocks

The heated water may pass through a heat exchanger which produces the steam needed to drive the turbines. These drive the generators which produce electricity.

Advantages: Clean, constantly available source of renewable energy.

Disadvantages: Quite expensive to install.
Technical problems in maintenance.
Suitable rock is found only in a limited number of areas.

Power output: Fairly low.

Wave energy

Countries which have a long coastline must consider ways in which the movement of the waves can be used to generate electricity. Waves are created by the movement of the tides and the wind. The up-and-down motion of the waves is a continuous source of energy, providing it can be turned into a rotatory movement from which electricity can be generated. The use of wave generators of different designs has been tested but the results have not proved encouraging for use on a large scale.

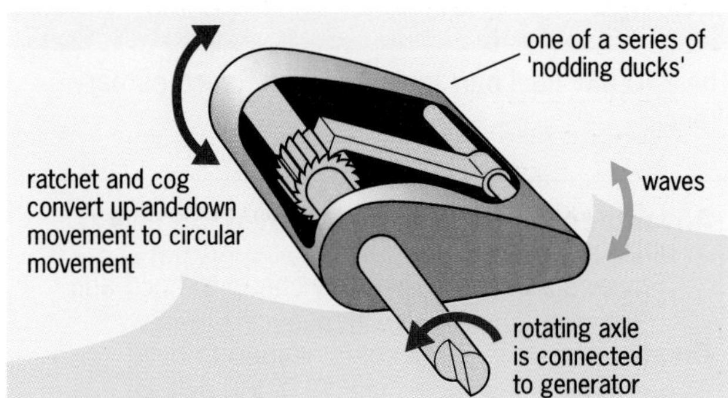

One form of wave generator

Advantages: Clean source of renewable energy.

Disadvantages: Initial costs are high.
Maintenance is difficult and costs are high.
Environmental problems – would stretch across many miles of coastline.

Power output: Fairly low unless technology is improved.

Tidal energy

The continuous motion of the tides can also be used to generate electricity using tidal barrages – large dams which are normally built across the narrower sections of river estuaries. As the tide moves in, water flows behind the barrage and the 'gates' are closed. Huge amounts of water are stored behind the barrage. The water is then allowed to flow out through large pipes. As it flows through the pipes it drives the turbines which in turn drive the generators.

The 240 MW tidal barrage across the Rance estuary, France

Advantages: Clean source of renewable energy. Reliable as tides rise and fall twice each day regardless of the weather.

Disadvantages: High costs needed to build barrages (currently around £10 000 million). Environmental effects – can damage natural habitats. May restrict movement of ships.

Power output: Fairly high – it is estimated that barrages across eight large estuaries in the UK could supply 15% of our electricity.

Nuclear energy

Nuclear power stations use non-renewable nuclear fuels such as uranium and plutonium. These materials release huge amounts of energy as changes take place inside the atoms. A single speck of uranium, for example, can produce the same amount of energy as a bucketful of coal.

Currently just over 20% of electricity in the UK is generated in nuclear power stations.

Nuclear fuels do not produce smoke or gases to pollute the atmosphere, but there are other potential dangers. Nuclear materials are radioactive (see page 194). If living things are exposed to radioactive emissions their health could be affected. The waste materials from nuclear power stations are classed as 'high-level' and 'low-level' waste, according to their level of radioactivity. Some low-level waste is washed into the sea. Small amounts of nuclear dust may get into the air. The high-level waste must be stored in complete safety for several thousand years before it will be safe.

Advantages: Lots of energy from small amounts of fuel.
Little atmospheric pollution, providing strict precautions are taken.
Generally reliable; little maintenance.
Low costs once up and running.

Disadvantages: Non-renewable.
Can be dangerous – strict safeguards are needed to ensure safety.
High cost of building power stations.
High cost of dismantling power stations when they can no longer be used.
Waste materials need to be stored for several thousand years and are potentially highly dangerous – there are many unknown factors about waste disposal.

Power output: Very high – 1 kg of uranium produces as much energy as 3000 tonnes of coal.

★ THINGS TO DO

1 Make a table showing which of the following energy sources are renewable and which are non-renewable, and whether they could produce electricity reliably throughout the year.

coal, nuclear, solar, gas, wind, waves, oil, hydroelectricity, geothermal

2 This table shows the cost of producing 1 kWh of electrical energy using different sources.

Source	Cost
Coal	1.2p
Oil	1.35p
Nuclear	0.8p
Hydroelectricity	0.23p
Wind	2.6p

a) Which of these methods produces the cheapest energy? Why do you think it is the cheapest?
b) Wind is free. Why do you think it costs so much to make electricity from the wind?
c) Some sources of energy are described as 'dilute'. This means that relatively large amounts are needed to produce small amounts of useful energy. Which sources of energy to you think are 'dilute'? Explain your answers.

3 Tidal barrages may provide much of the electricity we need in the future. One which is proposed would stretch 16 km across the mouth of the Severn estuary and would cost in excess of £12 000 million. The generators would produce about 7% of the energy currently supplied by all other power stations. Some people are worried about the environment.

By referring to the cartoon below, make a table showing the advantages and disadvantages (to both people and animals) of building the Severn barrage. Try to add some of your own.

Finally give your own opinions about whether the barrage should be built. Try to support what you say by giving reasons.

4 This table shows how the temperature of rocks below the surface changes with depth.

Depth/m	**Temp.**/°C	**Depth**/m	**Temp.**/°C
500	37	4000	162
1000	53	4500	179
1500	70	5000	200
2000	86	5500	215
2500	103	6000	230
3000	120	6500	250
3500	140	7000	269

a) Draw a graph of temperature against depth. What information can you obtain from the shape of the graph?
b) What is the temperature of the rocks at a depth of 3200 metres?
c) Why will water arriving at the surface not be at the same temperature as the rocks through which it passed at its lowest level?

IT WILL BE AN EYESORE ON THE LANDSCAPE
THE POLLUTION FROM UPSTREAM IS CARRIED AWAY BY THE TIDES AT THE MOMENT. IF THE BARRAGE IS BUILT THIS POLLUTION WILL BUILD UP TO DANGEROUS LEVELS. ANIMAL LIFE WILL BE TOTALLY WIPED OUT
THEY ARE GOING TO BUILD SPECIAL PASSES WHICH WILL ALLOW FISH TO MOVE UPRIVER FROM THE SEA. MOST OF THESE WILL PROBABLY BE KILLED WHEN THEY ARE WASHED BACK THROUGH THE TURBINES
THE POPULATION OF BIRDS AND OTHER ANIMALS WILL INCREASE. THE TIDE AT THE MOMENT STIRS UP MUD FROM THE RIVER BOTTOM. IF THERE ARE NO TIDES, THE WATER WILL BE CLEARER AND THE PLANTS WILL GROW BETTER. THE FISH AND OTHER ANIMALS WILL BE BETTER OFF

1.17 Solar power

The solar cells on this car produce the current needed to drive the motor

Your calculator may be powered by solar cells. Solar or 'photovoltaic' cells convert solar energy from sunlight into an electric current. In recent years they have also been used to power cars, aeroplanes, and the electrical equipment on satellites.

Electricity can be produced cleanly using solar cells – no raw materials are needed other than sunlight and the silicon for the cells themselves, and there is no pollution when they are used.

Power for underdeveloped countries

People in remote areas of the world cannot enjoy the benefits of an electricity supply. They cannot switch on the lights when it gets dark, they cannot use electrical tools or water pumps. However, solar cells are now being used in some areas to provide electricity on a small scale.

One particular benefit is a solar-powered refrigerator, which enables medicines and vaccines to be stored in warm areas of the world with no electricity supply. It is powered by a panel of solar cells and batteries. During the day the solar cells convert the sun's radiation into electricity. Some is used to power the fridge. Excess electricity is used to charge the batteries.

During the night the batteries provide the electricity to power the fridge.

The cost is high

Solar cells need little maintenance other than cleaning. They are reliable and will last for up to 25 years. The big disadvantage of solar cells is their high initial cost. They cost about ten times more than a petrol or diesel generator which could be used to supply electricity.

Cheaper solar cells are currently being developed which convert more of the sun's energy into electricity. The lower costs and higher efficiency will make them a much more feasible way of generating electricity.

On a larger scale

Solar furnaces use energy from the sun to produce superheated steam which can then be used to drive a turbine to generate electricity. Mirrors collect solar energy from a large area and focus it on a small area of the 'furnace' where it is absorbed.

The mirrors are computer-controlled so that they track the sun throughout the day

The reflected sunlight can raise the temperature inside the furnace to 3000 °C

★ THINGS TO DO

1 Why would solar cells be more useful in India than in Northern Europe?

2 Excess electricity generated by solar cells during the day can be used to charge lead-acid cells similar to car batteries. During the night, the cells supply the electricity which is needed.

A group of pupils decided to investigate the factors which affect how much energy could be stored in lead-acid cells. This was what they planned to do.

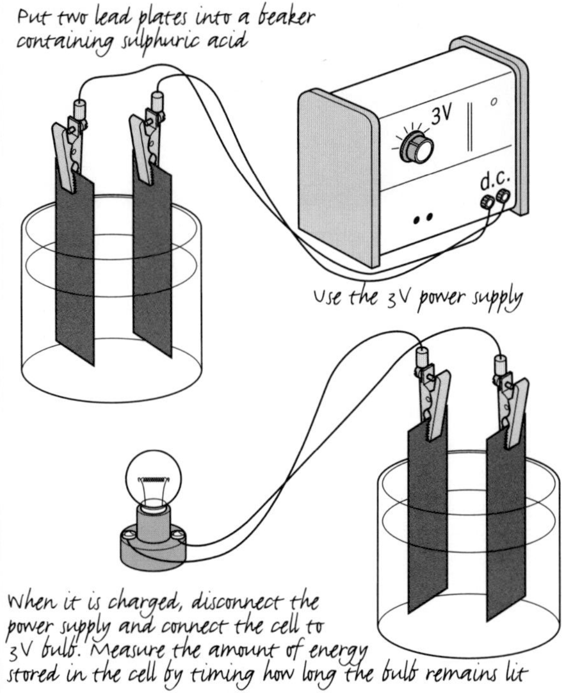

Put two lead plates into a beaker containing sulphuric acid
3V
d.c.
Use the 3V power supply
When it is charged, disconnect the power supply and connect the cell to 3V bulb. Measure the amount of energy stored in the cell by timing how long the bulb remains lit

a) Make a list of the factors which you think will affect how much charge can be stored by the cell.
b) Think about what kind of relation there might be between each factor and the energy stored. You may, for example, think that if you double the strength of the acid then you will double the amount of energy stored. Make a list of your predictions. Try to add a reason for each one.
c) Plan how you would carry out some tests to check your predictions. When your teacher has checked your plans you may be able to carry out your tests.
d) Record all measurements in a table and then describe what they tell you.

3 Solar panels can be used to heat water by absorbing energy from the sun (see page 27). This table shows the amount of solar energy striking a 1 m^2 solar panel at different times throughout the year.

Month	**Amount of energy striking panel** /MJ **when panel is tilted to the horizontal at an angle of**					
	20°	30°	40°	50°	60°	70°
March	17.2	17.4	17.5	17.5	17.3	17.1
April	23.8	24.9	24.8	24.1	22.7	20.5
June	29.2	29.2	27.4	25.2	22.3	19.1
August	25.6	25.9	26.3	24.8	22.7	20.5
October	19.4	19.9	20.6	20.8	19.8	19.4

a) Why does more energy strike the solar panel in August than in April?
b) Copy and complete this table showing the best angle for the solar panel in each month. Why does the angle need to change throughout the year?

Month	Best angle
March	40°–50°
April	
June	
August	
October	

c) Most houses would need solar panels covering 6 m^2 to produce sufficient energy to make them worthwhile. How much energy would fall on a 6 m^2 panel during a good day in July?
d) Why is the energy transferred by the solar panel likely to be significantly lower than the amount of energy striking the panel?
e) Why are the values in the table likely to be average values?

1.18 The cost of 'alternative energy'

At peak times generating stations must supply 45 000 MW of electricity to meet demand in the UK. The cost of producing this electricity determines the cost of goods produced by industry, and the heating and lighting costs in offices and homes.

Although renewable sources of energy are less polluting, the energy is so 'dilute' that the costs of producing electricity from it are high. Additionally, the installation costs, the annual costs of maintenance, and the useful life of the buildings, materials and machinery must be considered. The table below shows some of these economic details for alternative sources of energy.

The relatively low cost of energy production, the reliability of rainfall in certain areas, and the ability to switch production on and off to match demand, make hydroelectricity the most economic of alternative sources in the UK

Source	**Potential output**	**Installation costs** /£ per kW	**Annual costs** /£ per kW per year	**Construction time**/years	**Lifetime** /years	**Concerns**
Onshore wind energy	1 kW–3 MW per turbine	800–1200	12–18	1	15–25	Noise Visual effect TV and radio interference
Large-scale hydro-power	over 5 MW	1000–3000	2.5–7.5	4	100 +	Visual effect Environmental damage
Tidal power	30 MW–9 GW	1200–1500	5–10	3–10	100 +	Visual effect Environmental damage
Wave power	1 MW–2 GW	1000–3000	40–90	1–10	25–35	Obstacle to navigation and fishing
Solar cells	up to 0.5 MW	1500–1700	unknown	0.2–1	25	Visual effect
Geothermal energy	3.3 MW	12 000	300	5	20	Visual effect Water requirements Radon gas emissions Noise

★ THINGS TO DO

1 Use the information in the table opposite to help answer the following questions. In each case support your answer with a clear reason.

a) Which of the renewable sources could potentially provide the highest output?

b) Which source has the highest installation costs? Why are the costs so high?

c) Why are the annual costs for geothermal and wave energy much higher than the costs for other alternatives?

d) Investigations into the use of wave power and geothermal energy have proved largely unsuccessful. Why do you think this is so?

e) Some people argue that the environmental advantages are far more important than the additional costs of installing and using these alternative technologies. What do you think of this argument?

2 These figures are for the proposed Severn barrage, sketched below.

Length	16 km
Number of generators	216
Rated output of each generator	40 MW
Estimated annual output	17 million MWh

a) Calculate the amount of electrical energy which would be produced by the generators in one hour assuming they are 100% efficient.

b) A pupil carried out this calculation to find out how much energy would be produced in one year by the barrage:

energy produced by one generator in one hour
= power x time
= 40 MW x 1 h = 40 MWh
energy produced by 216 generators in one hour
= output of one generator x number
= 40 MWh x 216
= 8640 MWh
energy produced by generators in one day
= output of all generators x number of hours
= 8640 MWh x 24
= 207 360 MWh
energy produced each year = daily output x number of days
= 75 686 400 MWh

On looking at the figures above he noticed that his calculated output was much higher than the official estimated output. Explain why there is such a large difference between the official figures and the pupil's calculated output.

c) The typical annual energy output from the Hinkley B nuclear power station is 4 877 000 MWh.

i) Which will produce most energy each year, Hinkley B or the Severn barrage?

ii) Why could tidal barrages not replace other types of power station?

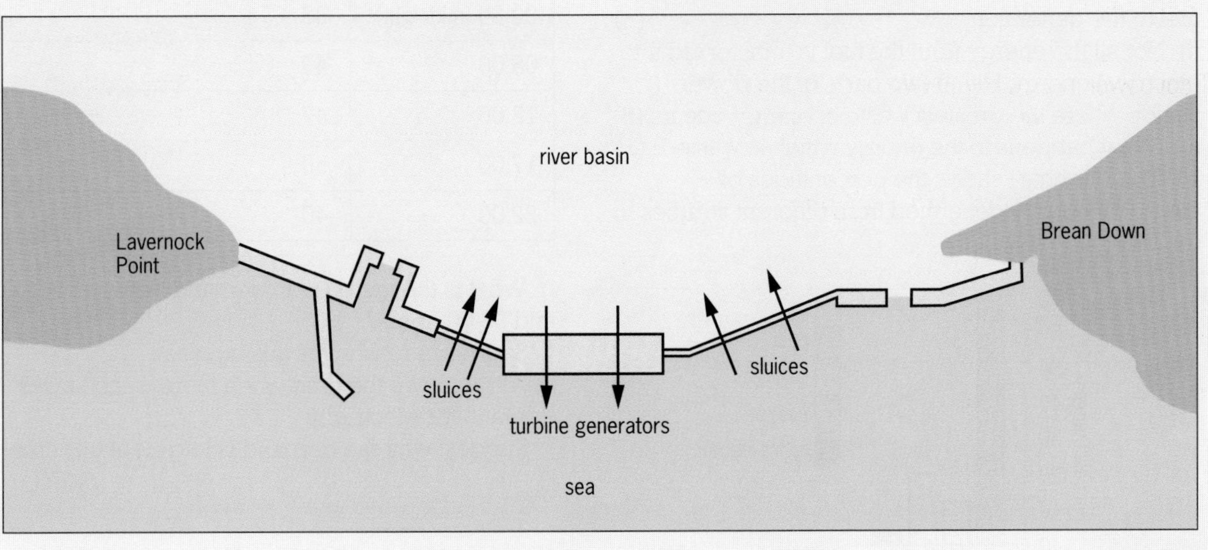

Exam questions

1 The diagrams show three appliances which use electricity.

[Copy and] complete the sentences by choosing the best words to describe the energy transfer in each appliance. Choose words from the following list:

heat **light** **movement** **sound**

The kettle is designed to change electrical energy into ……… energy.
The radio is designed to change electrical energy into ……… energy.
The lamp is designed to change electrical energy into ……… energy. (3)

(MEG, 1995)

2 a) The diagram shows part of a power station.

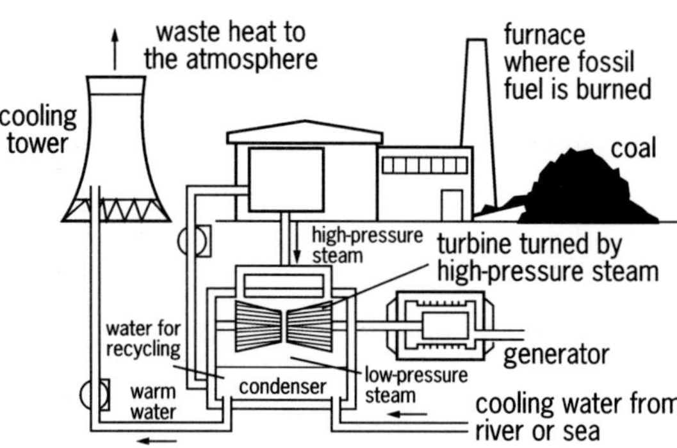

i) Describe how the energy is transferred from the fuel to the generator. (2)
ii) Not all the energy from the fuel is transferred into electrical energy. Name **two** parts of the power station where the greatest waste of energy occurs. (2)
iii) What happens to the energy which is wasted? (1)
b) The bar chart shows the percentages of electrical energy generated from different sources in the UK.

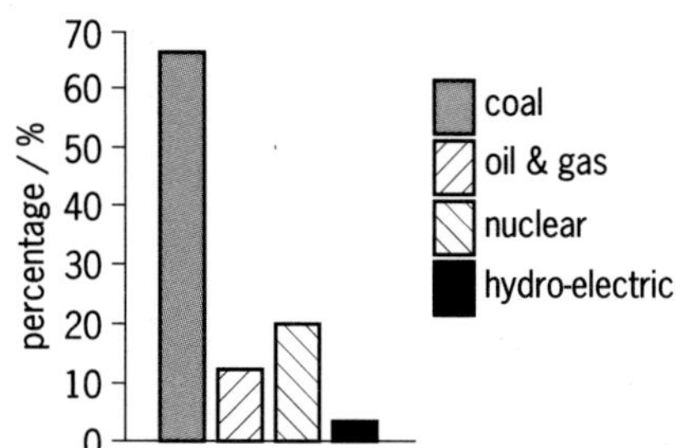

i) Which of the energy sources shown in the bar chart is renewable? (1)
ii) State **two** advantages of using renewable energy sources. (2)
iii) Suggest **one** reason why only a small proportion of the electrical energy generated in the UK comes from renewable sources. (1)

(MEG, 1995)

3 a) The diagram shows a hydroelectric power station in which water is used to generate electricity.

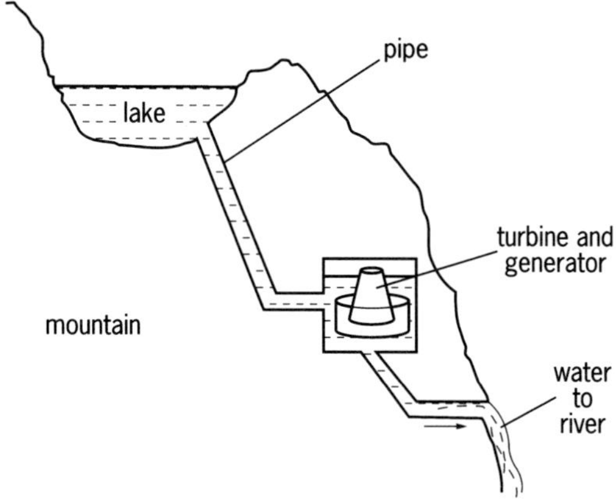

i) What type of energy does the water have when it is in the lake at the top of the mountain? (1)
ii) What happens to this energy as the water flows down the pipe? (1)
b) The figures below show the demand for electricity in the UK expected on a typical winter day.

Time/hours	*Demand*/thousands of MW
00.00 (midnight)	33
08.00	43
12.00	47
17.00	50
22.00	40

i) What is the increase in demand between 00.00 and 08.00 hours?
Suggest a reason for this increase. (2)
ii) Write down the time when there is the largest demand for electricity.
Suggest why the demand is largest at this time. (2)

(MEG, 1995)

4 Electricity can be generated in several different ways.

a) Describe how the energy in coal is transferred to drive generators in coal-fired power stations. (3)

b) The diagram shows a section through a tidal power generating system.

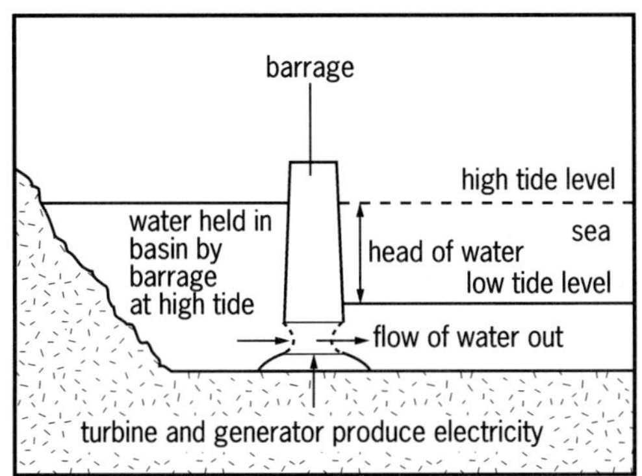

Describe fully how this method of driving turbines to generate electricity is **different** from using coal. (2)

(NEAB Specimen Paper, 1998)

5 On a very windy hilltop there are two wind generators side by side. The bar charts show the lengths of the turbine blades and the electrical outputs of the two wind generators.

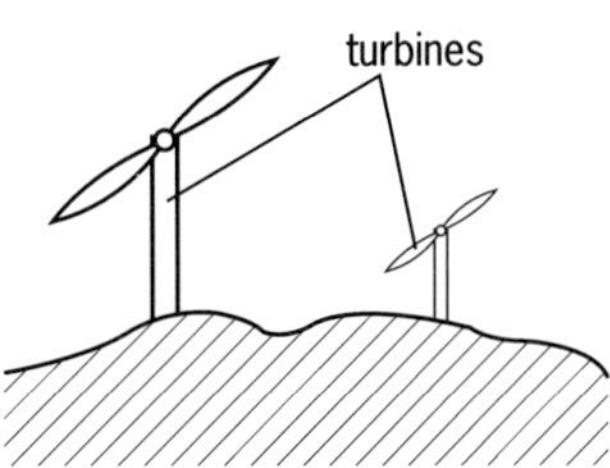

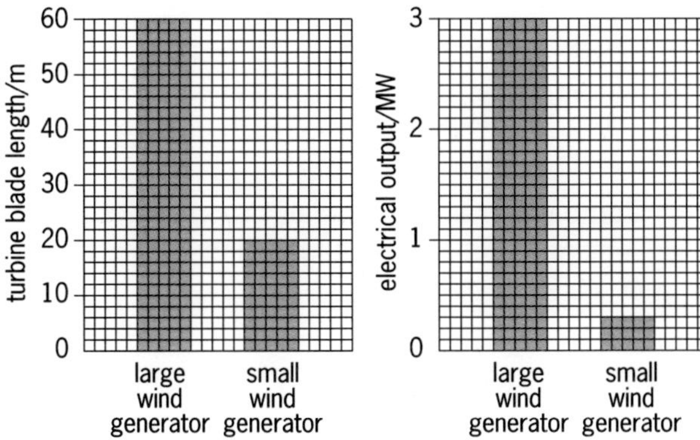

[Copy and] complete the following table. (3)

	Length of turbine blade (m)	Electrical output (MW)
Large wind generator	60	
Small wind generator		

(NEAB, 1995)

6 The illustration shows an advertisement used by a lamp company.

SAVE MONEY !

CF lamp

Ordinary Filament lamp

- Don't buy inefficient filament lamps.
- Buy our Compact Fluorescent (CF) lamps now!
- One 20W CF lamp will give out the same amount of light as one 100W filament lamp.
- Only £13.20 for one CF lamp.
- Just plug in like an ordinary lamp.
- One CF lamp will last 8000 hours, compared with 1000 hours for a filament lamp.

a) Many power stations use fossil fuels, such as coal, oil and gas.

Explain why the use of CF lamps can help to reduce problems caused by countries using large amounts of fossil fuels for generating electricity. (5)

b) The cost of electricity can be calculated from

cost of electricity = kilowatts × hours used × cost of one kWh

The table shows a comparison of the costs for the two types of lamp.

	CF lamp	Filament
Power (kW)	0.02	0.1
Time used (hours)	8000	8000
Cost of 1 kWh (£)	0.08	0.08
Cost of electricity (£)		64.00
Number of lamps needed	1	8
Cost of one lamp	13.20	0.50
Total cost (£)		

i) Give the **three** pieces of missing information. (3)

ii) CF lamps can give large savings on the cost of electricity but many people still buy filament lamps instead of CF lamps.

Suggest **two** reasons for this. (2)

(ULEAC, 1994)

7 The diagram shows a rock face and two climbers. Jennifer, who has a mass of 60 kg, is going to climb up to Christopher, who has a mass of 80 kg.

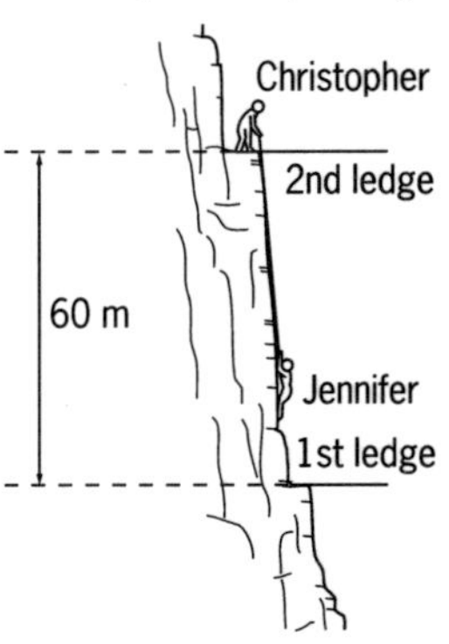

a) Calculate, showing your working:

i) Jennifer's weight; (2)

(Take the acceleration due to gravity (g) as $10\,m/s^2$.)

ii) the **least** amount of work Jennifer will do when she climbs from the first ledge to the second ledge; (3)

iii) the average power of Jennifer if she takes 10 minutes to complete the climb. (2)

iv) State **one** reason why the work Jennifer actually does will be more than you have calculated in (ii). (1)

b) In the diagram, Christopher has more potential (positional) energy than Jennifer. State **two** reasons why. (2)

(SEG, 1994)

8 The diagram below shows the structure of an electric storage heater. The power rating of the heater is 3.5 kW.

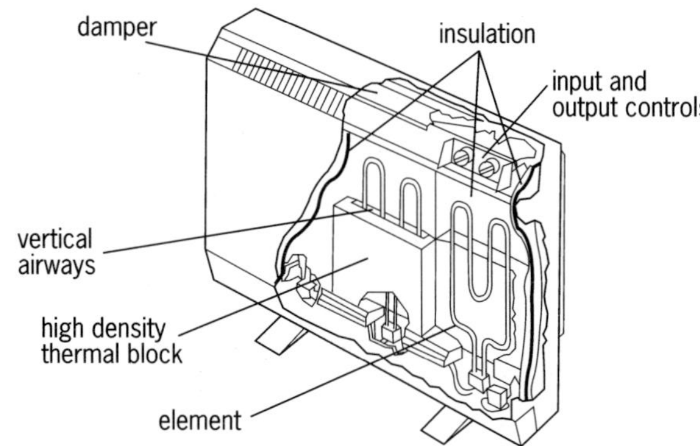

The electrical elements are used to heat the high density thermal blocks overnight. During the daytime the heat energy stored is released to the room.

a) During the day the thermal energy stored in the heater during the night is released into the room.

i) Explain how this energy transfer takes place from the storage heater and how the rate of transfer can be controlled. (3)

ii) The Electricity Board claims that this method of heating is one hundred percent efficient.

Explain what they mean by this and whether the claim is justified. (2)

iii) Explain what the drawbacks of this method of heating would be if there were sudden changes in weather. (2)

b) The Electricity Board charges 0.8p for each kilowatt hour during the period midnight to 5 a.m. In the daytime, they charge 8p for each kilowatt hour.

i) Explain why the Electricity Board charges different rates. (3)

ii) Calculate the weekly cost of running the storage heater at the night-time rate. (2)

c) Explain why it is necessary in the design of the storage heater to include insulation between the high density blocks and the outer metal casing of the heater. (1)

(ULEAC Specimen Paper, 1994)

9 The diagram shows a heated greenhouse.

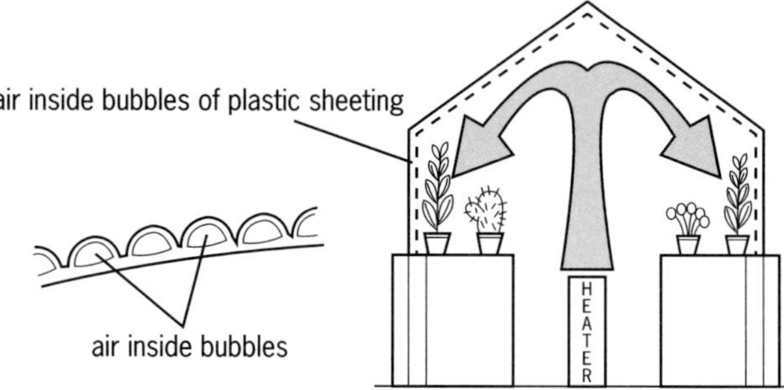

The arrows on the diagram show how moving air transfers heat in the greenhouse.

a) What is this method of heat transfer called? (1)

b) To save fuel in winter, bubble plastic sheeting is clipped to the inside of the windows.

Explain, in as much detail as you can, how the bubble plastic works. (4)

c) On a cold day, the 3000 W heater is switched on for 12 hours.

Calculate how many Units of electricity this uses. (3)

(NEAB, 1992)

10 Two of the ways used to generate electricity in the UK are coal-fired power stations and hydroelectricity schemes.

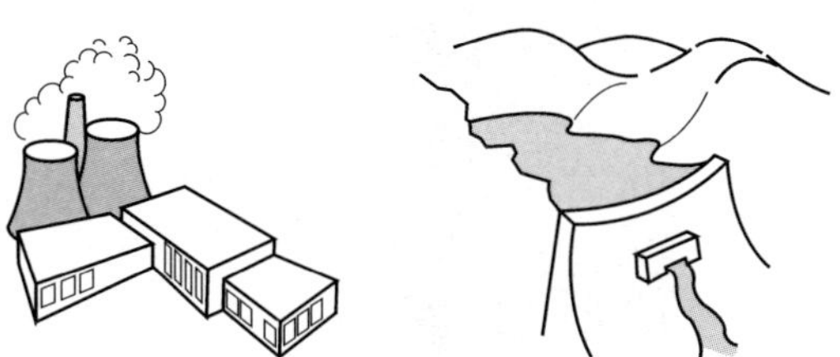

Compare, in as much detail as you can, the advantages and disadvantages of these two ways of generating electricity. (9)

(NEAB, 1992)

11 a) Different fuels can be used to heat a house.

Name a solid fuel which could be used.

Name a liquid fuel which could be used.

Name another type of fuel which could be used to heat a house. (4)

b) Why are these substances all called fuels? (2)

(NEAB, 1992)

ELECTRICITY

2.1

What a shock!

People have known about electricity and some of its effects for thousands of years, but it was not until 300 years ago that people tried to find out more about it. Even then its real importance was not realised, and electricity was used for fun. People were suspended and 'charged' with electricity by stroking them with a dry cloth until their hair stood on end, or until sparks jumped from their bodies to the ground!

People began to take electricity seriously in the 18th century. Benjamin Franklin, an American statesman and scientist, thought that lightning was a giant electric spark. He flew a kite into thunderclouds during a storm, and collected electricity from them in a simple storage jar. Others who tried the same thing were killed by a huge electric shock as the electricity passed through them instead of into the storage jars.

We now know that thunderclouds become covered with a layer of static electricity – a huge store of energy. Eventually the static electricity passes to the Earth as lightning.

You may have heard 'crackles' when you remove your clothes. In a darkened room you could see that the crackles are due to small sparks which jump between your clothes and your body. 'Static' electricity builds up on some materials when they rub against one another. The sparks are created as this electricity passes from the clothes to your body.

Static electricity also builds up on vehicles and aircraft – generated by friction between the air and the sides of the moving object. Precautions are taken to reduce the risk of accidents and injury. Static electricity on petrol tankers must be 'discharged' before petrol is transferred, because any sparking could ignite the petrol vapour.

Benjamin Franklin discovered that lightning was an electrical effect

Static electricity builds up on helicopters during flight. The winch cable must touch the ground before anyone touches it. The electricity then passes to earth and not through the person

What produces the static electricity?

We now know that there are two types of static electricity – **positive electric charge** and **negative electric charge**.

The atoms of all materials contain particles called protons, neutrons and electrons (although the hydrogen atom is an exception because it has no neutrons). The protons have positive charge and are found in the nucleus of the atom, along with the uncharged neutrons. The electrons have negative charge and swirl around outside the nucleus.

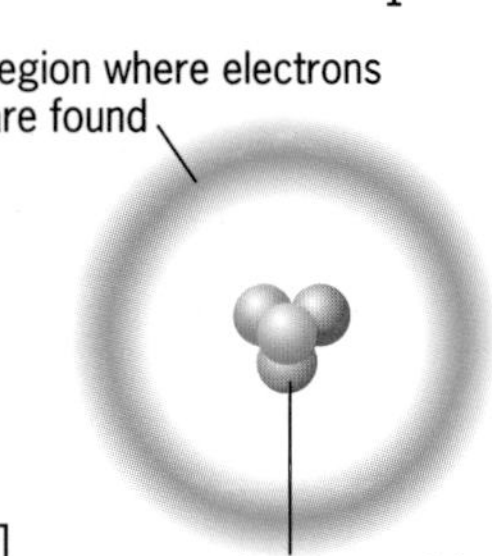

The positive charge of the nucleus is usually exactly balanced by the negative charge on the electrons – there are the same number of protons and electrons in the atom and they have opposite charges, so the atom as a whole is uncharged.

Some materials become charged when they are rubbed with a duster. **Friction** causes some of the electrons to be pulled off one material and onto the other. Only electrons are transferred – protons are 'locked' inside the nucleus. When polythene, for example, is rubbed with a duster it gains extra electrons from the duster. It then has more negatively charged particles than positively charged particles. The 'extra' negative charges make the polythene negatively charged.

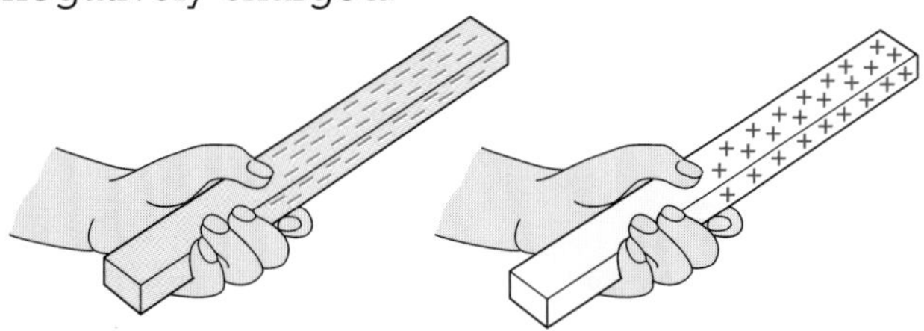

Polythene becomes negatively charged when rubbed with a duster

Perspex becomes positively charged when rubbed with a duster

The opposite happens with perspex. When it is rubbed, electrons are transferred from it to the duster. This leaves the perspex with more positively charged particles than negatively charged particles, so it becomes positively charged. The duster, because it gains electrons, becomes negatively charged.

Attraction and repulsion

Charged objects can exert forces on other things although the forces are generally quite small. When a negatively charged rod, for example, is brought close to another negatively charged rod they can be seen to repel one another.

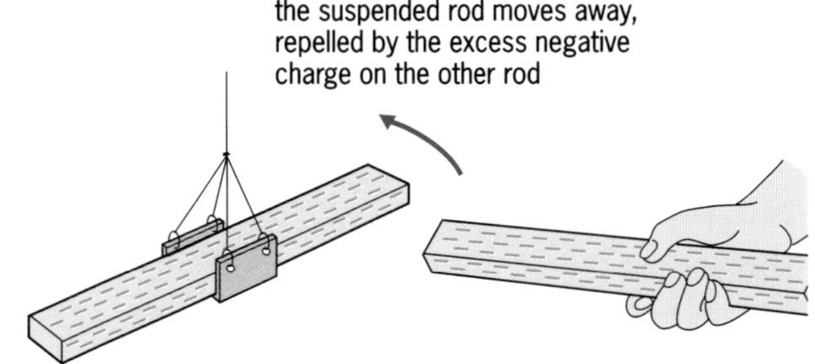

the suspended rod moves away, repelled by the excess negative charge on the other rod

Electrostatic repulsion

The same happens when two positively charged rods are brought close together – they also repel one another. We can say that objects with similar charges repel one another – *like charges repel*.

If, on the other hand, a negatively charged rod is brought close to a positively charged rod they attract one another – *opposite charges attract*.

Polishing furniture, especially plastics or glass such as a television screen, can have the opposite effect to what is intended – it can charge the surface so that it attracts dust particles from the air.

★ THINGS TO DO

1 Rub a strip of polythene with a duster. Try to pick up some small pieces of paper from the desk. Try rubbing other materials and find out which will attract the paper. Make a note of what you find out and try to explain your observations.

2 Charge up the polythene again and bring it close to the stream of water running from a tap. What happens?

3 A car travelling along the road can lose some electrons due to friction between the air and the car body. The car becomes charged, and if you touch the metal you get a shock as the charge flows through you to earth.

Some people fit 'earthing straps' to the back of the car. The strap contains a metal band which touches the road surface.

Explain how an earthing strap helps prevent the build-up of static charge on a car.

2.2 Charge on the move

Sometimes the static charges which build up on things can become very concentrated. This concentrated charge is a store of electrical potential energy. The area where concentrated charge builds up can be described as having a high 'potential' (or voltage). Areas of less concentrated charge have a lower potential. When there is a large difference in potential between two points, charge may pass between them. The Earth is considered to be at zero potential, so surfaces at a high potential may become 'discharged' as electrons pass to or from the Earth.

A van de Graaff generator covers you with electric charge which makes your hair stand on end!

Shocking but true

The van de Graaff generator shown in the photograph produces a high concentration of charge on the dome – the dome becomes an area of high potential. The charge spreads across anything which touches it, including this girl – producing some hair-raising effects! If the girl was standing on the ground, then instead of the charge spreading across her, it would pass through her to earth.

If the girl is standing on a wooden stool when she touches the dome, the charges spread across her. Each strand of hair becomes covered with similar charges. The charges repel one another, making the strands of hair separate and stand on end. The charges do not pass to earth because the wood of the stool is an insulator

If the girl stood on the floor and put her finger close to the dome, the concentrated charge would pass from the point of high potential (the dome) to the point of lower potential (earth) through her body. As the charge passed through her she would receive an electric shock. A spark would be seen as the charge 'jumped' the gap between the dome and her finger

If the dome was connected to earth by a conducting wire, then the charge would flow directly through the wire to earth. Even if the girl touched the dome she would not receive a shock – the charge would pass through the wire rather than through her because the wire is a better conductor than her body. A sensitive current meter connected in the wire would show that a current was flowing. The electric current is a movement of charged particles (electrons) through the conductor as they pass from the point of high potential to a point of lower potential

Current is a flow of charge

The van de Graaff generator demonstrates four important ideas.

1 An **electric current** is a flow of charged particles (electrons) through a conductor.

2 Charge will only flow when there is a difference in potential between the two ends of the conductor. It flows from a point of high potential to a point of lower potential.

3 The current is able to pass through materials such as copper, which are **conductors**, but cannot pass through other materials such as wood, because they are electrical **insulators**.

4 Under normal circumstances, the current always flows to earth.

York Minster was severely damaged in a fire caused by lightning

Protecting buildings

Lightning can cause severe damage if it strikes buildings and passes through them to earth. To reduce the risk of damage, most tall buildings are fitted with lightning conductors – strips of copper connecting the ground to a tall pointed post above the building.

Thunderclouds can build up huge amounts of electric charge (created by friction between water droplets and air particles as they move around in the clouds). They have a high potential compared with the Earth. As charge continues to build up, negative charges gather in the lower part of the cloud. These draw positive charge towards the surface of the Earth. Eventually the charges become so concentrated (and the potential difference between the two points so great) that a spark (the lightning) jumps between the cloud and the ground.

The lightning conductor works in two ways.

- The conductor itself can become charged as positive charges are drawn from the Earth by the concentrated negative charge on the underside of the cloud. At the point of the conductor, positive charge builds up in the air. Some of this may cancel out some of the negative charge on the cloud, making it less likely that lightning will strike.
- If lightning does strike then it will strike the highest point – the lightning conductor. The copper strip provides a good conducting path through which the electricity flows to earth without damaging the building. Because the Earth is so large, the extra electrons it gains have no real effect on it.

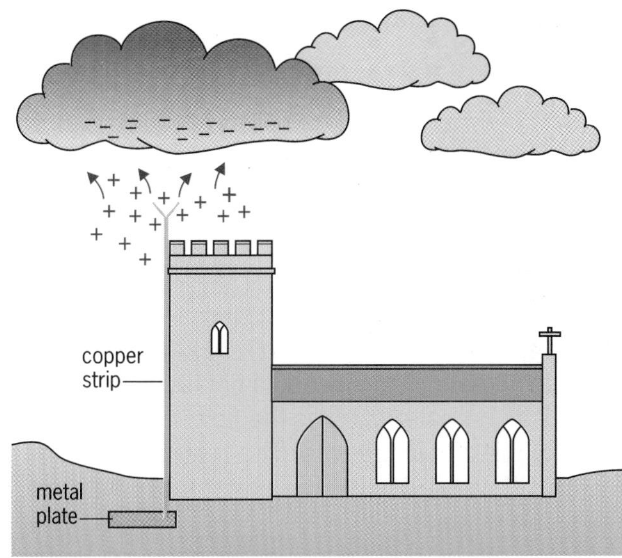

Some of the charge around the lightning conductor cancels some of the opposite charge in the thundercloud

Applications of electrostatics

Many modern applications use the ideas that charged particles repel or attract one another. For example, in an electrostatic crop spray gun the particles of spray are charged positively and repel one another, creating a more even spray pattern. Paint sprays work similarly.

Dust and flue-ash from power station chimneys can be removed by 'electrostatic precipitation' – the particles are charged and are then attracted to large collecting plates.

Conductors and insulators

The ideas about electrons described in topic 2.1 help us to understand why some materials are electrical insulators whilst others are conductors. In an insulator the electrons are held strongly by the positive charge in the nucleus of the atoms. The electrons cannot move. In a metallic conductor, however, some of these electrons are not so tightly bound and are free to move through the material.

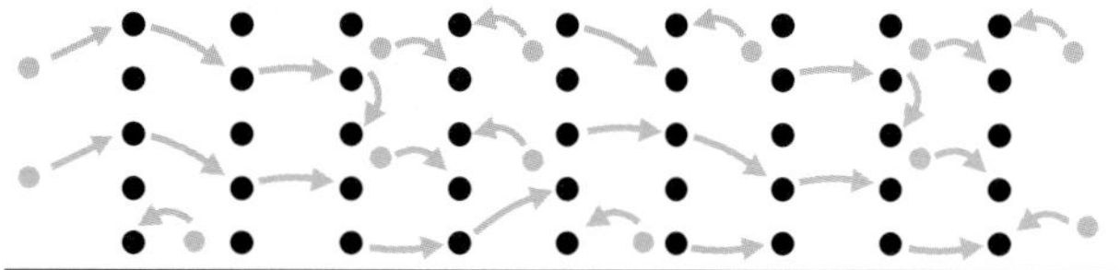

Normally the 'free' electrons move around randomly from atom to atom

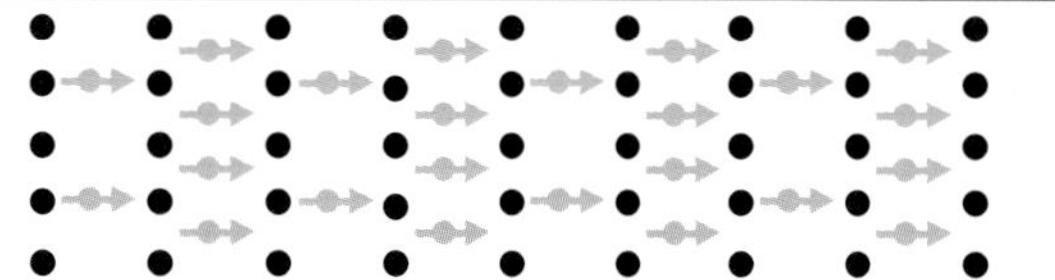

When the conductor is connected to a battery, the potential difference created between the ends of the conductor forces the 'free' electrons to drift in the same direction

The movement of the electrons through a conducting wire connected to a battery is the electric current. The current is not, therefore, 'made' in the battery, but is the flow of electrons already present in the wire. The battery provides the 'push' needed to get the electrons moving in the same direction.

Metals are all good conductors, although some are better than others. Non-metals, with the exception of carbon, are generally insulators.

Electrolysis

Some substances are electrical insulators when they are solid, but when they are melted or dissolved in water they become conductors. These substances are compounds made up of electrically charged particles called ions. It is possible to separate the constituents of such a compound by passing an electric current through the molten substance or a solution of the substance. This process is called **electrolysis** (see *GCSE Science Double Award Chemistry,* topic 1.11).

Electrolysis is used to extract some metals such as aluminium from their natural ores

Electrolysis can be used to apply a coating of one metal onto another – a process called electroplating. The handlebars of a bicycle are made from steel, which rusts fairly readily unless it is protected. Electroplating with chromium helps to protect them and also improves their appearance.

Bicycle handlebars are electroplated to prevent them from rusting

The steel handlebars are first electroplated with nickel, because chromium will not attach itself to steel directly, but will attach itself to nickel. They are plated with nickel by placing them into a solution of a nickel compound – the 'electrolyte'. The handlebars form the negative terminal of the electrolysis cell – the 'cathode'. A block of nickel is used as the positive terminal – the 'anode'. When a large electric current is supplied, positively charged nickel ions pass from the anode to the cathode and so coat the handlebars.

As with all electrolysis cells, the amount of metal deposited on the handlebars depends on:

- the current which is flowing – the bigger the current, the more metal is deposited in any given time, and
- the time for which the current is flowing – the longer the time, the more metal is deposited.

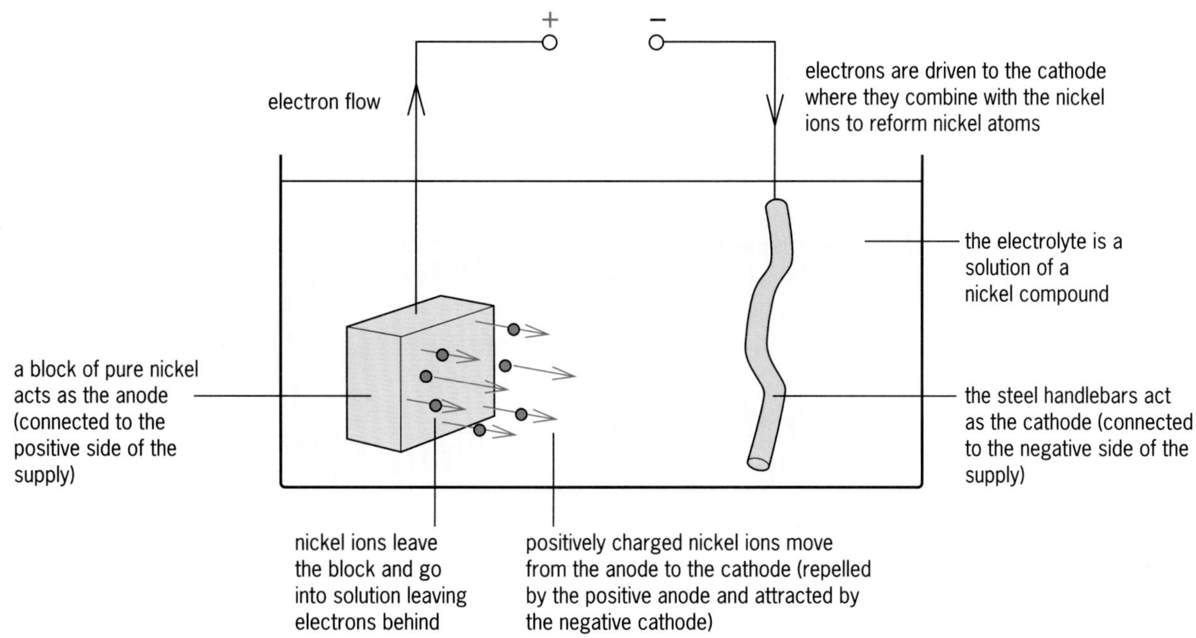
+
–
electron flow
electrons are driven to the cathode where they combine with the nickel ions to reform nickel atoms
the electrolyte is a solution of a nickel compound
a block of pure nickel acts as the anode (connected to the positive side of the supply)
the steel handlebars act as the cathode (connected to the negative side of the supply)
nickel ions leave the block and go into solution leaving electrons behind
positively charged nickel ions move from the anode to the cathode (repelled by the positive anode and attracted by the negative cathode)

Electroplating handlebars in an electrolysis cell

★ THINGS TO DO

1 During flight, aeroplanes build up a high concentration of charge due to friction. The tyres of an aeroplane are not ordinary rubber (which is an insulator) but contain a compound which allows the rubber to conduct electricity. Explain how the conducting material in the tyres helps prevent accidents which could occur during refuelling.

2 A small craft firm is about to begin making a new kind of jewellery. They intend electroplating small iron or steel ornaments with copper. This is their sketch of how they intend doing it.

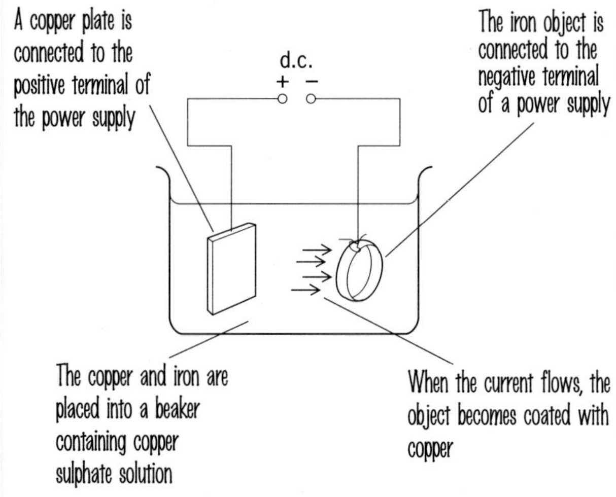
A copper plate is connected to the positive terminal of the power supply
d.c.
+ –
The iron object is connected to the negative terminal of a power supply
The copper and iron are placed into a beaker containing copper sulphate solution
When the current flows, the object becomes coated with copper

Imagine they have written this letter to your class, asking for help before they start production.

....Obviously we are concerned about the cost of producing the jewellery but we feel that we must produce the best quality possible. At the moment we have a number of questions which we would like answered.

1. How does the current affect the amount of copper which is deposited on the iron?

2. How does the concentration of the copper sulphate solution affect how much copper is deposited on the iron?

3. Would it be better to apply the coating using a small current for a long time, or a larger current for a short time?

We would be grateful for any help you could give us in this matter and look forward to hearing from you soon.

Yours sincerely,

Do some tests which would help answer their questions. When you have finished, prepare a report outlining what you have found out. Don't forget to include any results which would help them to understand what you have done and what you found out. You should also include any steps which you took to make sure your tests, and the results you obtained, are reliable.

2.3 Safety around your home

Each year in the UK 2500 people are killed or injured by electric shock and over 28 000 fires are caused by faults in electrical appliances.

The commonest dangers include plugs which are fitted with the wrong fuses, incorrectly wired or cracked plugs, and poor earth connections. The cables on vacuum cleaners and hairdriers, in particular, often become twisted, which can weaken the insulation inside the outer cable. Regular checks should be made to find any faults before they cause an accident.

Twisted cables can be dangerous

Plugs

Most appliances are connected to the socket via a plug. Plugs are generally made from plastic or rubber, both of which are electrical **insulators** (electricity cannot pass through them). This prevents electricity flowing through the plug and then to earth through you.

The three pins are metal. Metal is a good **conductor** so electric current flows easily through the pins. The cables must be connected properly.

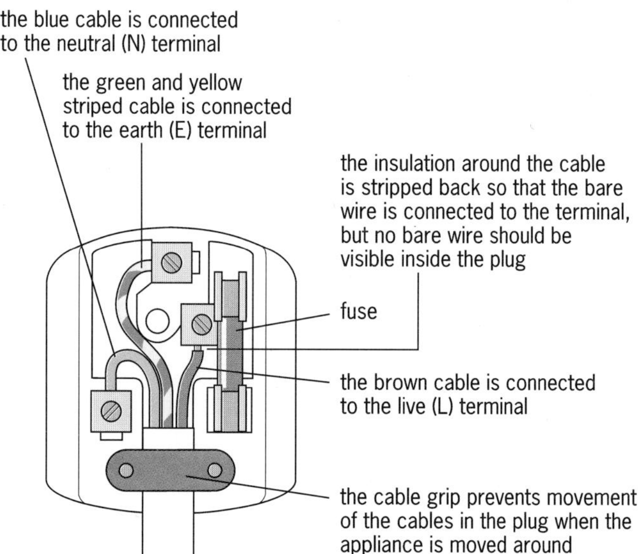
the blue cable is connected to the neutral (N) terminal
the green and yellow striped cable is connected to the earth (E) terminal
the insulation around the cable is stripped back so that the bare wire is connected to the terminal, but no bare wire should be visible inside the plug
fuse
the brown cable is connected to the live (L) terminal
the cable grip prevents movement of the cables in the plug when the appliance is moved around

Why are there three cables?

The *live* and *neutral* cables in our homes are connected directly to the power station. Alternating current (a.c.) pulses to and fro through these cables, supplying the energy which appliances need.

The *earth* wire is there to protect you. Any appliance which has exposed metal parts, such as a microwave oven or a washing machine, should have an earth connection. If a fault develops the electricity takes the path of least resistance to earth – through the earth connection in the socket, not through you. Some appliances are 'double insulated' – the electrical parts inside are completely insulated from the outer parts which will be handled. An earth wire is then not needed.

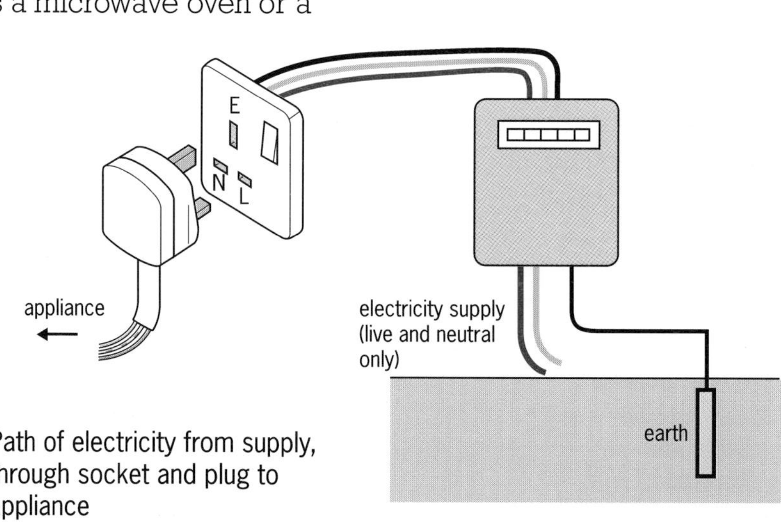
E
N
L
appliance
electricity supply (live and neutral only)
earth

Path of electricity from supply, through socket and plug to appliance

Safety devices

Extra protection is sometimes advisable when hand-held appliances such as lawnmowers are being used. When a fault develops in an appliance, the 'return' current through the neutral cable falls. Some safety devices, such as the one shown here, detect any small difference in the current flowing through the live and the neutral cables. When they do, they immediately switch off the current to the appliance, preventing injury to the user.

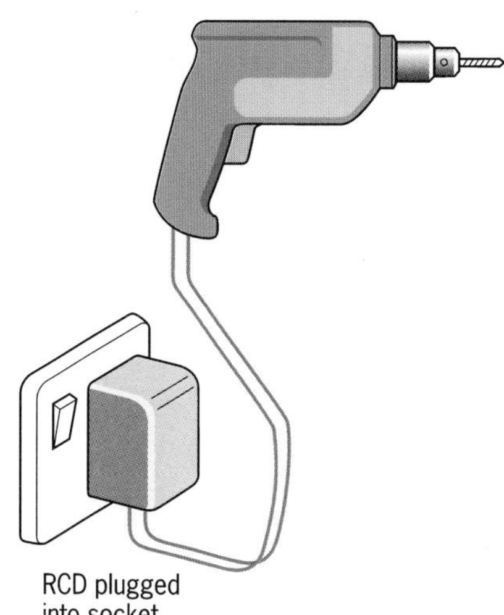

Use of a residual current device (RCD)

Fuses

Current must flow through the fuse inside a plug and then to the appliance. The fuse limits the current which can flow through the appliance. Without a fuse, too much current might flow and the appliance or the cables could overheat, possibly causing a fire. (All conductors get warm when a current flows through them.)

A cartridge fuse is a thin strand of metal wire inside a glass or ceramic tube. As current flows through the fuse wire it gets hot. If the current is too big the fuse wire melts, making a 'gap' in the circuit and cutting off the current. A 3 amp fuse will melt when the current reaches 3 amps (or thereabouts). A 13 amp fuse will melt when the current is bigger than 13 amps.

Your home may also have a fuse box which adds extra protection to the circuits around the house.

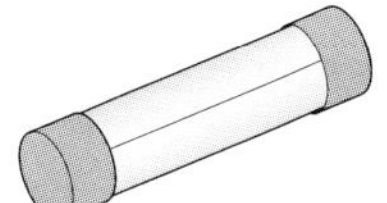
Cartridge fuse

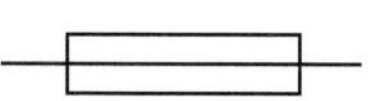
Symbol for a fuse

★ THINGS TO DO

1 Each of these diagrams shows a plug with a different fault. For each one
a) describe what the fault is, and
b) say what should be done to put it right.

i ii iii

2 This leaflet describes the correct fuses for different appliances. Mr Brown checked the plugs in his house, noting which fuses were in each plug. He wrote the information in a table.

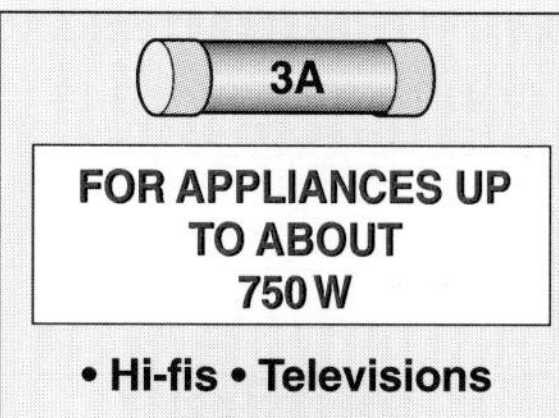

FOR APPLIANCES UP TO ABOUT 750 W

- Hi-fis • Televisions
- Table lamps
- Radios
- Answerphones

13A

FOR APPLIANCES WITH A POWER RATING ABOVE 750 W

- Irons • Kettles
- Washing machines
- Tumble-driers
- Dishwashers • Hairdriers

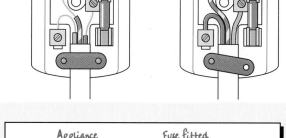

Appliance	Fuse fitted
TV	3 A
Hi-fi	13 A
Washing machine	13 A
Bedside lamp	13 A
Hairdrier	3 A

Make a list of those appliances which had the wrong fuse fitted. For each one say which fuse should have been fitted.

2.4 Portable power

Alessandro Volta and his 'voltaic pile'

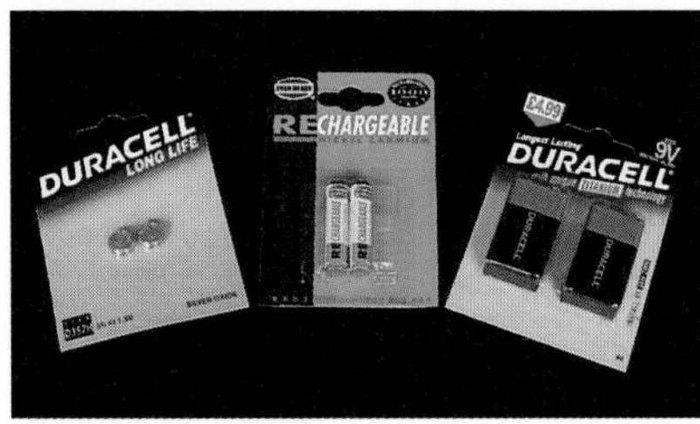

Modern dry cells

In 1795 an Italian scientist, Alessandro Volta, discovered that electricity could be produced by some chemical reactions. He developed the first battery – a pile of silver and zinc discs separated by paper soaked in brine. However, the weight of the metal discs soon squeezed the brine from the paper and the battery stopped working.

Modern batteries are small and light so they are easily carried. Considering their small size, they transfer a lot of electrical energy. The batteries which you use in a personal stereo or a torch are 'dry cells' – there are no liquids to leak out and cause damage.

When a cell is used the chemicals inside it react and supply electrical energy which is carried to the devices in the circuit.

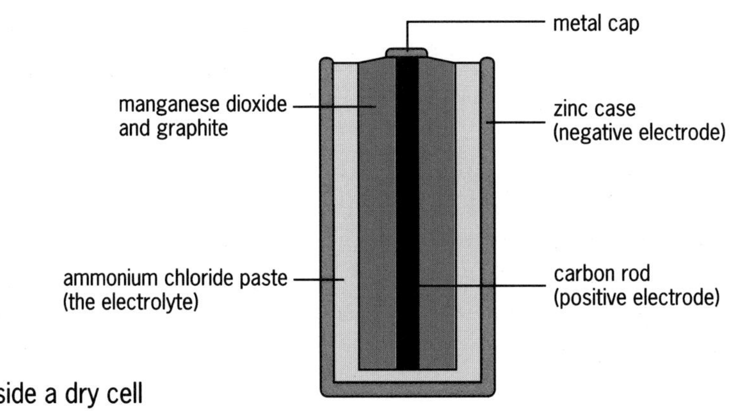

Inside a dry cell

We can write this energy transfer as:

chemical energy ⟶ electrical energy

As the cell is used, the original chemicals change and new substances are formed. Eventually most of the original chemicals become 'used up' and the reaction stops. The cell must then be replaced (or recharged).

Getting the energy to where it is needed

Electrical appliances only work when energy is transferred to them. To light a small bulb, for example, connecting wire is used to form a circuit (or loop) through which electrons flow, carrying energy from the cell to the bulb. The electrons then return to the cell where energy is again transferred to them.

The flow of electrons through the circuit is the **electric current**. All cells produce 'direct current' (d.c.). Direct current always flows in the same direction through a circuit – from the positive terminal to the negative terminal.

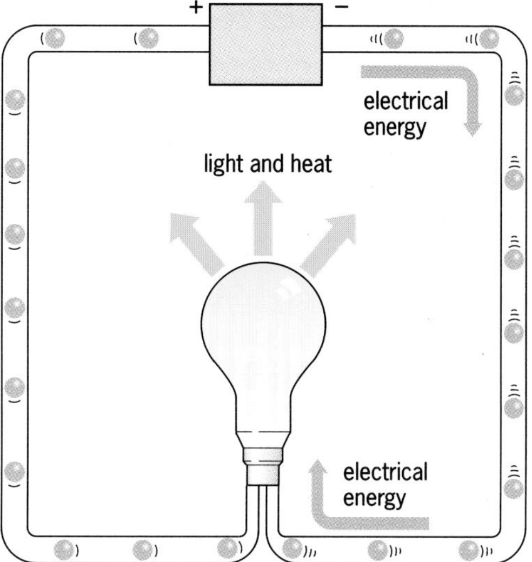
The chemical reaction inside the cell transfers extra energy to the electrons
+
−
electrical energy
light and heat
The electrons return to the cell where more energy is transferred to them
The electrons flow through the wire. Electrons flow from the negative terminal of the cell back to the positive terminal, although for historical reasons we say that current flows from positive to negative
electrical energy
As the electrons pass through the bulb, some of their energy is transferred to the filament. The temperature of the filament rises. Eventually it becomes 'white hot' and produces white light

Electron flow through a circuit

★ THINGS TO DO

1 Some battery makers claim that their batteries last longer than any other make. Write a plan saying how you could test their claims. It is particularly important to make sure that your tests are 'fair'.

2 Young children have difficulty understanding how electricity flows. Draw a 'strip cartoon' describing the journey of an electron through a circuit containing a cell and a buzzer.

3 Car batteries contain lead plates which dip into sulphuric acid. A group of pupils made a model car battery by putting lead plates into sulphuric acid in a beaker. They then charged up the cell by connecting the plates to a power supply. They tested the amount of charge stored by the cell by connecting the plates to a bulb and timing how long the bulb remained lit. Their results are shown.

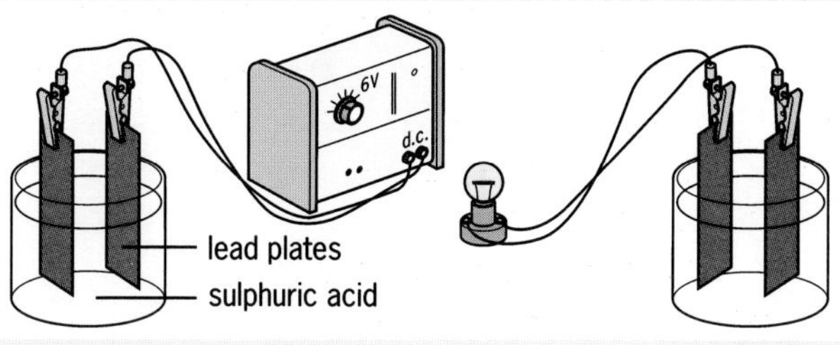
6V
d.c.
lead plates
sulphuric acid

a) What two things did they change during their investigation?
b) What do you think they did to make their investigation 'fair'?
c) What conclusions can they draw from their results?
d) One of the pupils said that their results showed that if the area of the plates was doubled, the charge stored was doubled. Their teacher said that they did not have sufficient information for their conclusion to be reliable. What could they do to improve their investigation?

Time for which plates were charged /min	Area of plates covered by acid /cm^2	Strength of acid /mol dm^{-3}	Time for which bulb was lit
8	25	1	6 min 45 s
12	25	1	7 min 49 s
16	25	1	8 min 17 s
8	50	1	13 min 30 s
12	50	1	17 min 03 s
16	50	1	21 min 43 s

2.5 Measuring voltage and current

The reaction inside a cell releases the energy which electrons carry around a circuit. As the electrons pass through the cell, energy is transferred to them. The energy difference between the electrons leaving and the electrons entering the cell is called the **potential difference** (p.d.) of the cell and is measured in units called **volts** (V). The p.d. is often just referred to as the **voltage**.

There is also a potential difference across every device in a circuit (because energy is transferred to the devices by the current). The potential difference is measured using a voltmeter connected to the two points across which the difference is to be measured.

In a **series circuit** (one in which everything is connected end-to-end) the potential difference across the supply is always equal to the sum of the potential differences across all the devices in the circuit.

On most cells you will find a number which is the voltage

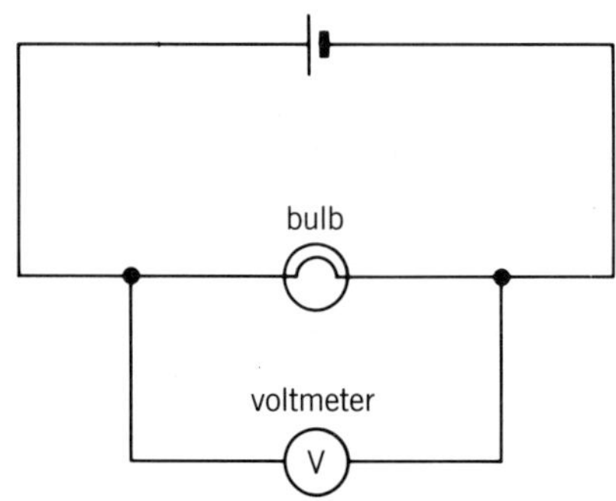

The voltmeter measures the potential difference across the bulb

4.5 V
V
1.5 V 1.5 V 1.5 V
bulb
motor
V
V
1.25 V
3.25 V

In a series circuit the total potential difference across all the devices is equal to the total potential difference of the supply

Connecting cells in series

Some devices need more energy than others to work. Larger currents are needed to supply the extra energy. To provide a larger current, several cells may be connected in series (end-to-end). The total potential difference (voltage) is found by adding the voltage of each cell. Three 1.5 V cells connected in series, for example, will give a total potential difference across the supply of 4.5 V.

Cells are an expensive way of supplying electrical energy. A cheaper and often more convenient way is to use a mains power supply. The power supply packs used in school laboratories have the added advantage that they cut the mains voltage down from 230 V to about 12 V, making it safer to use. Most power packs can supply either d.c. (direct current) or a.c. (alternating current).

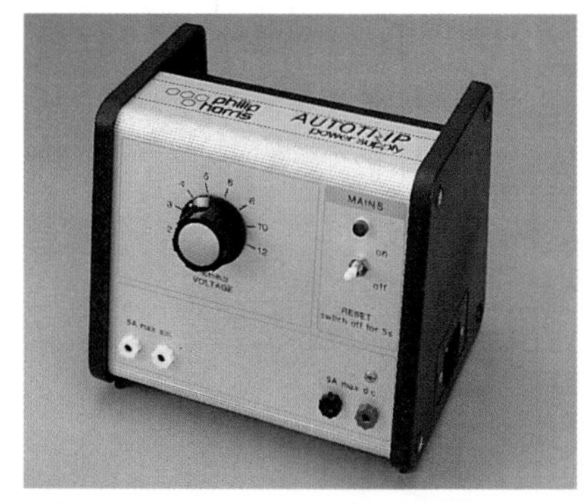

Laboratory power pack

Measuring current in a circuit

An ammeter is used to measure the current flowing through a circuit. The units used to measure current are **amperes**, abbreviated to **amps** (A). An ammeter is connected in series with everything else in the circuit. The current is the same at all points in a series circuit.

Ammeters have low resistances so they have little effect on the current through the circuit.

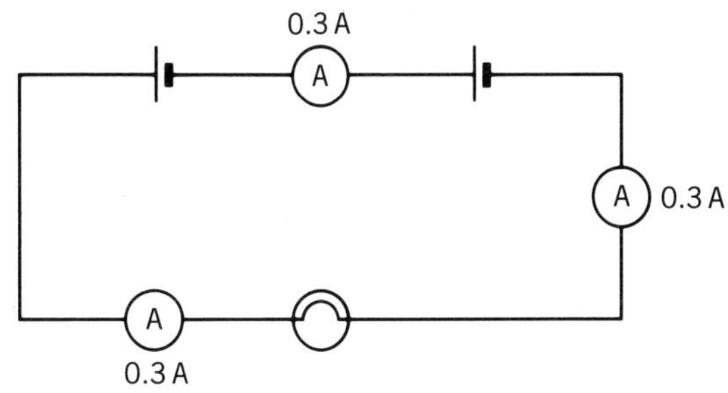

In a series circuit the current is the same at all points

★ THINGS TO DO

1 Copy the passage below into your notebook. Fill in the blank spaces with words or phrases from this list. Some may be used twice.

thin *connecting wires* *energy*
hot *electrons* *light energy*
electrical energy *plastic* *chemical*

An electric current is a flow of charged particles called .... is transferred to them by the cell in the circuit. A cell contains chemicals which react when the cell is connected into a circuit. In the cell .... energy is transferred to the current as .... The current flows through .... which are covered by an insulating material such as .... In a bulb in the circuit .... is transferred to the filament. The filament is a .... wire which gets .... as the current flows through it. Some of the electrical energy is converted into ....

2 Some cables used to connect circuits have thick copper wire. Others have thinner wire.

Connecting wire

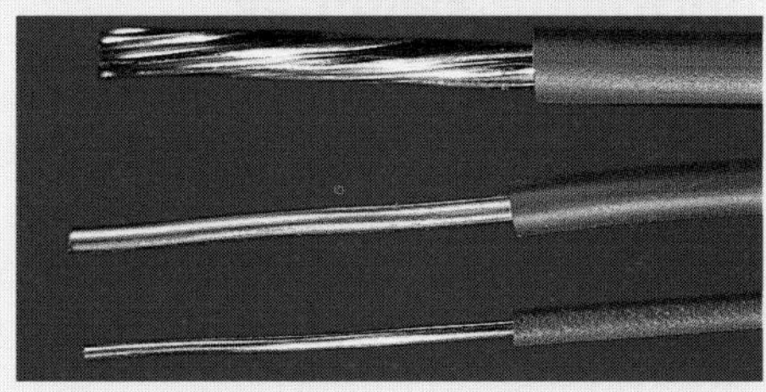

How do you think the diameter of the wire will affect the current which flows through a circuit? Make a note of your ideas and plan how you could test them. Check with your teacher before starting your tests.

Keep a record of any measurements you make and use them to prepare a report.

3 Compare what happens in an electric circuit with the way water flows through a central heating system such as that shown below.

Make a list of similarities between the way the electric circuit and the water circuit work. Make a second list describing the differences.

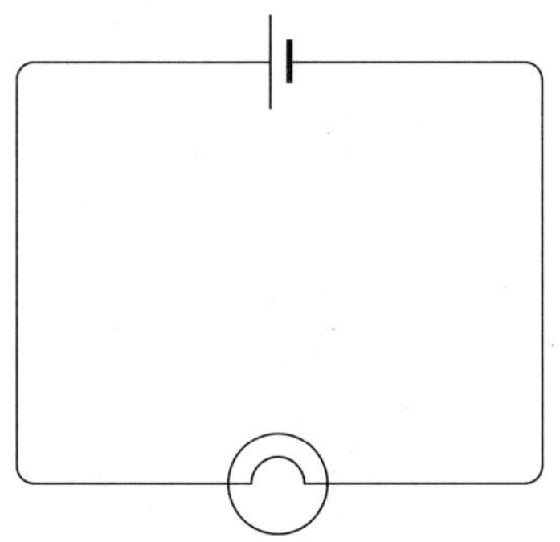

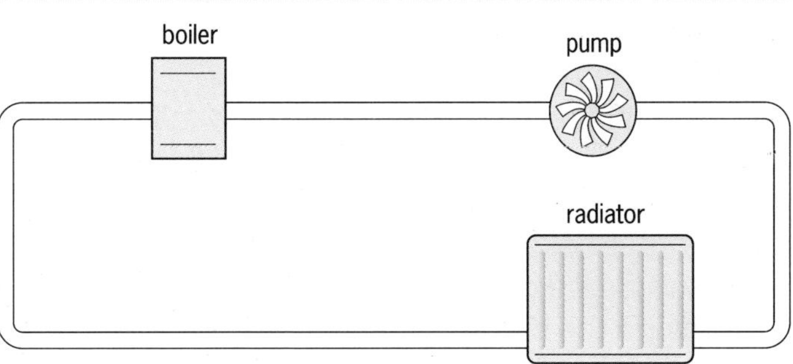

Is an electric circuit like a central heating circuit?

2.6 Switched on

Electric circuits are meant to work for us – to do the things we want them to do. We therefore need to know how to control the flow of the current.

A switch is a simple form of control device. Many switches are mechanical – they need to be pushed or pulled.

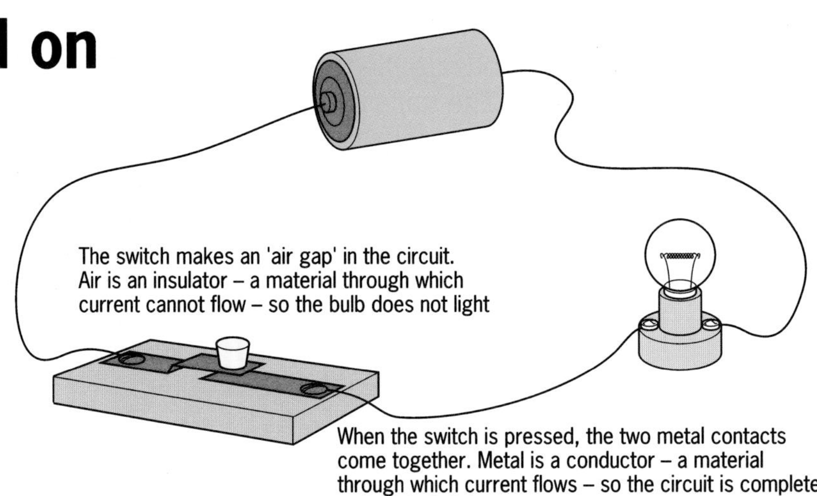

The switch makes an 'air gap' in the circuit. Air is an insulator – a material through which current cannot flow – so the bulb does not light
When the switch is pressed, the two metal contacts come together. Metal is a conductor – a material through which current flows – so the circuit is completed and the bulb lights

Temperature-controlling switches

A temperature switch, or *thermostat*, can be used to switch a circuit on or off at a certain temperature.

Some Christmas tree lights flash on and off regularly. They have a special switch inside one of the bulbs. Whether the switch is open or closed depends on its temperature.

As the current flows through the bimetallic strip the temperature rises and the strip bends away, breaking the circuit. The bulbs go out and the strip cools down. As it cools it straightens, making contact again and the bulbs light. This process is then repeated, making the bulbs switch on and off.

Thermostats are also used:

- to control the temperature of an iron,
- to control the temperature inside an oven, and
- to control the central heating system in your home.

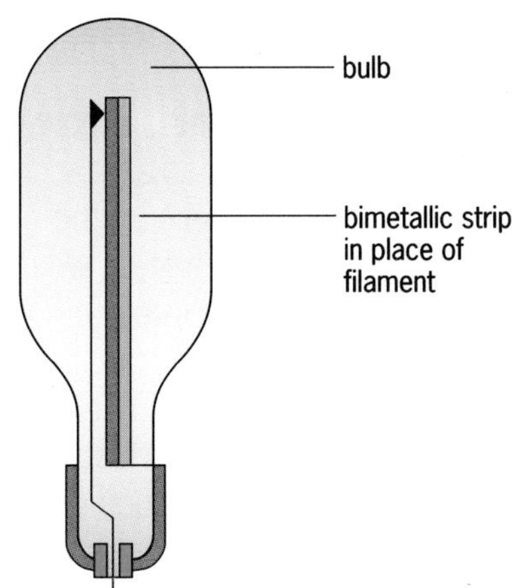

Temperature-controlled switch in a set of flashing Christmas tree lights

Magnetic switches

The doors to your home may have a switch as part of a burglar alarm system. If the door is opened by an intruder, the alarm sounds.

The switch illustrated here is a *reed switch*, operated by permanent magnets attached to the door and door frame. When the door is closed, the magnetic effects of the magnets in the door and frame cancel, so the two contacts inside the switch remain apart, making a break in the circuit. If, however, the door is opened, the reeds are magnetised and they spring together, completing the circuit and sounding the alarm.

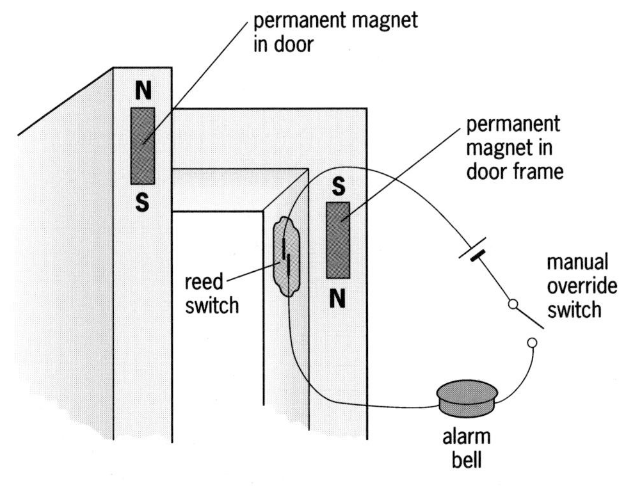

Reed-switch activated burglar alarm

Automatic switches

Some switches operate when they detect movement, light, or heat. They are called *sensors*.

◀ The sensor above these doors detects movement and opens the doors automatically

▶ This security device detects the heat from someone's body and switches on the light

★ THINGS TO DO

1 Copy and complete this table describing what you must do to get each bulb to light in the circuits on the right.

Bulb	What to do
A	Close switch(es) ....
B	
C	
D	

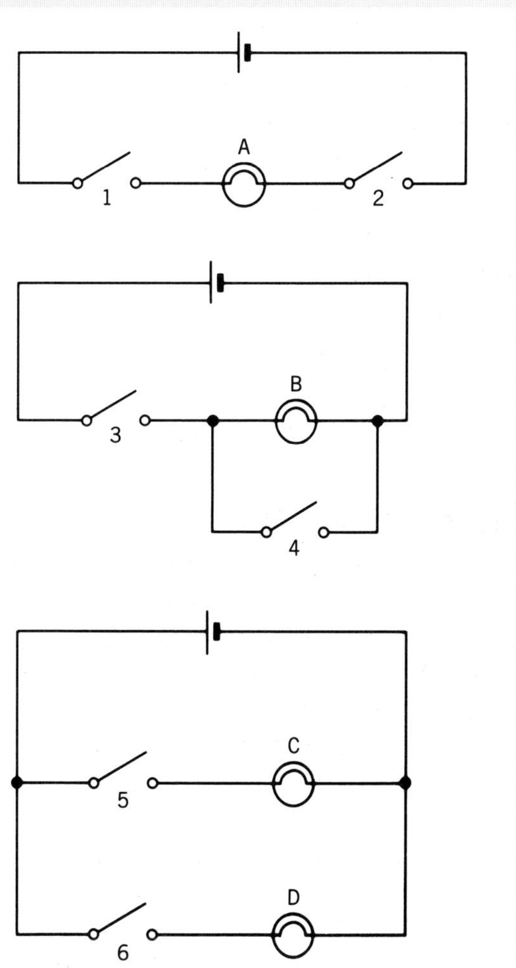

2 Design and test your own reed switch alarm using a buzzer or bell for the alarm. You will need to think about which materials to use for your reed switch, how far apart they must be placed, and where the magnet(s) should be.

3 Look at the circuit in a torch. Draw what you see, explain how it works and then draw a circuit diagram for the torch.

Describe how you could use a torch to test the fuses used in 3-pin plugs.

4 Design a circuit which will let you test materials to find out whether they are conductors or insulators. Test some materials and organise your results in a table showing which materials are conductors and which are insulators.

2.7 Christmas tree lights

Christmas tree lights are usually connected in one long line – in series. The main problem with series circuits is that everything must be on or everything must be off – you cannot have some parts on and others off.

It follows that if the filament inside one of the bulbs melts, then the whole circuit is broken and every bulb goes out. This is another weakness of series circuits – if one part fails, everything else stops working.

When one of the bulbs on your Christmas tree 'blows' all the lights may go off

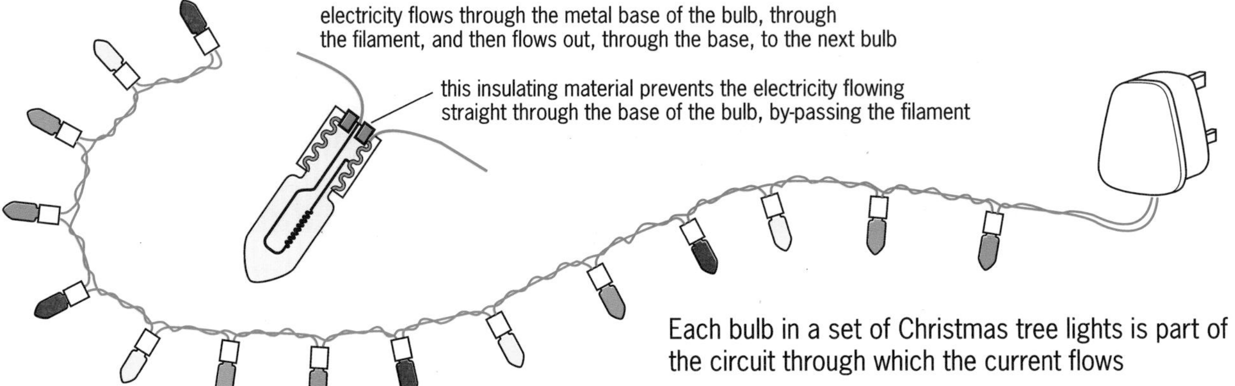

electricity flows through the metal base of the bulb, through the filament, and then flows out, through the base, to the next bulb
this insulating material prevents the electricity flowing straight through the base of the bulb, by-passing the filament

Each bulb in a set of Christmas tree lights is part of the circuit through which the current flows

Potential difference in series circuits

In series circuits the energy from the supply is 'shared' between the devices in the circuit. This is another way of saying that *the potential difference across the supply is equal to the sum of the potential differences across all the devices* in the circuit. (Remember that the potential difference across a device is a measure of the electrical energy transferred to it.) The more devices which are added, the lower the potential difference across each one – so the less energy each one receives (assuming the supply does not change).

If further bulbs were added to the circuit illustrated, the potential difference across each one would fall until there was insufficient energy to light the bulbs. Similar effects would be noticed with other devices – motors, for example, would run more slowly.

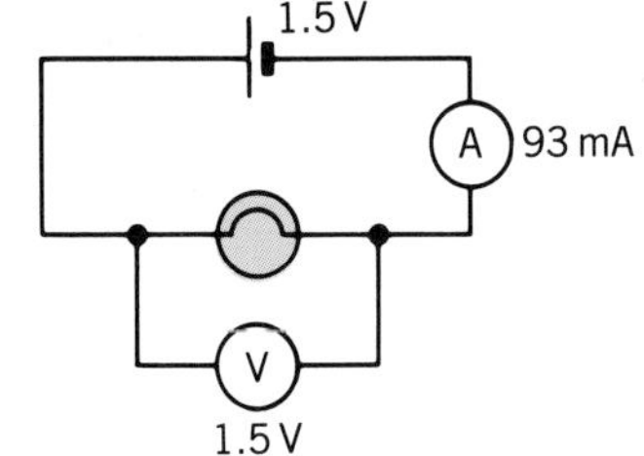

Here there will be a potential difference of 1.5 V across the bulb

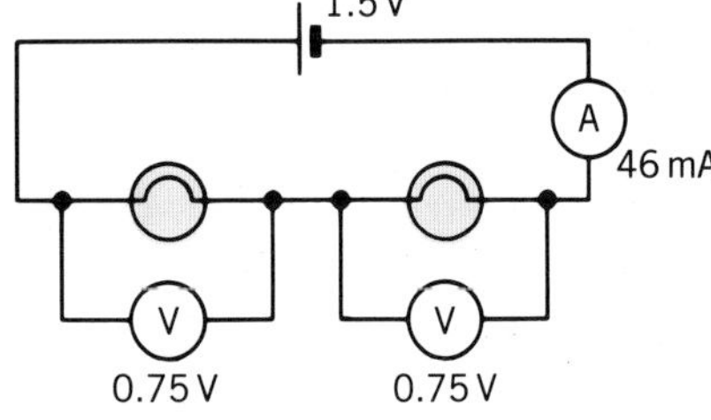

Now the potential difference of the supply is 'shared' between two identical bulbs. The potential difference across each bulb falls to 0.75 V and each bulb is dimmer

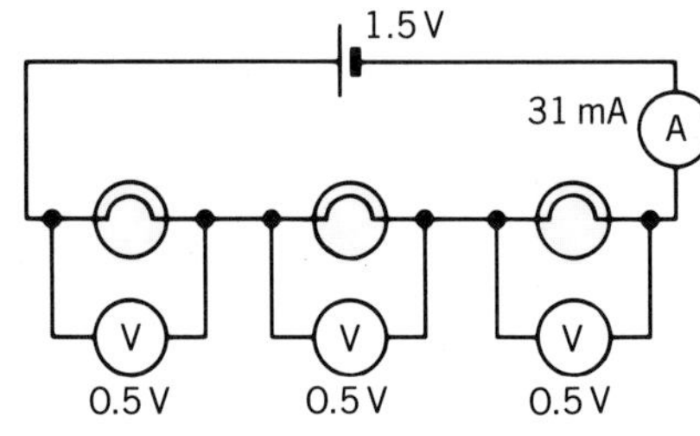

When a further (identical) bulb is added the potential difference across each one falls to 0.5 V and each bulb becomes even dimmer

Resistance

In the circuits shown on the opposite page you will notice that each time an extra bulb is added, the current decreases. This is because each bulb tries to resist the flow of charge – it provides a **resistance** against the current. Every part of a circuit – the connecting wire, bulbs, motors, buzzers, bells, even the cell itself – provides resistance. The resistance of good copper connecting wire is so small, however (copper is a very good conductor) that it can normally be ignored. The resistance of the cell is also generally ignored.

The resistance of a device is measured in units called **ohms** (Ω). The more devices there are in a series circuit, the bigger the resistance and the smaller the current. In a circuit containing two bulbs and a buzzer like those shown below the total resistance would be 366 ohms – the sum of their resistances.

As we will see later, the resistance of a device changes if its temperature changes.

Different components have different resistances

1 metre of 0.5 mm resistance wire 5 Ω

2 metres of 0.5 mm resistance wire 10 Ω

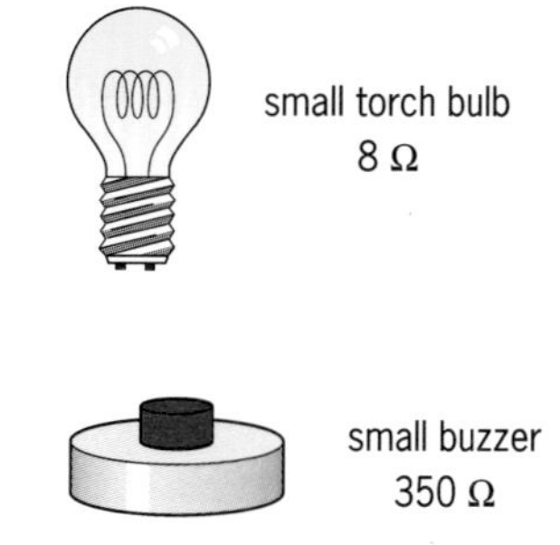

★ THINGS TO DO

1 Design an investigation to find out how the current flowing in a series circuit depends on the number of bulbs in the circuit. Check your plans with your teacher before carrying out your investigation. Keep a record describing what you do, and use your results to suggest what might be happening in the circuit.

2 Draw each of these circuits in your notebook. Alongside each of the meters write down what you think the reading will be.

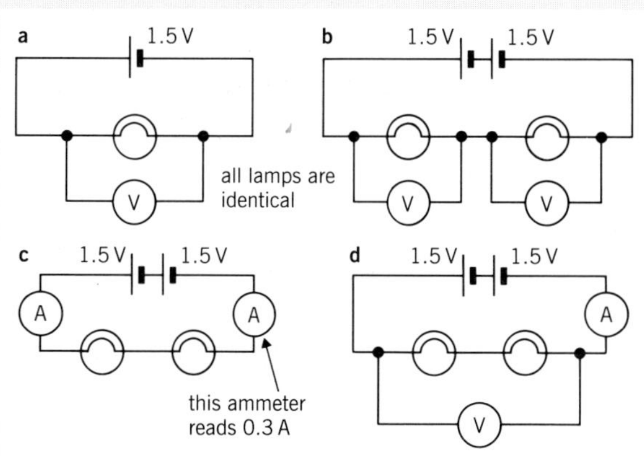

3 Mr Brown bought some Christmas tree lights. There were twenty bulbs in the circuit. Assume the mains supply is 240 V.

a) What will be the potential difference across each bulb?

b) If he added more bulbs to the set of lights, what difference would he see? Explain your answer.

c) The lights went out and he found one of the bulbs was broken. In the shop there were two types of bulb, with the information shown here.

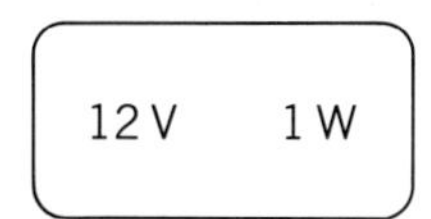

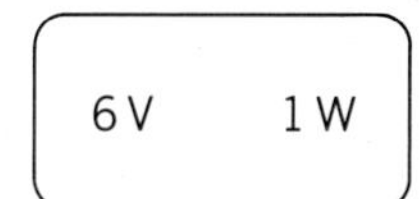

i) Which should he buy? Explain your answer.

ii) What would be the difference between a set of tree lights using 12 V bulbs and a set using 6 V bulbs? Explain your answer.

2.8 The lights in your house

Household lighting circuits are connected in a way which allows each light to operate independently – one can be on while others are off. The lights are connected in a **parallel circuit**.

If you look at the circuit diagram on the right you should be able to see that if switch A is pressed, then the living room light would come on but the others would remain off. Another advantage of this type of circuit is that if one of the bulbs fails, the others will continue to work.

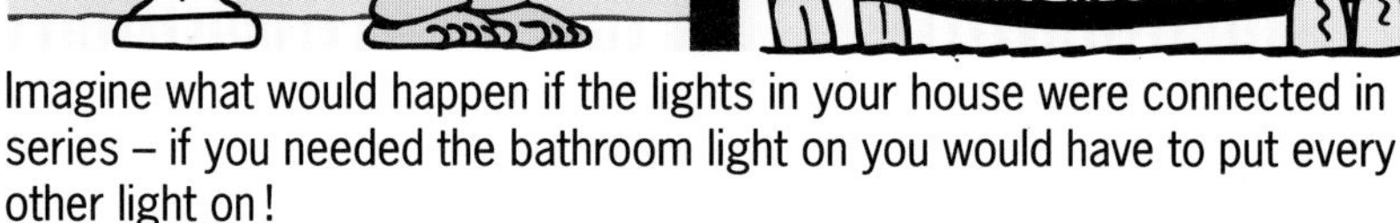

Imagine what would happen if the lights in your house were connected in series – if you needed the bathroom light on you would have to put every other light on!

The sockets in your house are connected in the same way, so that you can have one socket in use while others are off. The sockets that are switched off are 'by-passed' by the current so it can still reach the sockets that are in use and operate any appliances connected to them.

Downstairs lighting circuit of a house, simplified

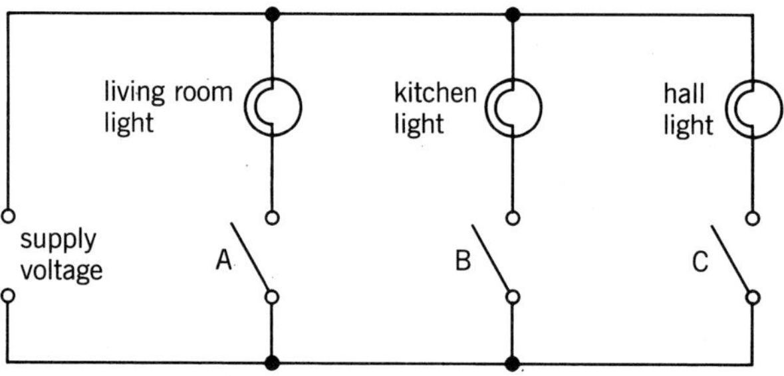

Current through parallel circuits

Parallel circuits consist of two or more 'loops' in which the components are connected. One loop 'branches' off another. As the current flows through the circuit, it divides at each branch, with some flowing through one loop and the rest flowing through the second loop.

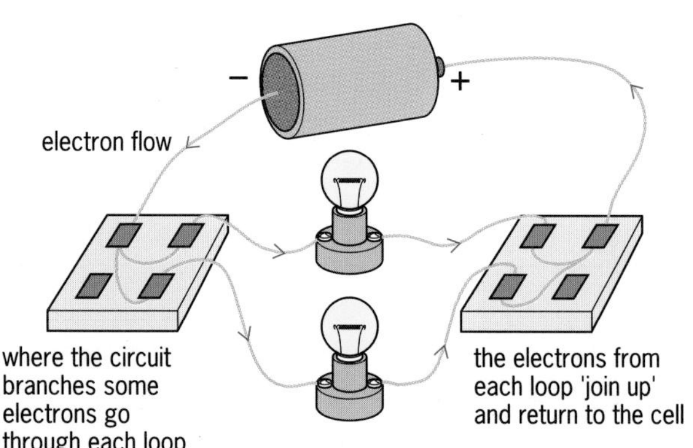

The current divides at a branch

Note that *the sum of the currents in each loop is always equal to the current from the cell.*

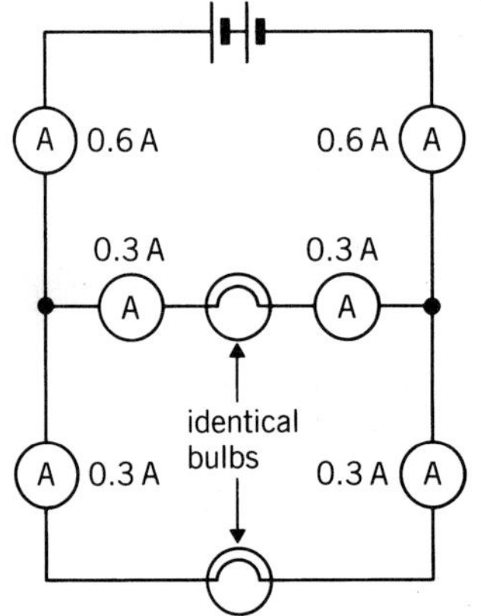

If the two bulbs are the same the current divides equally through each loop

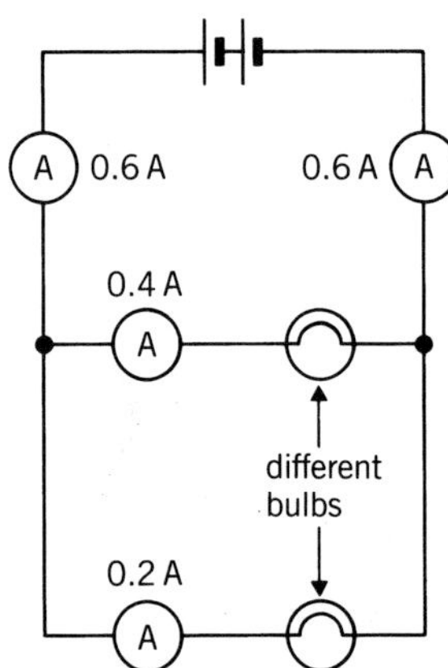

If the bulbs have different resistances then most current takes the path of least resistance

Potential difference in parallel circuits

We saw that in a series circuit the total potential difference across all the devices in the circuit was equal to the potential difference across the supply. In parallel circuits we find a quite different result.

The potential difference across the device(s) in each loop of a parallel circuit is equal to the potential difference of the supply. No matter how many bulbs are added to this circuit, the potential difference across each one would remain at 3 V, so the brightness of each would always be the same.

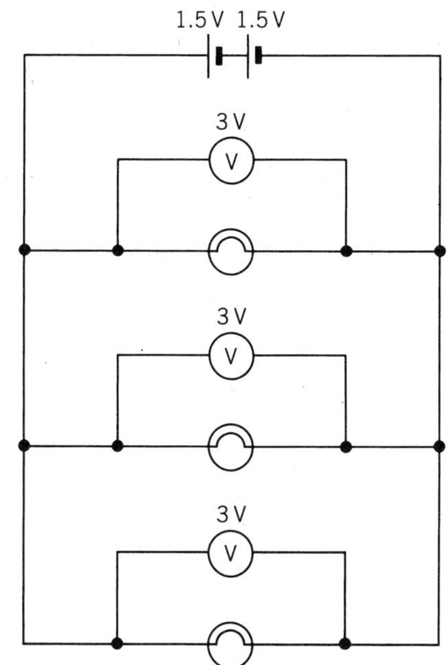

The p.d. across each bulb is exactly the same (3 V) and is equal to the p.d. across the cells (3 V)

★ THINGS TO DO

1 Connect the circuit shown here.

a) Copy this circuit diagram. Use an ammeter to measure the current at each of the points A–H and put the values in a table.

Make a note of, and explain any similarities and differences in, the values in your table.

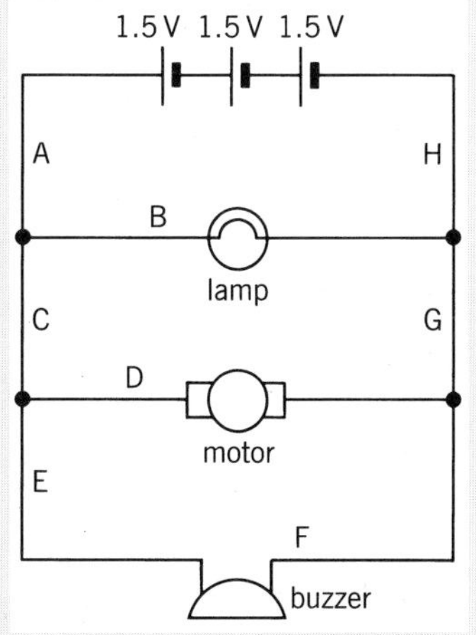

b) Measure the potential difference across the lamp, the motor and the buzzer. Put your results into a table.

c) Now connect the same three components in series with three cells.

i) Make a note of any similarities and differences you notice between what happens when they are connected in series and in parallel.

ii) Measure the potential difference across each component when connected in series. Do the values differ from those obtained in **b**?
If so, why?

2 Copy these circuit diagrams into your notebook. Add what you think the missing readings on the meters will be.

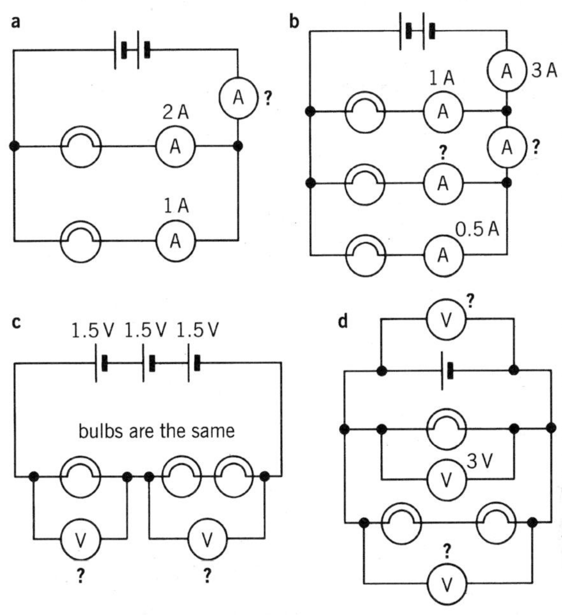

3 Car headlamp bulbs have two filaments. One is for 'dipped' headlights, the other is used when the lamps are placed on 'full beam'. Draw a circuit which would allow each filament to be operated independently by the driver, but which could also operate both filaments together.

2.9 Current, potential difference and charge

Current and charge

An electric current is a flow of charged particles (electrons) from a point of high potential to a point of lower potential. Some appliances need large currents to supply the energy they need to work effectively. Others need only small currents.

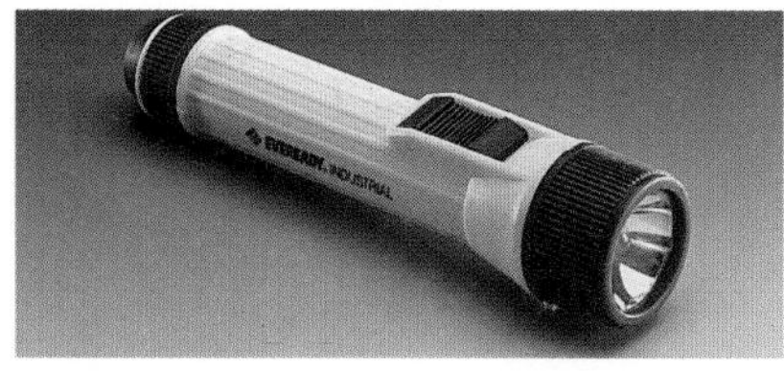
EVEREADY INDUSTRIAL

A torch bulb needs a current of about 0.2 amps to supply the energy it needs

Russell Hobbs

A current of about 8 amps may flow through the element of a kettle

A cooker may need a current of 16 amps if every part of it is in use

The charge on a single electron is very small, and huge numbers must flow through circuits to supply the energy needed. The size of the current at any point depends on the amount of charge which flows past that point in one second. The more charge flowing, the bigger the current. Current, charge and time are mathematically related:

$$\text{current (amps)} = \frac{\text{charge (coulombs)}}{\text{time (seconds)}}$$

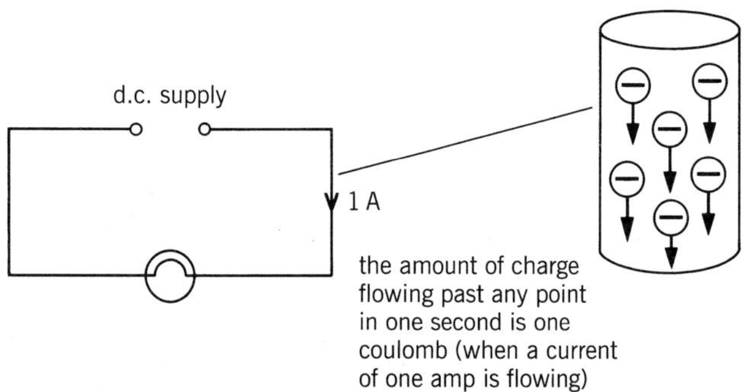
d.c. supply
1 A
the amount of charge flowing past any point in one second is one coulomb (when a current of one amp is flowing)

Put another way, the amount of charge passing a point depends on the current which flows, and the time for which it flows. Rearranging the equation above:

$$\text{charge (coulombs)} = \text{current (amps)} \times \text{time (seconds)}$$

Using this relationship we can get a definition for the unit of charge – the **coulomb**. *One coulomb is the amount of charge carried by a current of one ampere which flows for one second.*

If, for example, 1 amp flows for 2 seconds, then 2 coulombs of charge will have been transferred by the current. If 2 amps flow for 6 seconds, then 12 coulombs of charge will have been transferred.

Potential difference and charge

The potential difference (or voltage) of a cell is the amount of energy which it transfers to each coulomb of charge which passes through it. A 1.5 volt torch battery, for example, transfers 1.5 joules of energy to each coulomb which passes through it. A 12 volt car battery transfers 12 joules of energy to each coulomb. This helps us to define the unit of potential difference – the **volt**.

A cell has a potential difference of one volt if each coulomb of charge passing through it gains one joule of energy. The potential difference is therefore the number of joules of energy transferred to each coulomb of charge, so we can write:

$$\text{potential difference (volts)} = \frac{\text{energy transferred (joules)}}{\text{charge (coulombs)}}$$

Potential difference in series and parallel circuits

As we have seen, the potential difference across components connected in series and parallel is quite different. Thinking about what happens in terms of the flow of charge can help us to understand why the components behave so differently when connected in different ways. Consider the circuits shown here.

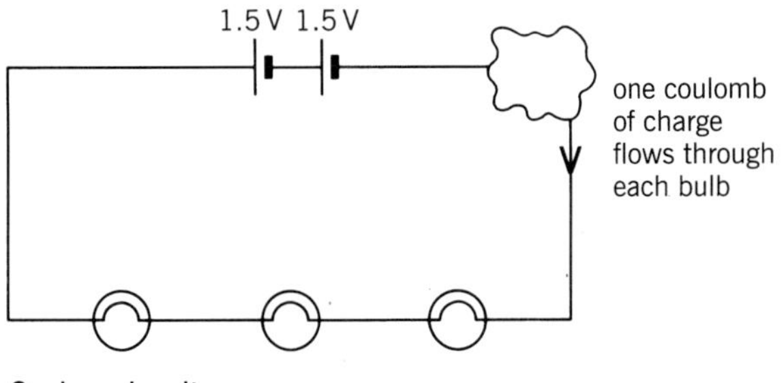

Series circuit

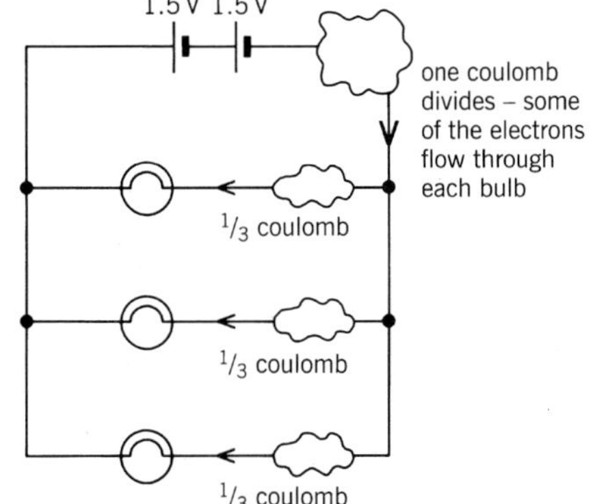

Parallel circuit

In both cases we will assume that the resistance of the connecting cables and the cells are negligible and so any effects of their resistance on energy transfer can be ignored.

In both circuits, the cells transfer 3 joules of energy to each coulomb of current flowing through them (because the p.d. across the cells is 3 volts).

In the series circuit, all electrons pass through all three bulbs. As they do they transfer the energy they gained from the cells to the bulbs. The bulbs will therefore have a total of 3 joules of energy transferred to them by each coulomb of charge which flows through them. If they are identical, each will receive one-third of this energy, i.e. 1 joule from each coulomb of current. The potential difference across each bulb will therefore be 1 volt. The energy transferred to the current by the cells is shared equally between all three bulbs.

In the parallel circuit, each coulomb of charge flowing will divide, with some passing through each loop in the circuit. Assuming the bulbs are identical, one-third of the electrons will flow through each loop of the circuit (so the current will be the same in each branch). In each loop, therefore, the energy transferred to the bulb will be 1 joule per ⅓ coulomb (because ⅓ coulomb passes through each loop and will carry ⅓ the total energy supplied by the cells to a full coulomb). The energy transferred to each bulb will therefore be 3 joules per coulomb – the same as the potential difference across the cells.

If the bulbs used in the parallel circuit were not identical, the potential difference across each would still be 3 volts. This is easier to understand if you consider potential difference as the energy transferred by one full coulomb to each part of the circuit.

★ THINGS TO DO

1 Calculate the amount of work done (or energy transferred) in transferring 4 coulombs of electric charge between two points which have a potential difference of 12 V.

2 The current through a 230 V electric kettle is 7 A. Calculate the amount of energy transferred by the current in 5 minutes.

3 A current of one amp means that one coulomb of charge passes each point in the circuit each second. One coulomb of charge is equivalent to 6.24×10^{18} electrons.

a) Calculate the number of electrons per second flowing through the filament of a 60 W light bulb if the current through the bulb is 0.25 A.

b) Calculate the amount of energy transferred by the filament of the bulb in 30 minutes. (Remember that 1 W = 1 J per second.)

2.10 Well in control

Each day we use things which are designed to control the flow of current.

The child makes the cars go slower or faster using the hand controller. This changes the potential difference across the motor and the current which flows through it

There are many examples of devices which control the current through the appliances in your home.

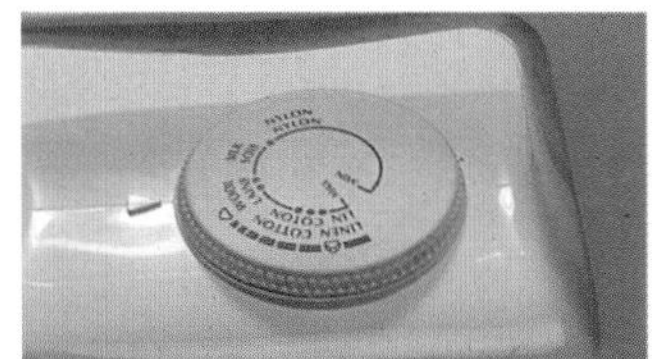

- The control on an iron adjusts the temperature.
- Dimmer switches adjust the brightness of your room lights.
- A fan can be switched from low to high speeds.
- Volume controls adjust the loudness of your audio equipment.
- The fast-forward control on your tape recorder makes the tape wind faster.

These changes are all brought about by changing the resistance in the circuit. This changes the current flowing through the components in the circuit and affects how they work.

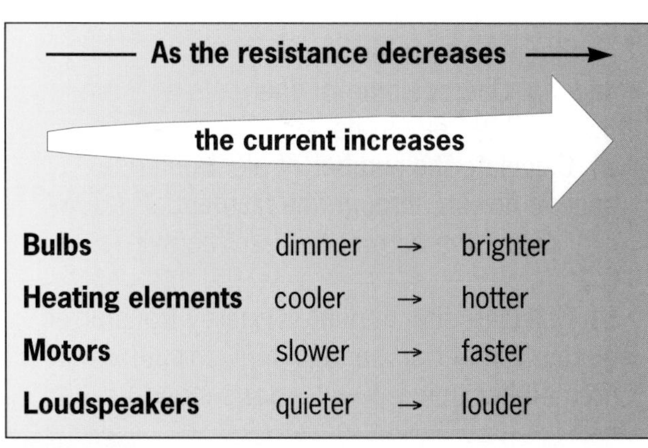

As the resistance decreases →

the current increases

Bulbs	dimmer	→	brighter
Heating elements	cooler	→	hotter
Motors	slower	→	faster
Loudspeakers	quieter	→	louder

Resistance wire

The metals used for connecting wire are good conductors. They have a low resistance which means little energy is 'wasted' as the current flows through the wire. Other metals which are not such good conductors, such as nickel chrome, provide more resistance to the flow of current. Wire made from these metals is generally called 'resistance wire'. The circuit here can be used to show the effect of changing the length of resistance wire in a circuit. The table shows some pupils' results.

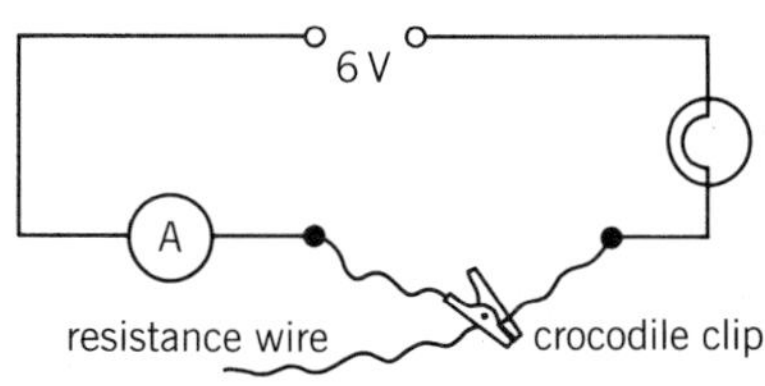

Length of resistance wire / cm	Current / mA	Brightness of bulb
20	46	bright
40	42	slightly dimmer
60	38	dim
80	34	just glowing
100	30	not lit

You can see that as the length of resistance wire in the circuit is increased, the current decreases and the bulb gets dimmer. Notice that in the final row, although the bulb was not lit, current was flowing through the circuit. There was simply not enough current to supply the energy needed to light the bulb.

By designing a circuit in which we can change the amount of resistance, we can control the current and hence control the appliances in the circuit.

Variable resistors

Variable resistors allow us to vary the current in a circuit just by turning a knob. The volume controls on your radio and hi-fi are variable resistors. Some types of variable resistor or 'potentiometer' are shown in the photograph.

In some (low-power) appliances the potentiometer has a carbon track in place of the coil of resistance wire.

Variable resistors are shown on circuit diagrams by the symbol

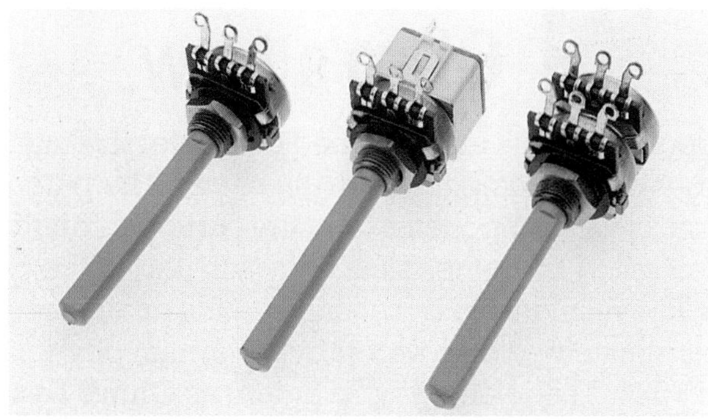

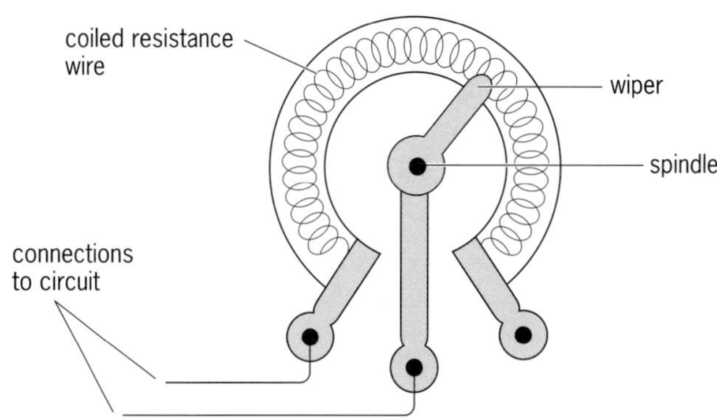

Inside the outer case of this variable resistor is a coil of resistance wire. As the control knob is turned, a sliding contact (the wiper) passes across the coil. The amount of resistance wire in the circuit depends on the position of the wiper

Fixed resistors

Modern electronic circuits contain small components called resistors to control the current in each part of the circuit.

They are normally made from a mixture of carbon and some other conducting material. Two short lengths of wire project from each end, allowing the resistor to be connected into the circuit. Resistors such as these have a fixed value, from less than one ohm to millions of ohms.

The symbol for a fixed resistor is

★ THINGS TO DO

1 This circuit was drawn for a remote-control car kit. The instructions given to the designer were that:
- it should include a switch which would make the car go forwards and backwards,
- it should be possible to make the car go faster or slower,
- there should be a switch which would control the front and rear lights,
- another switch should sound a buzzer.

a) Make a list of components that would be needed for this part of the circuit.
b) When it was tested two errors were found. Work out, from the circuit diagram, what the errors were. For each one say how you would correct it.

2 Design, build, and if possible, test a circuit for a two-speed hairdrier. Write a report which includes a description saying how the circuit changes the speed of the motor.

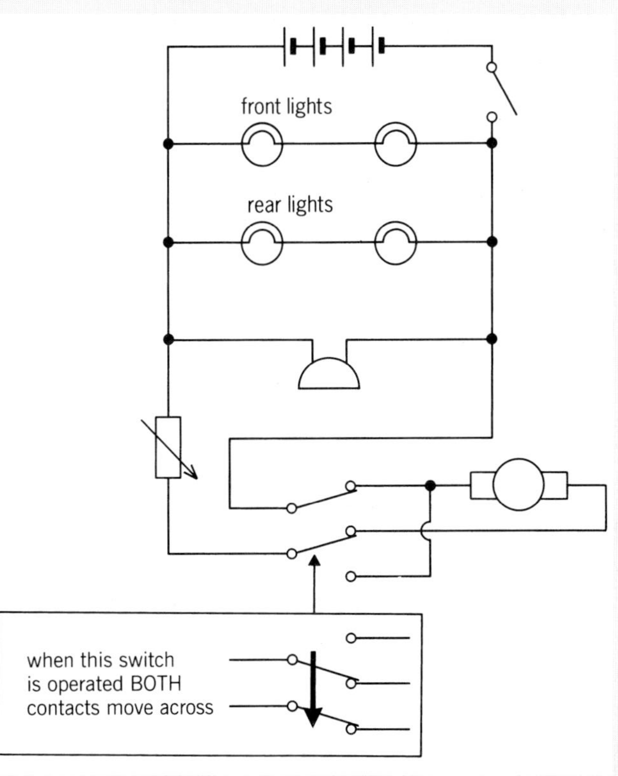

2.11 Ohm's Law

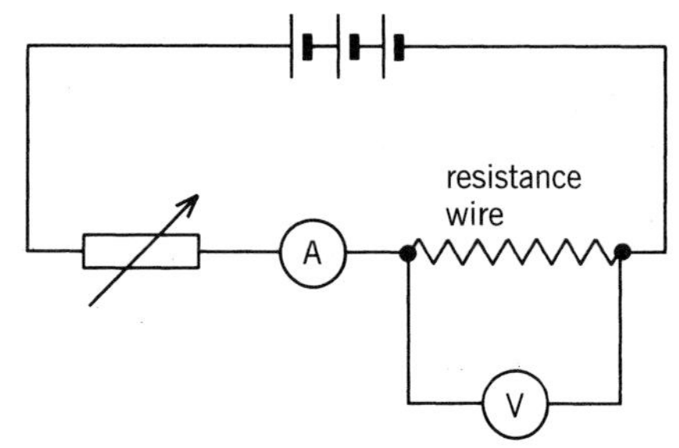

Electric circuits are designed to transfer just sufficient energy to operate the components in the circuit. The potential difference across the components (and the current through them) are carefully controlled by the resistance in each part of the circuit.

The relationship between potential difference, current and resistance was discovered by a German physicist, George Ohm, in 1826. The relationship is known as **Ohm's Law** and can be demonstrated experimentally as shown here.

Circuit for determining the relationship between potential difference across a resistance wire and current through it when the resistance of the circuit is varied, and typical results

Potential difference across resistance wire /volts	Current flowing through circuit /amps	Potential difference / Current
2	0.18	10.1
2.4	0.25	9.6
3.0	0.3	10.0
3.5	0.36	9.7
3.9	0.38	10.2

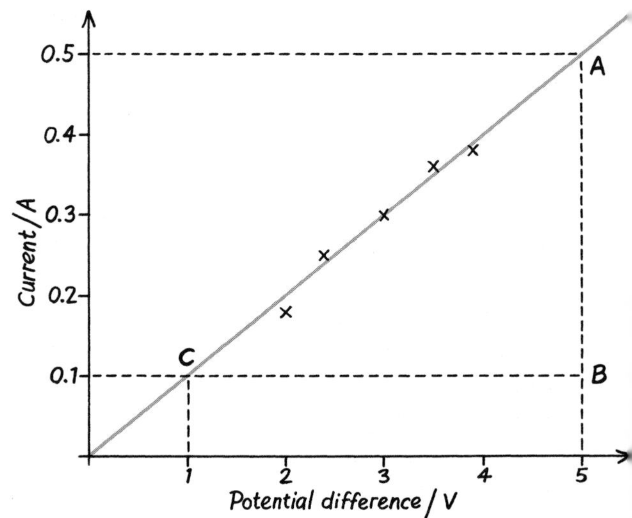

You can see from the table that as the potential difference across the resistance wire increases, the current through it increases. The relationship is shown more clearly when the values for current and potential difference are plotted on a graph.

The straight line illustrates Ohm's Law, which states that *the current through a metallic conductor is directly proportional to the potential difference across its ends, providing the temperature remains constant.*

This relationship is used to define **resistance**:

$$\text{resistance} = \frac{\text{potential difference across the ends of a conductor}}{\text{current flowing through the conductor}}$$

The resistance of the wire in the experiment above can be found by calculating the inverse of the gradient (or slope) of the graph, for example BC/AB. The gradient has the same value, regardless of which two points are used to calculate it. Because the gradient is constant, the resistance of the conductor must be constant across the range of potential differences used, and under the particular conditions of the experiment, i.e. constant temperature.

Other types of metallic conductor show the same relationship but the gradient of the line will be different.

Using symbols

The standard symbols used in electricity calculations are:

current = I
potential difference = V
resistance = R

Using these symbols, the relationship alongside can be written as:

$$R = \frac{V}{I}$$

This equation can be easily rearranged to give values for I and V:

$$I = \frac{V}{R} \quad \text{and} \quad V = I \times R$$

Temperature

Ohm's Law only applies providing the temperature of the conductor does not change. In some cases we cannot keep the temperature constant. When current flows through a filament bulb, for example, the temperature of the filament rises. By studying a graph of current against potential difference across a filament bulb, we can see how the resistance of the filament changes.

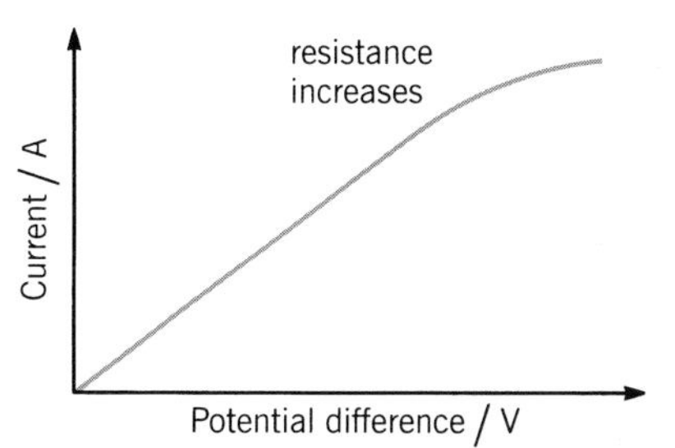

Current against potential difference for a filament bulb

You can see that for low values of the potential difference the filament seems to obey Ohm's Law – the graph is a straight line and the resistance of the filament remains constant. At higher values of the potential difference, however, the temperature of the filament increases considerably (by as much as 1000 °C) and the resistance increases. *The higher the temperature of a conductor, the higher its resistance.*

Using the equation *R* = *V*/*I*

This relationship can be used to find the value of the potential difference, current or resistance if any two of the quantities are known. Suppose, for example, we needed to calculate the value of the current in this circuit.

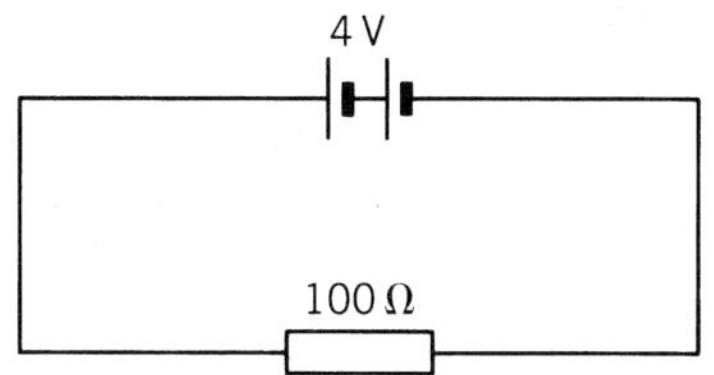

Because we know the potential difference across the resistor and the value of its resistance we can use:

$$I = \frac{V}{R} = \frac{4\,\text{V}}{100\,\Omega} = 0.04\,\text{A}$$

So the current through the circuit is 0.04 A, or 40 mA.

★ THINGS TO DO

1 Design and carry out an experiment to calculate the resistance of a small motor when a potential difference of 3 V is applied across it.

2 Calculate the value of the unknown quantity in each of the circuits shown here.

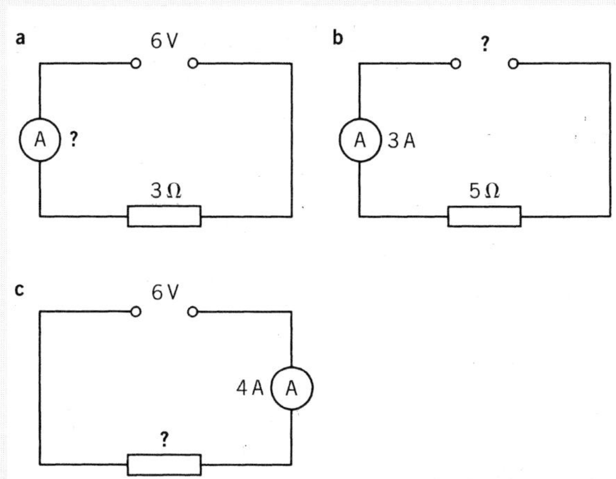

3 Diodes are used to control the direction in which current flows through a circuit. They allow current to flow in one direction but not in the opposite direction. The band on a diode represents the end which is the cathode – the end which would normally be connected to the negative terminal of the power supply.

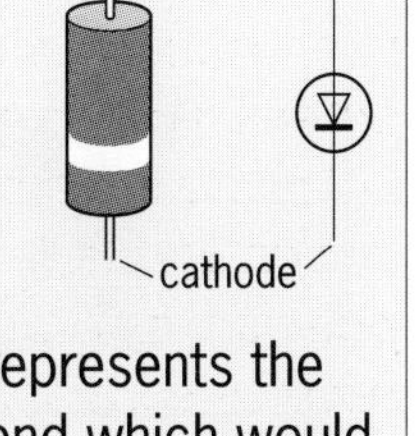

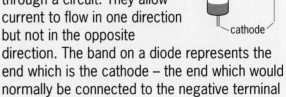

a) Build a simple series circuit containing a battery and a small bulb. Put a diode in series with the bulb and note what happens. Now reverse the diode and note any differences.
b) Use the circuit on page 72 to plot a graph of the current through the diode at different values of the potential difference across it.
c) Use the information from your graph to explain why the diode has the effect you noticed in part **a**.

2.12 LDRs and thermistors

We have seen that the current through a circuit can be varied by changing the resistance in the circuit. In the applications we have studied so far this could only be done by physically changing the length of resistance wire in the circuit. A variable resistor can do this, but it must have some form of mechanical control.

The petrol tank in some cars, for example, contains a float connected to a variable resistor. The resistor is part of the circuit containing the fuel gauge.

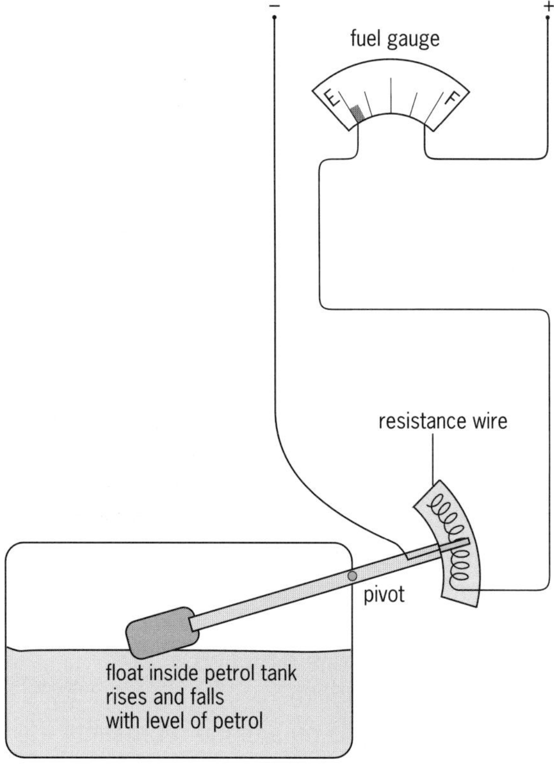

A fuel gauge circuit contains a variable resistor

As the fuel level in the tank changes, the float rises and falls. The variable resistor changes the potential difference across the fuel gauge, and consequently the position of the needle.

The resistance of some components, however, depends on their temperature, or on the amount of light falling on them. They can be used to control circuits automatically.

They are called temperature-dependent resistors (or 'thermistors') and light-dependent resistors (or LDRs).

Motorway lights automatically light up when the light level falls

▼ This sprinkler system is operated automatically if the temperature rises beyond a 'safe' level

Thermistors are used in circuits which are designed to be controlled by temperature, such as the sprinkler system above

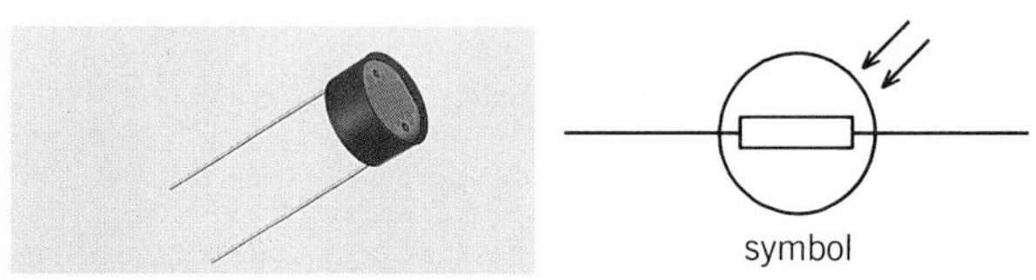

Light-dependent resistors are used in circuits which are designed to be controlled by light level, for example to switch on lights when darkness falls

Using LDRs and thermistors

We have seen that, in a series circuit, the sum of the potential differences across the components is equal to the supply voltage. If one of the components in the circuit has a higher resistance than the other, the potential difference is divided between them so that the component with the higher resistance has a greater potential difference across it.

If one of the resistors in the circuit on the right is replaced by a light-dependent resistor then the potential difference across the second resistor becomes controlled by the resistance of the LDR.

The same principles also apply to the use of thermistors to control the potential differences across the components in a circuit.

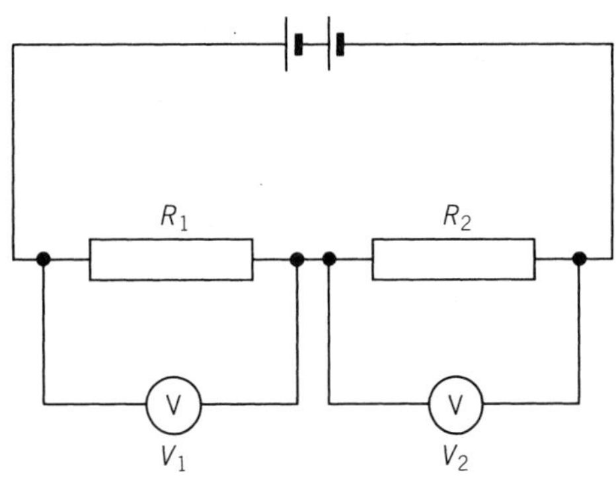

If $R_1 > R_2$ then $V_1 > V_2$

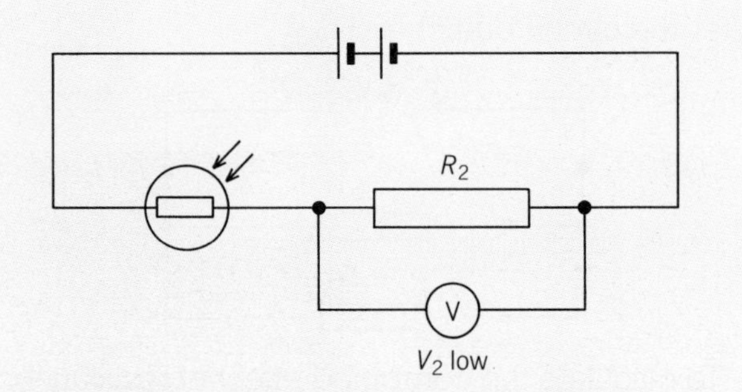

In the dark the resistance of the LDR is high so the potential difference across it is high. The potential difference across R_2 must therefore be low. In reality it will be almost zero

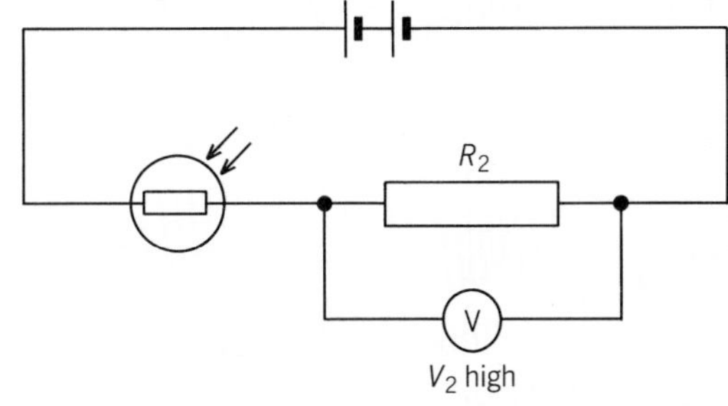

If a light shines on the LDR its resistance decreases dramatically, so that it is now well below that of the other resistor. The potential difference across R_2 therefore becomes high, whilst the potential difference across the LDR becomes low

★ THINGS TO DO

1 This graph shows the relationship between temperature and resistance for a thermistor.

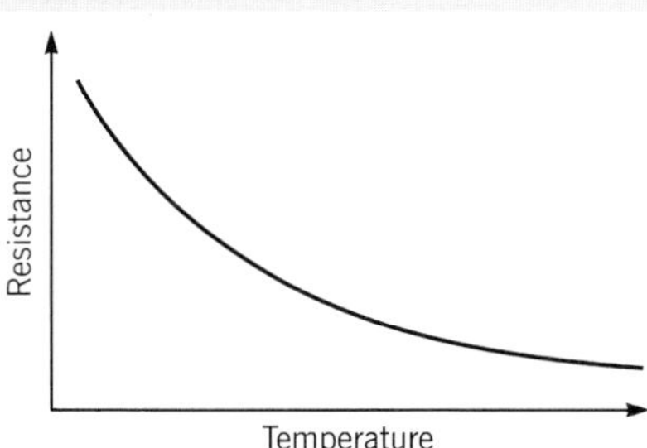

a) Comment on the shape of the graph.

b) Plan how you could use the circuit shown on the right to find out how the resistance of the thermistor depends on its temperature.

When your teacher has approved your plans, carry out your tests and prepare a report describing your findings.

Describe how you could calibrate the meter so you could use this circuit as the basis for an electrical thermometer. If possible, test your ideas and prepare a brief report.

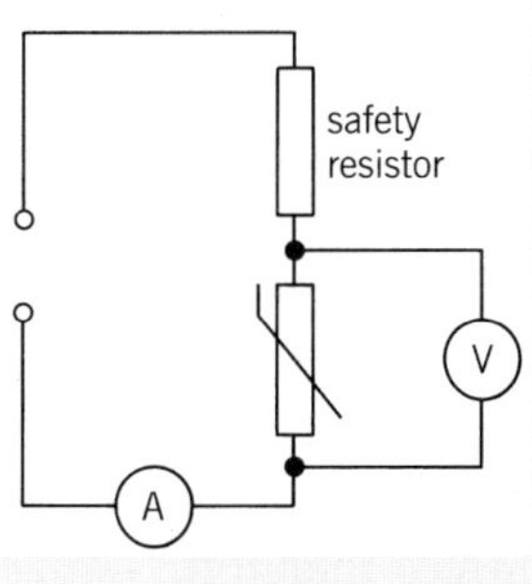

2.13 Resistances in series and parallel

In series

Every component in a circuit provides some resistance to the flow of current. The more components there are in a series circuit, the bigger the resistance and the smaller the current. *Their total resistance is the sum of the resistances of each one.*

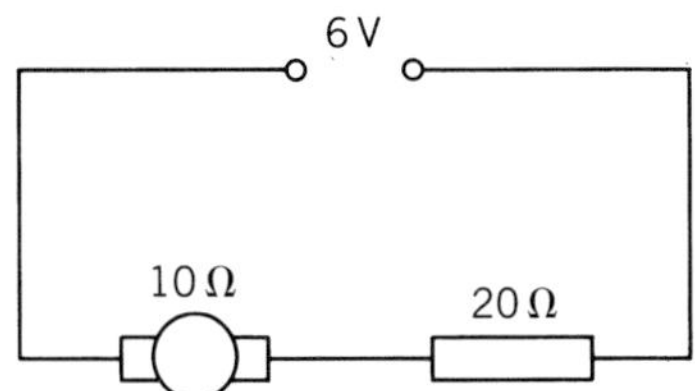

In the circuit illustrated the total resistance will be:

total resistance = resistance of motor + value of fixed resistor

$= 10\,\Omega + 20\,\Omega$

$= 30\,\Omega$

The current flowing through the circuit can be calculated using Ohm's Law:

$$\text{current } I = \frac{V}{R} = \frac{6\,\text{V}}{30\,\Omega} = 0.2\,\text{A}$$

Note that the value of the resistance used in calculating the current is the *total* resistance in the circuit.

Resistance and potential difference

Because the resistor has a higher resistance than the motor, more energy is transferred by the current in the resistor than in the motor. The potential difference across the resistor will, therefore, be greater than the potential difference across the motor (see page 75). The potential difference of the supply (6 V) is divided between the motor (2 V) and the resistor (4 V).

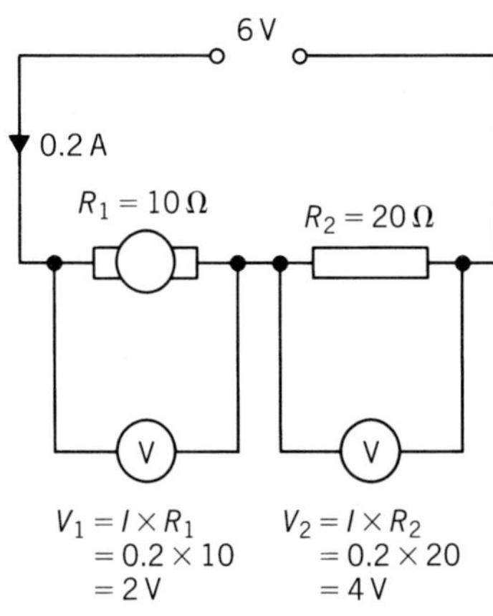

If the resistor were changed to one with a lower value, the potential difference across the motor would increase and it would turn faster (energy would be transferred from the current at a greater rate).

In parallel

When components are connected in parallel, some of the current flows through one loop of the circuit and the rest passes through the other loop(s). The current in each loop will be the same only if the resistances in each are the same. The sum of the current through the loops will be the same as the current in the main circuit before and after the circuit branches.

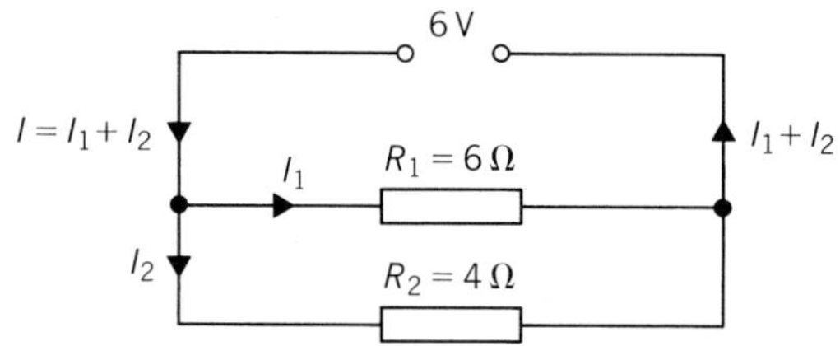

To calculate the combined effect of resistances in parallel this equation must be used:

$$\frac{1}{R} = \frac{1}{R_1} + \frac{1}{R_2} + \frac{1}{R_3} \text{ etc.}$$

Where only two resistors are involved:

$$\text{combined value of resistors} = \frac{\text{product}}{\text{sum}}$$

$$R = \frac{R_1\,R_2}{R_1 + R_2}$$

The values of R_1 and R_2 in the circuit illustrated are $6\,\Omega$ and $4\,\Omega$, so:

$$\text{combined resistance} = \frac{\text{product}}{\text{sum}} = \frac{6 \times 4}{6 + 4} = \frac{24}{10} = 2.4\,\Omega$$

Notice this is *less* than either resistance alone.

The current supplied by the cells depends on the combined value of the resistors, i.e. $2.4\,\Omega$ (their combined effect on the current flowing in the circuit is the same as if they were replaced by a single resistor with this value). Therefore:

$$\text{current supplied, } I = \frac{V}{R} = \frac{6\,\text{V}}{2.4\,\Omega} = 2.5\,\text{A}$$

How much current passes through each resistor?

When the current reaches the branch in the circuit most takes the 'path of least resistance', i.e. most of the current passes through the 4 Ω resistor. The rest passes through the 6 Ω resistor. How much current passes through each one depends on their respective values. To calculate the current through each one you need to appreciate that the potential difference across each is equal to the potential difference across the supply (6 V).

$$\text{So the current through } R_1 = \frac{V}{R_1} = \frac{6\,\text{V}}{6\,\Omega} = 1\,\text{A}$$

$$\text{and the current through } R_2 = \frac{V}{R_2} = \frac{6\,\text{V}}{4\,\Omega} = 1.5\,\text{A}$$

Notice that the sum of these values is equal to the current supplied by the cell, 2.5 A.

★ THINGS TO DO

1 Calculate the combined resistance of each of these combinations of resistors.

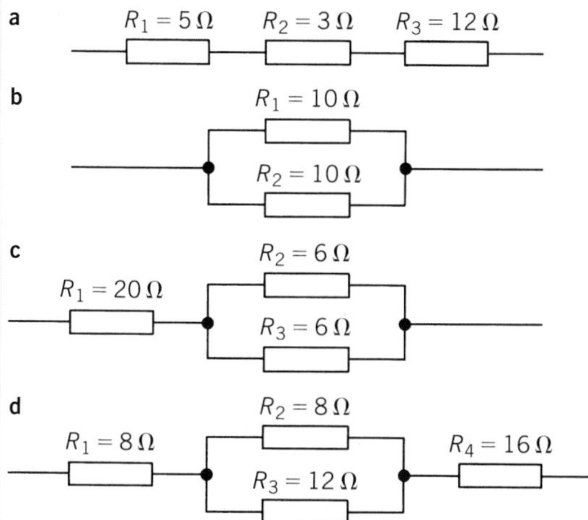

2 Calculate the value of the current from the cell(s) in each of these circuits.

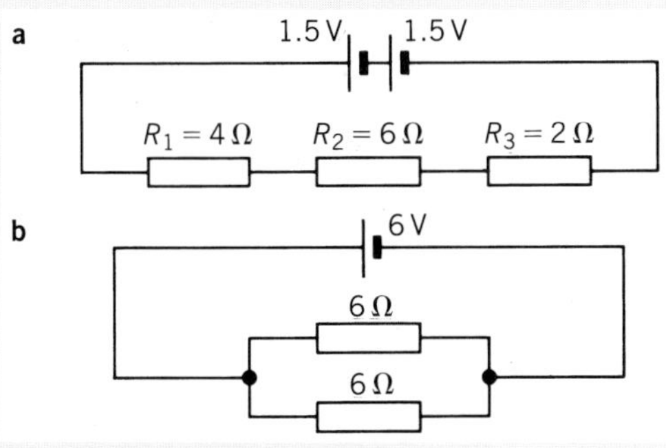

3 In each of these circuits calculate the current shown by ammeters A1, A2 and A3.

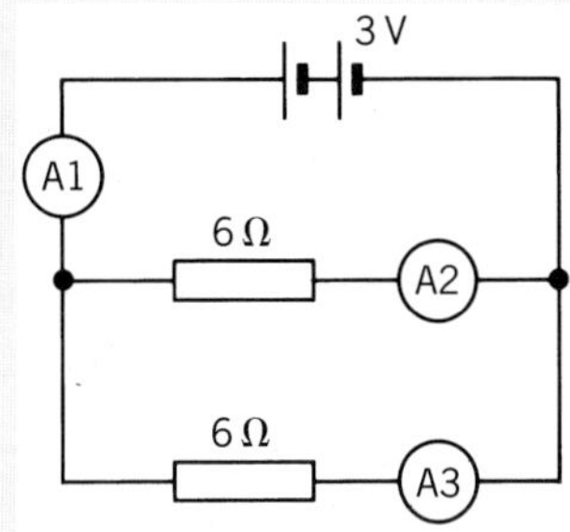

b
5 V
A3
6 Ω
4 Ω
A1
A2
6 Ω
4 Ω

4 A pupil designed this circuit which she thought could be used to measure the amount of petrol in the tank of a car.

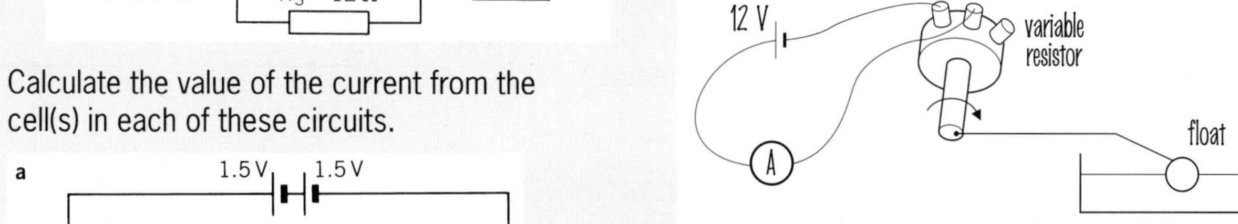

a) If the meter can read a maximum of 1 amp, what must be the smallest value of the resistance coil when the tank is full?
b) What should be the value of the resistance for the meter to read 'half full'?
c) If the 0–1 A ammeter was replaced with a 0–2 A meter, but everything else was kept the same, what difference would she notice? Explain your answer.
d) If the resistance coil was replaced with one which had the same length of resistance wire but which had a larger resistance per centimetre, what differences would be noticed? Explain your answer.

Electrical power

As electricity flows through an appliance, it transfers energy from the supply. When a motor is working, for example, electrical energy is transferred from the current to the motor as kinetic energy. We can think of the energy as being 'transformed' – changed into some other, more useful form. How quickly a device transforms energy is a measure of its **power**.

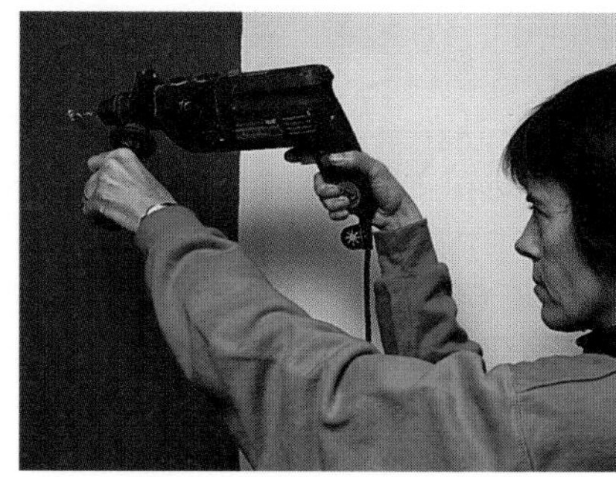

Electrical energy is transformed into kinetic energy. A smaller amount of energy is transferred to the air as heat and sound

Calculating the power of an appliance

As we saw on page 10, power is the amount of energy transferred each second, and is calculated using the equation:

$$\text{power (W)} = \frac{\text{energy transferred (J)}}{\text{time (s)}}$$

The amount of energy transferred by an electrical appliance depends on:

- the current flowing,
- the potential difference across the device, and
- the time for which the current flows.

These are related by the equation:

$$\text{energy transferred (J)} = \text{current (A)} \times \text{potential difference (V)} \times \text{time (s)}$$
$$= I \times V \times t$$

(Note that here the standard symbols for current (I), voltage (V) and time (t) are used to simplify the equation.)

Combining the equations above:

$$\text{electrical power (W)} = \frac{\text{energy transferred by the current (J)}}{\text{time for which the current flows (s)}}$$
$$= \frac{I \times V \times t}{t}$$
$$= I \times V$$

The power of an electrical appliance = current flowing through it × potential difference across it.

From Ohm's Law, page 72, potential difference $V = I \times R$ for a metallic conductor of resistance R. The above equation for power can therefore be changed into an alternative form:

$$\text{power} = I \times V = I \times (I \times R) = I^2 R$$

For an electrical appliance this is the rate at which electrical energy is transferred as heat due to its resistance R.

The current is a measure of the rate of flow of electrons. Increasing the current increases the rate at which electrons flow through the motor (assuming the p.d. across the motor stays the same). The greater the current, the more energy is transferred per second

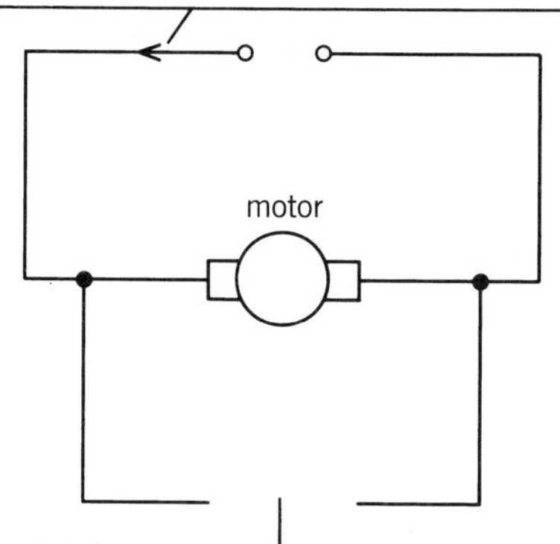

The potential difference is a measure of the energy transferred by each coulomb of charge as it passes through the motor. The bigger the potential difference, the more energy is transferred each second (assuming the current stays the same)

The energy transferred per second by an appliance – its power – depends on the current flowing and on the potential difference across the device

Choosing a fuse

Fuses normally used are '3 A' or '13 A'

If we know the power rating of an appliance we can calculate the current flowing through it under working conditions. Knowing the current allows us to choose the correct fuse for the plug.

Imagine, for example, a sunbed is shown to have a power rating of 200 W and operates from a 230 V supply. Using:

$$\text{power (W)} = \text{current (A)} \times \text{voltage (V)}$$

the current drawn by the sunbed is given by:

$$\text{current} = \frac{\text{power}}{\text{voltage}}$$

$$= \frac{200\,\text{W}}{230\,\text{V}} = 0.87\,\text{A}$$

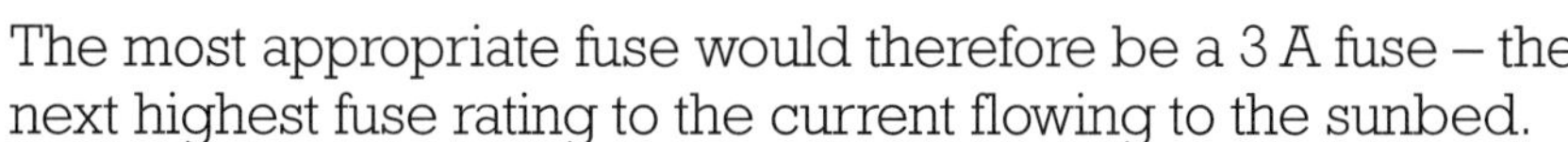

The most appropriate fuse would therefore be a 3 A fuse – the next highest fuse rating to the current flowing to the sunbed.

★ THINGS TO DO

1 A kettle has a power rating of 2200 W. It takes 3 minutes to boil the water. How much energy is transferred in this time?

2 A torch bulb is rated at 3.5 V, 0.3 A. The bulb is connected correctly to a 3.5 volt supply.
a) How much energy will be transferred to the bulb in 10 minutes?
b) If the batteries work continuously for 3 hours before becoming 'flat', how much energy will they have supplied?

3 A bedside lamp is rated as 230 V, 60 W.
a) Calculate the current which will flow when the lamp is in use.
b) Why would it be safe to use a 3 A fuse in the plug?

4 Mr Brown connected the following appliances to a single 13 A socket using a 4-way extension lead. (A 13 A socket is designed to allow a current of 13 A to be drawn safely from it.)

- a 3 kW electric kettle
- a 2 kW tumble-drier
- an 800 W iron
- a 1300 W toaster

a) Calculate the current through each appliance, assuming the supply voltage is 230 V.
b) What would happen if he attempted to use all the appliances at the same time, assuming the plug from the extension lead contained a 13 A fuse? Explain your answer.

Magnetic effects

The trains of the future

As a train moves along the railway track much energy is 'wasted' in overcoming friction. The trains of the future, however, may carry you at over 500 km/h (300 miles per hour) quietly and smoothly without touching the track.

The trains will be supported by a process called Maglev, or magnetic levitation – they will ride on an air 'cushion' supported by magnetic fields. The trains will be powered by a kind of magnetic motor called a linear motor. A Maglev train already runs on a section of track near Tokyo in Japan.

Japan's Maglev train has reached a speed of 500 km/h in tests

How Maglev works

The magnetic suspension system works by utilising the forces between powerful electromagnets. Electromagnets are attached to the vehicle, suspended so that they are below electromagnets in the track.

When current flows, a strong magnetic field builds up between the electromagnets on the train and those in the track in such a way that the train rises. The train is supported above the track, by the magnetic field.

The electromagnets on the Japanese train are kept at very low temperatures by liquid helium. At these temperatures they become superconductors – they offer virtually no resistance to the flow of current so hardly any energy is needed to maintain them at full strength.

Much smaller (and slower!) Maglev trains take passengers between Birmingham Central railway station and Birmingham International Airport

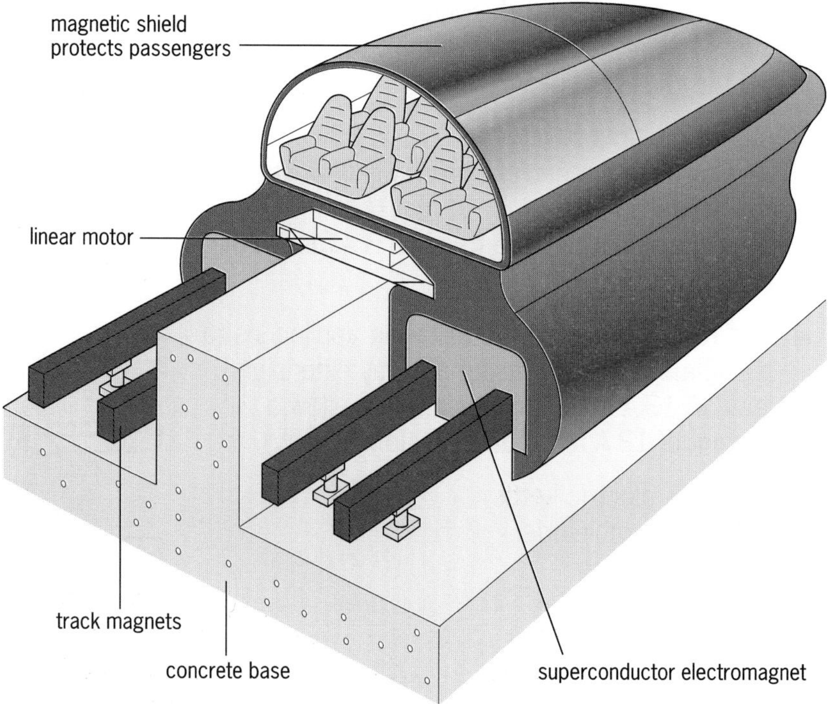

Magnetic forces cause the train to hover

Magnetism and electricity

The magnets used in the Maglev suspension system are **electromagnets** – magnets created and controlled by electricity. Wherever there is electricity you will find magnetism. When a current flows through a conductor, a **magnetic field** forms around it. There is a magnetic field around every cable in your house – but only when current is flowing. A magnetic field is a space in which magnetic forces can be detected.

The magnetic field around a long straight wire when a current flows in it shows a pattern of concentric rings around the wire.

The direction of the magnetic field around a current-carrying wire can be deduced using the *right-hand grip rule*.

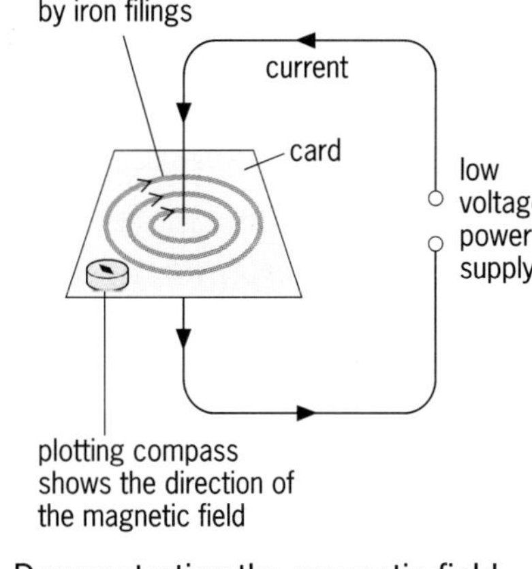

Demonstrating the magnetic field around a long straight wire

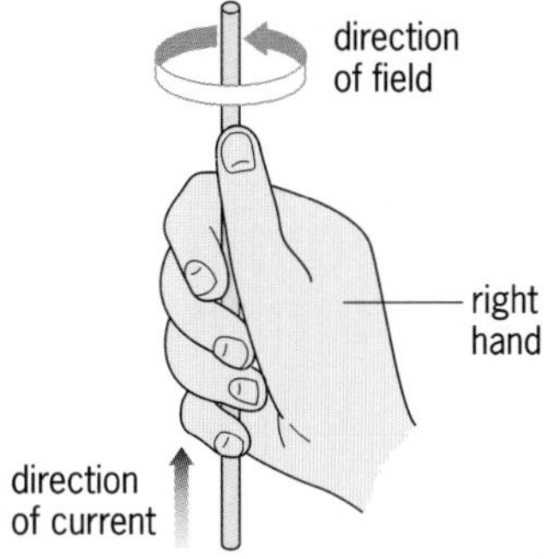

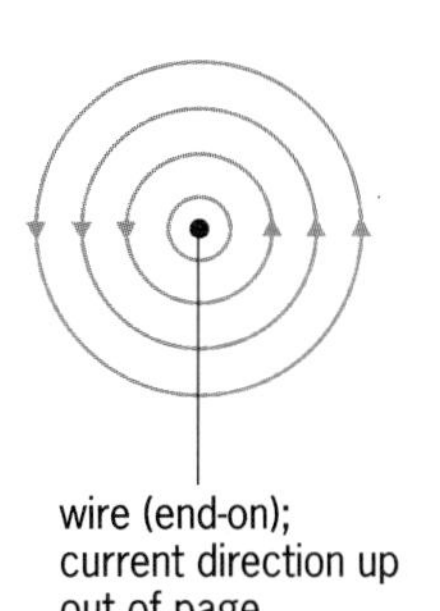

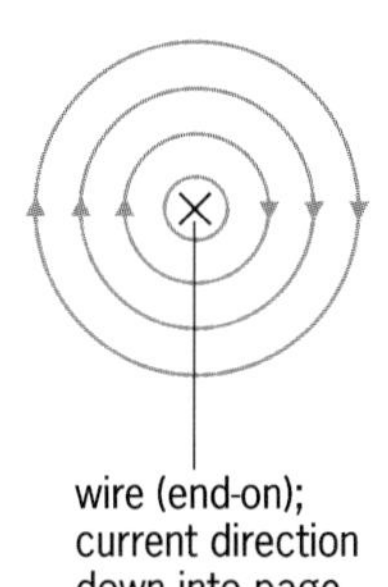

If the fingers of the right hand grip the wire, with the thumb pointing in the direction of the current, then the fingers show the direction of the magnetic field

A stronger field

The magnetic field due to a current can be made stronger if the wire is formed into a coil, called a solenoid. The magnetic field of each single coil builds up to produce a stronger field around the solenoid. The pattern of the magnetic field is very similar to that of a permanent bar magnet. In fact the solenoid behaves as if it were a weak magnet.

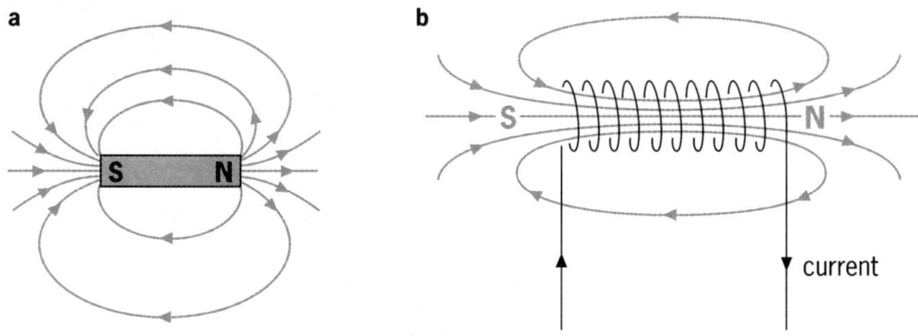

Magnetic field patterns due to **a** a permanent bar magnet and **b** a current-carrying solenoid

One end of the solenoid behaves as a north pole whilst the other end behaves as a south pole. The polarity depends on the direction in which current flows through the coil. It can be deduced using a *right-hand grip rule* similar to the one described above.

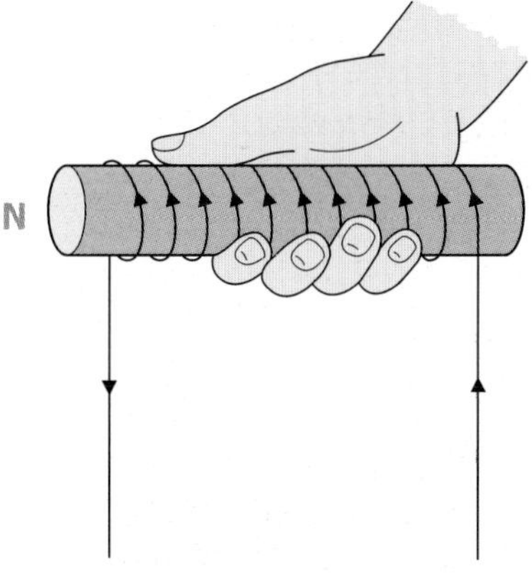

If the right hand grips the coil in such a way that the fingers point in the direction in which current is flowing, then the outstretched thumb points towards the north pole

An even stronger field

The magnetic strength of a solenoid can be increased considerably (at least a thousand times) if the wire is wrapped around a 'core' of soft iron (soft here means that the iron is *magnetically* soft – it does not 'store' magnetism like the steel of a permanent magnet). When current flows through the coil, the soft iron becomes magnetised.

When the current is switched off the magnetic field collapses and the iron becomes demagnetised. This is the principle of an electromagnet.

Electromagnets are versatile because they are so easily controlled. The strength of an electromagnet can be varied by:

- changing the number of coils of wire – the more coils, the stronger the magnet (assuming the current stays the same), and/or
- changing the current – the larger the current, the stronger the magnet (assuming the number of coils stays the same).

Electromagnets are used when really strong magnets are needed (such as in Maglev trains), or when the strength of the magnet needs to be controlled (such as in cranes), or where permanent magnets would weaken due to vibration (such as in the central locking mechanism in cars).

N

S

insulated copper wire

soft iron core

A simple electromagnet. If the current is reversed, the polarity is reversed

Electromagnetic relay

Many industries now use robots which can be programmed to do certain jobs such as welding car bodies.

Very high currents are needed to operate the robots. Thick cables are used to carry the current.

The robots are controlled by microprocessors. Microprocessor circuits have very small currents flowing through them – far too small to operate the robotic machinery.

An electromagnetic **relay** is used to allow the low-power microprocessor circuit (the 'primary' circuit) to control the high-power robot circuit (the 'secondary' circuit).

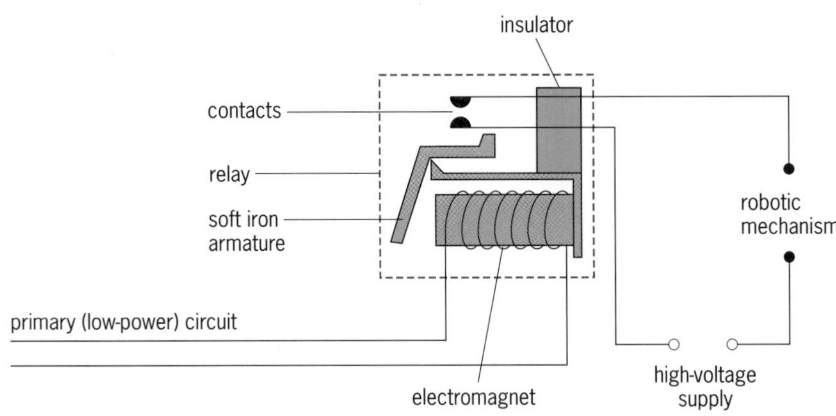

Relay switching circuit

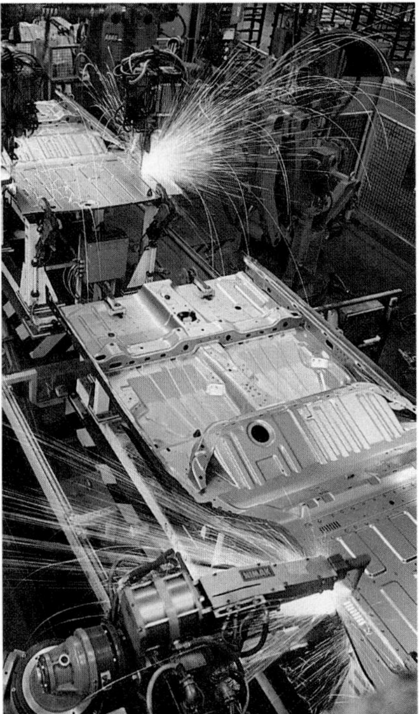

This robot welder on a car production line is controlled by a relay circuit

When current flows through the coil, a soft iron plate called the armature is attracted towards it. The armature pivots and closes the contacts, completing the secondary circuit. Current then flows in that circuit.

When the primary circuit is broken, the electromagnet loses its magnetism immediately. The armature falls back to its original position and the contacts open again, breaking the secondary circuit.

★ THINGS TO DO

1 An electromagnet can be made by wrapping insulated wire around any piece of soft iron. Make a list of things which could affect the strength of such an electromagnet. Try to give a reason why you think the strength of the magnet will be affected by each factor. Plan how you could test your ideas. When your plan has been approved by your teacher, you can go ahead and test your ideas.

Keep a good account of your investigation, including a table and a graph or chart showing your results.

In your summary include a section describing how the results support any predictions you made, and give an explanation of what your results show.

Can you say which of the things you tested has most effect on the strength of the magnet? If not, how could you have obtained data which would have allowed you to do this?

2 Build your own electromagnet by wrapping wire around a soft iron rod. Check the polarity of the ends using a plotting compass. What happens when you reverse the current?

3 a) This shows a pupil's design for a relay.

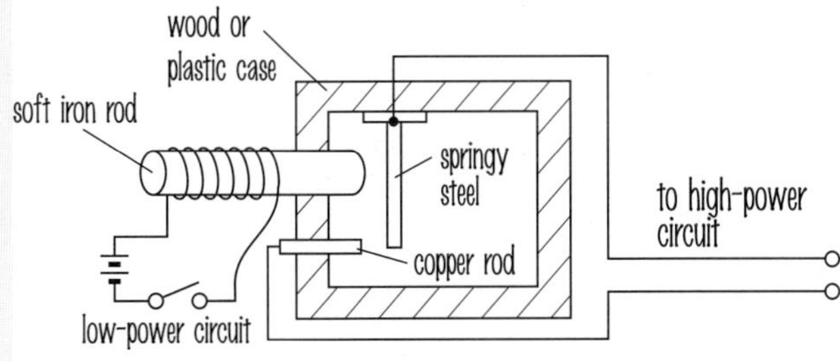

Write a short paragraph for a science book, explaining how the relay works.

b) Another pupil designed this relay which did not work.

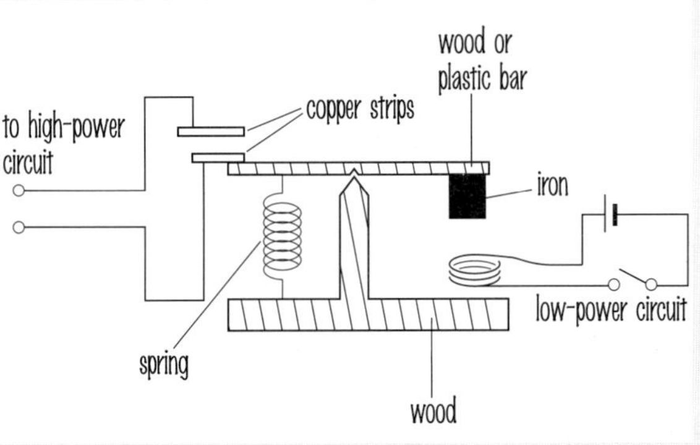

Describe what could be wrong with the design and how it could be made to work. If necessary, draw it with any changes shown in red.

4 The illustration below shows the circuit for an electric bell. Prepare a short article for a do-it-yourself book, describing how the bell works.

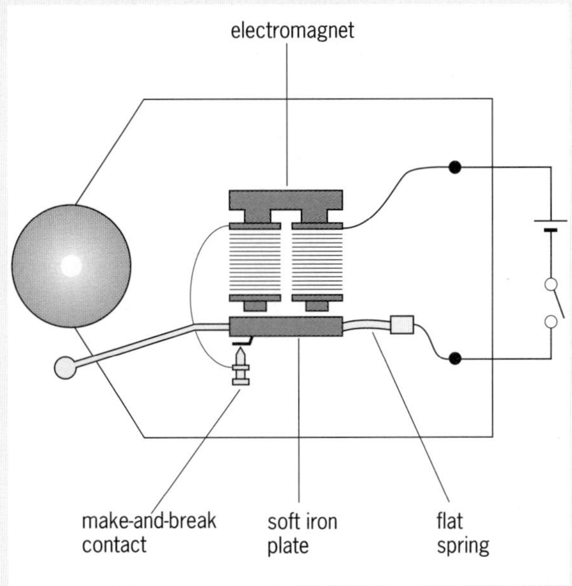

In a spin

Over 200 years ago Michael Faraday discovered a way in which an electric current could be used to produce movement. He had discovered the ideas behind the electric **motor**.

The basic idea behind the electric motor is that a force acts on a conductor through which an electric current flows if the conductor is in a magnetic field. This can be seen if a long straight wire is placed between the poles of a large magnet, as shown right.

Electric motors are now a part of our everyday lives

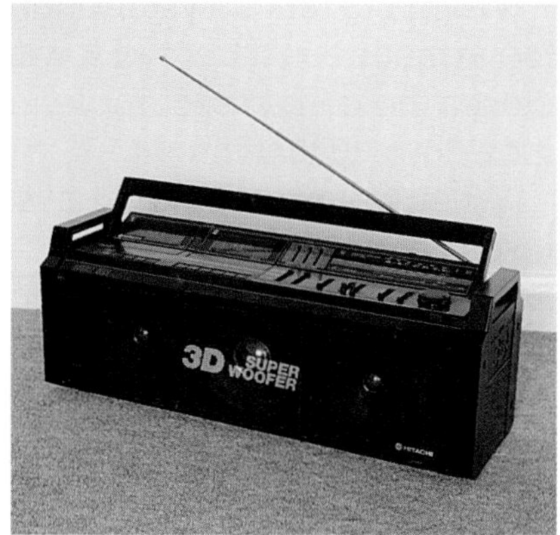
3D SUPER WOOFER

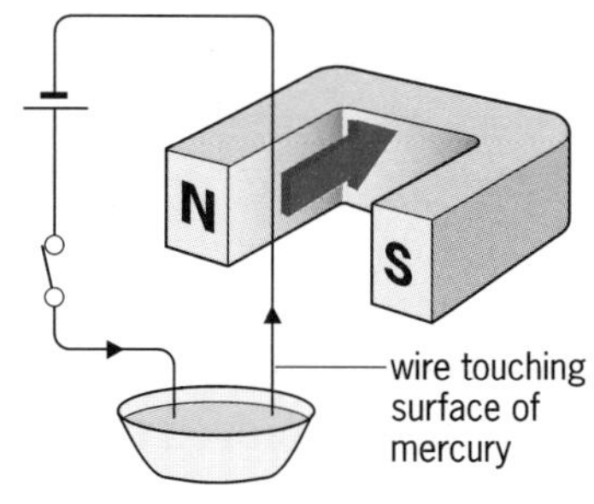
N
S
wire touching surface of mercury

When current flows through the wire, the force makes the wire 'kick'

The direction of the force (and so the movement of the wire) depends on:

- the direction of the current, and
- the direction of the magnetic field.

Reversing the current or the magnetic field reverses the direction in which the force acts on the wire. The direction can be predicted using the *left-hand motor rule*, shown right.

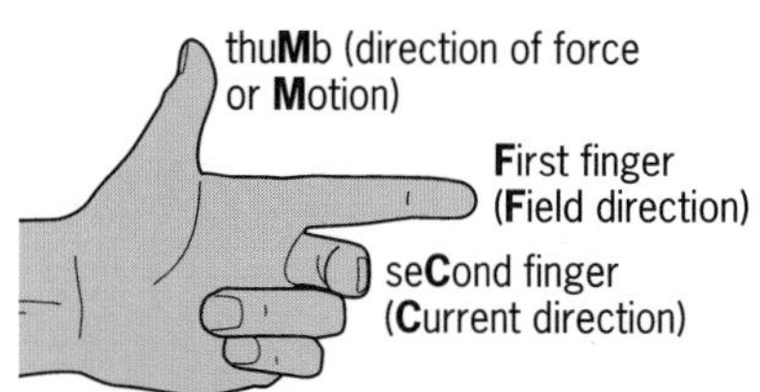
thuMb (direction of force or Motion)
First finger (Field direction)
seCond finger (Current direction)

If the thumb and first two fingers of the left hand are held at right angles to one another, the direction of the force is shown by the thumb

The size of the force depends on:

- the strength of the magnetic field, and
- the size of the current flowing through the wire.

Increasing either the magnetic field strength or the current increases the force on the wire.

Electric motors

The ideas described above help explain how an electric motor works. The illustration here shows the parts of a simple motor, such as the one found in a small hand-held fan or a toy car.

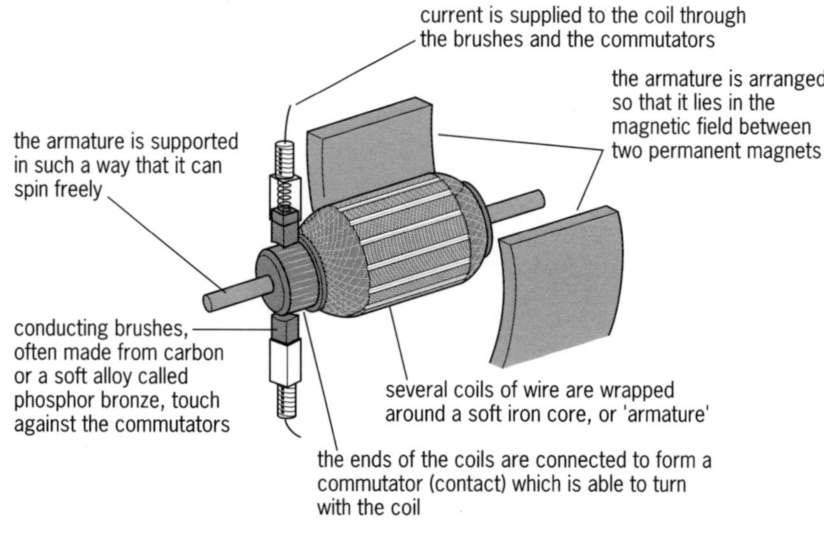
current is supplied to the coil through the brushes and the commutators
the armature is arranged so that it lies in the magnetic field between two permanent magnets
the armature is supported in such a way that it can spin freely
conducting brushes, often made from carbon or a soft alloy called phosphor bronze, touch against the commutators
several coils of wire are wrapped around a soft iron core, or 'armature'
the ends of the coils are connected to form a commutator (contact) which is able to turn with the coil

A simple electric motor

The force on the coil depends on its position in the field.

a

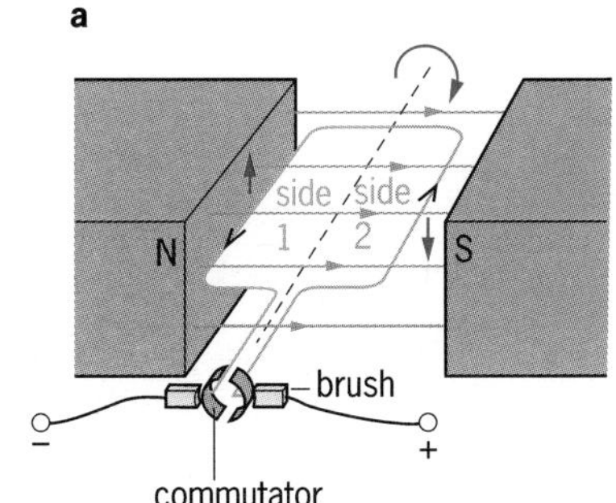

As current flows through the coil, a force acts on each side of the coil. Because the current flows in opposite directions in each side of the coil, the force on side 1 acts in the opposite direction to the force on side 2. You could check this yourself using the left-hand motor rule. The two forces form a 'couple' – a turning effect – which makes the coil rotate. The largest couple acts when the coil is at right angles to the direction of the magnetic field

b

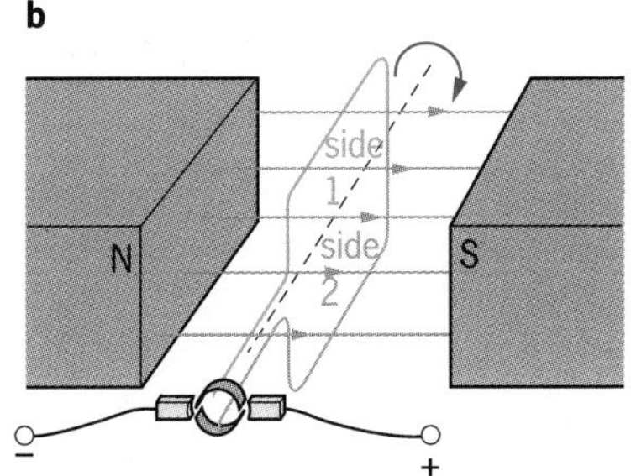

As the coil moves through the vertical position it moves parallel to the magnetic field. The commutator segments have rotated with the coil and are no longer in contact with the brushes. No current flows in the coil. No force acts on the coil in this position but its momentum carries it forward

c

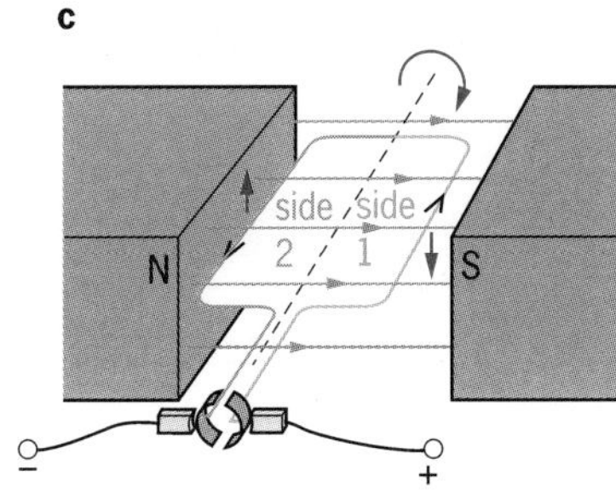

The coil rotates further and side 1 is now on the right, with its commutator segment touching the right-hand (positive) brush, so it has a downward force acting on it. Similarly, side 2 has an upward force on it. Thus the couple always acts in the same direction (clockwise) and the coil spins

The big weakness of simple motors is that a force acts on the coil for only part of the time – the coil relies on its momentum to keep it moving. Heavy-duty motors, such as those in vacuum cleaners and food-processors, have several coils, each with its own pair of commutator segments. Each coil contributes to the movement of the motor, producing more efficient and effective running. If a motor stops working, it can often be repaired by replacing the brushes, which tend to wear with time.

★ THINGS TO DO

1 **a)** Make a list of all the things in your home which have electric motors.
b) Some motors are more powerful than others. Re-organise your list so that the appliance which needs the most powerful motor is at the top and the one which needs the least powerful motor is at the bottom.

2 Build your own electric motor from a kit. Carry out a series of tests to find out what affects
a) its speed, and
b) its direction.
Draw a diagram of your motor and describe the tests you did and what they showed.

3 Use simple diagrams of an electric motor, such as those shown above, to:
a) explain what would happen if the commutator was a solid ring rather than a split ring as shown,
b) describe why the motor will rotate clockwise when the current flows,
c) explain why the direction of the motor would change if the magnetic field was reversed.

4 Describe how practical motors are different from the simple motor shown opposite, and explain how this would affect they way the motor works.

2.17 Electromagnetic induction

Many shops now have anti-theft alarms. A large coil of wire passes around the doorway. Items for sale are fitted with a magnet which is removed when the goods are paid for. If someone tries to leave without paying, the magnet causes a small current to flow through the coil which sets off an alarm

If part of a loop of wire is moved quickly down through a magnetic field, a small current flows through the wire, which can be detected by connecting a galvanometer (a sensitive current meter) in the loop. The current is called an 'induced' current, and the effect is called **electromagnetic induction**.

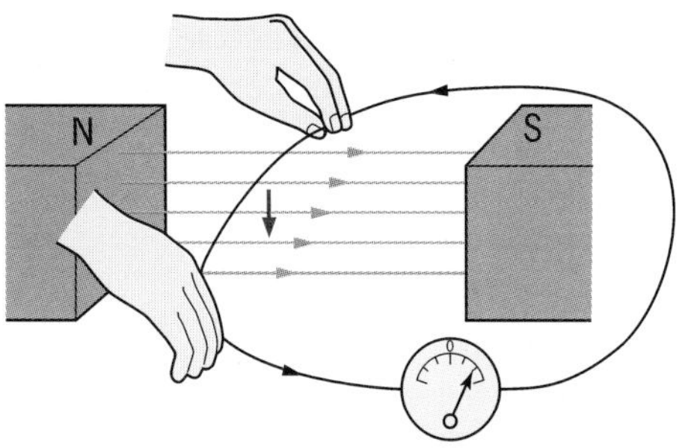

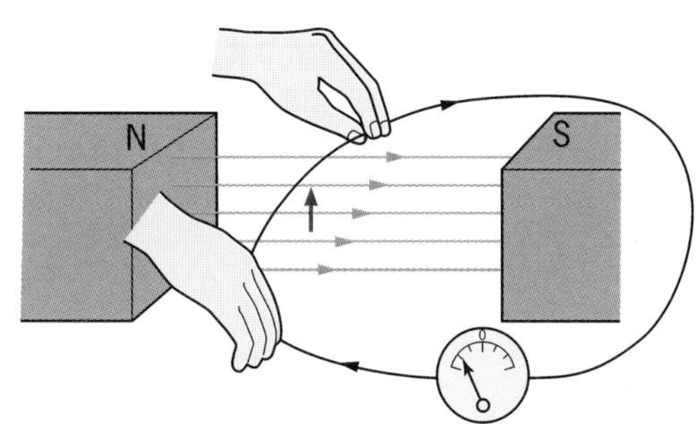

If the wire is raised through the magnetic field, a small current flows once again, but this time in the opposite direction.

If the wire is stationary in the magnetic field or moving parallel to it, no current flows – the wire must move *through* the magnetic field for induced current to flow.

▲ A small voltage is induced across the ends of a wire as it is moved through magnetic field lines. This produces a small current if the wire is part of a loop

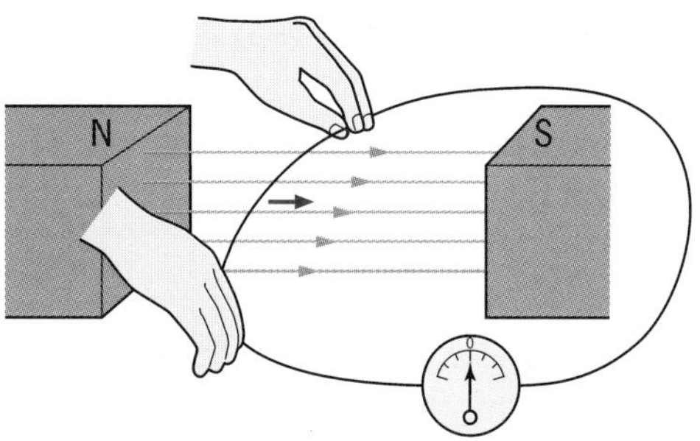

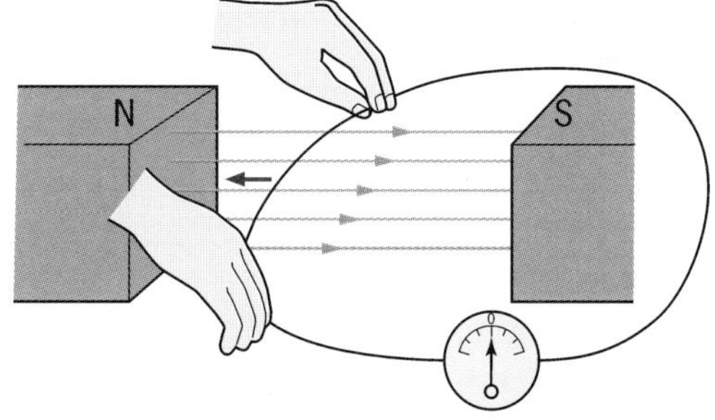

▲ No voltage is induced if the wire is moved parallel to the field lines, so no current flows

The size of the induced current can be increased by:

- moving the wire faster,
- using stronger magnets to produce a stronger magnetic field,
- increasing the amount of wire moving through the field, possibly by creating several loops of wire and moving them all through the magnetic field together.

An induced current is produced in the same way if a magnet is moved so that its magnetic field cuts through a coil of wire. This is what happens in the anti-theft alarm opposite.

If a bar magnet is moved in and out of a coil, an induced current flows first in one direction, then the other.

As the magnet moves into the coil an induced current flows

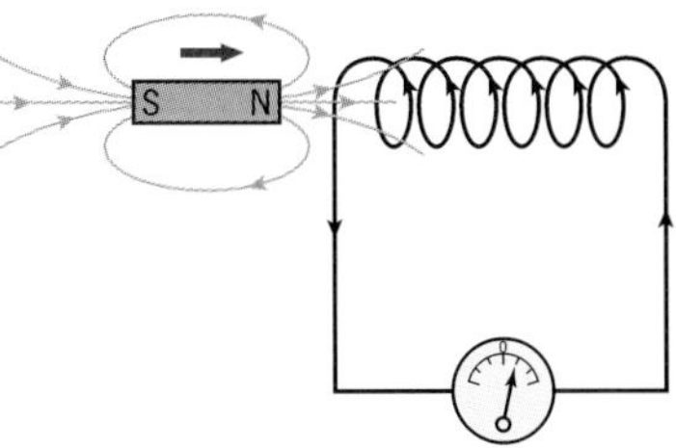

If the magnet is removed from the coil the induced current flows in the opposite direction

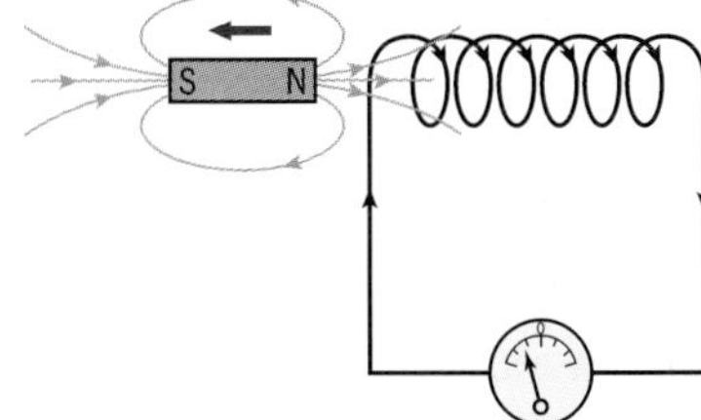

If the magnet is moved faster then the induced current is bigger

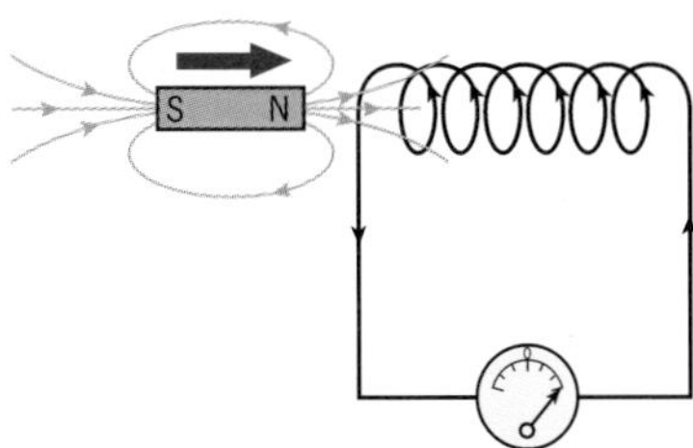

If there are more coils then the induced current is bigger

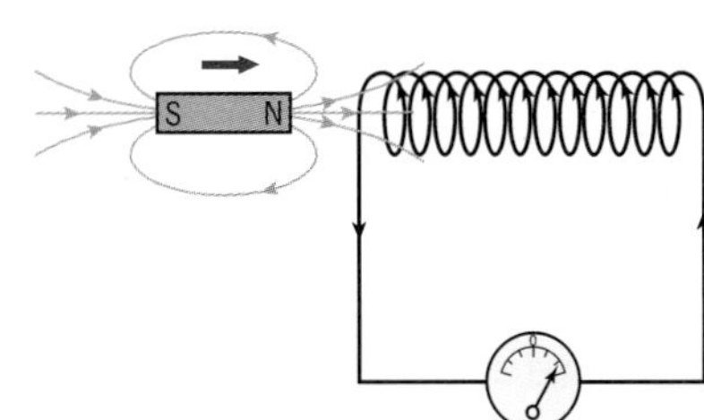

Direction of the induced current

The direction of the induced current in a straight conductor moving through a magnetic field can be deduced using the *right-hand generator rule*, shown right.

Predicting the direction of an induced current in a coil is rather more complicated. When current flows through a coil, a magnetic field is created in and around the coil. The coil behaves just like a permanent magnet, with a north and a south pole.

As the magnet moves into the coil, the induced current flows through the coil in such a way that the magnetic field created around it *opposes* the magnetic field of the moving magnet. This determines the polarity of the coil – see the illustration below. The direction of the current can then be found using the *right-hand grip rule*.

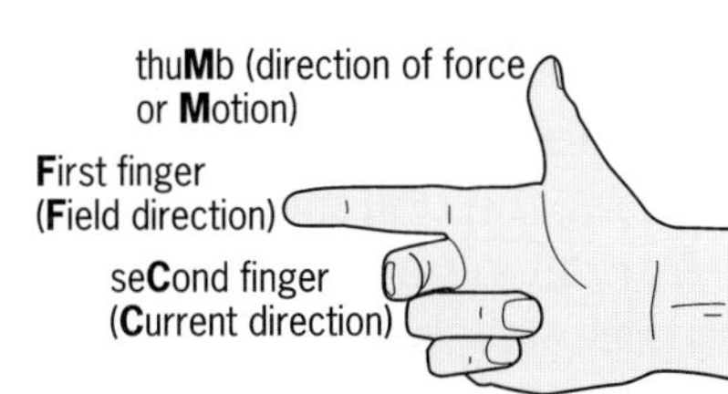

If the thumb and the first two fingers of the right hand are held at right angles to one another, the direction of the induced current in a wire is shown by the second finger

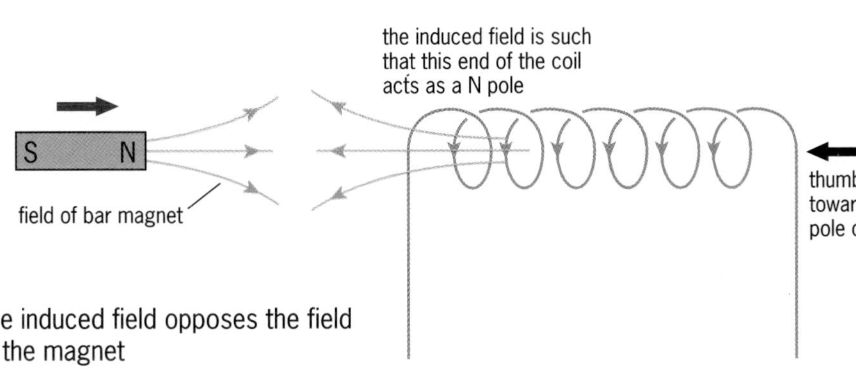

The induced field opposes the field of the magnet

Too loud!

Microphones, amplifiers and loudspeakers ensure that you hear the music at any concert.

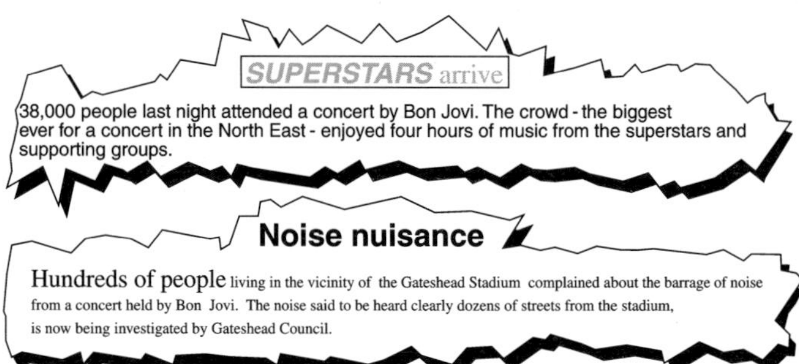

SUPERSTARS arrive

38,000 people last night attended a concert by Bon Jovi. The crowd - the biggest ever for a concert in the North East - enjoyed four hours of music from the superstars and supporting groups.

Noise nuisance

Hundreds of people living in the vicinity of the Gateshead Stadium complained about the barrage of noise from a concert held by Bon Jovi. The noise said to be heard clearly dozens of streets from the stadium, is now being investigated by Gateshead Council.

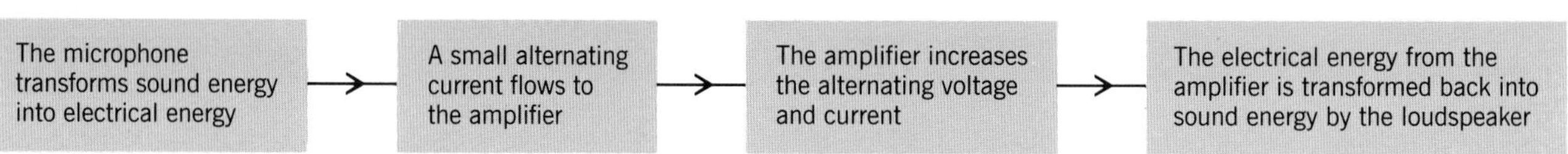
The microphone transforms sound energy into electrical energy
A small alternating current flows to the amplifier
The amplifier increases the alternating voltage and current
The electrical energy from the amplifier is transformed back into sound energy by the loudspeaker

The microphone

There are many types of microphone. One is a moving-coil microphone. When we speak or sing, the air molecules vibrate (move to-and-fro) – see page 159. These vibrations make the diaphragm inside the microphone vibrate. The diaphragm is connected to a small coil. As the diaphragm vibrates, the coil moves to-and-fro over a permanent magnet.

A small, alternating voltage is generated across the ends of the coil, which induces a small, alternating current. *Sound energy has been transformed into electrical energy.* The changes in the alternating voltage (and current) exactly match the changes in the frequency and amplitude of the voice.

circular magnetic pole pieces
moving coil
S
N
S
output
diaphragm

Moving-coil microphone

The loudspeaker

The construction of the loudspeaker is very similar to that of the moving-coil microphone. Small pulses of current from the amplifier pass to the coil which surrounds the pole of a permanent magnet.

As we have seen, when a current flows through a coil, a magnetic field is produced around the coil. The magnetic field from the coil interacts with the magnetic field of the permanent magnet. A force acts on the coil. The coil will be attracted to or repelled from the permanent magnet, depending on the direction of its magnetic field (which depends on the direction of the current through the coil).

As the coil vibrates to-and-fro, it causes the paper cone to vibrate at the same frequency. Sound is produced as the air molecules by the cone are made to vibrate. *Electrical energy has been transformed into sound energy.* The changes in frequency and amplitude of the sound have exactly the same pattern as those from the singer's voice.

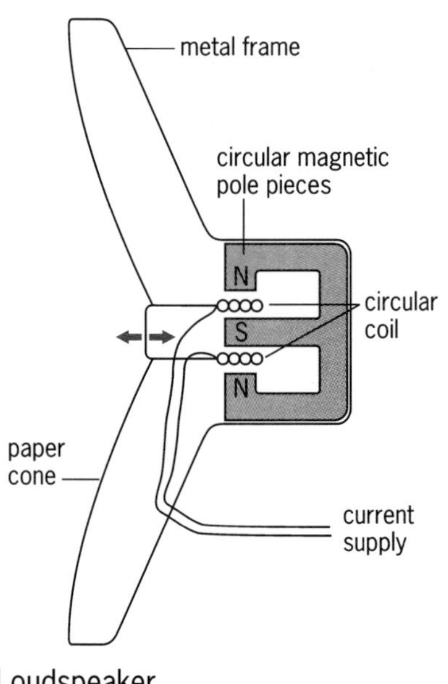
metal frame
circular magnetic pole pieces
N
S
N
circular coil
paper cone
current supply

Loudspeaker

★ THINGS TO DO

1 Design and build your own alarm system, similar to the one shown on page 86, for a shop. When you are sure it works well, demonstrate it and explain to someone how it works.

Write a letter to a manufacturing company, describing your design and how it works. Say how it could be made more sensitive, and how it would be used in a shop.

2 Electricity can be generated from moving air using a wind generator. The diagram shows a small wind generator.

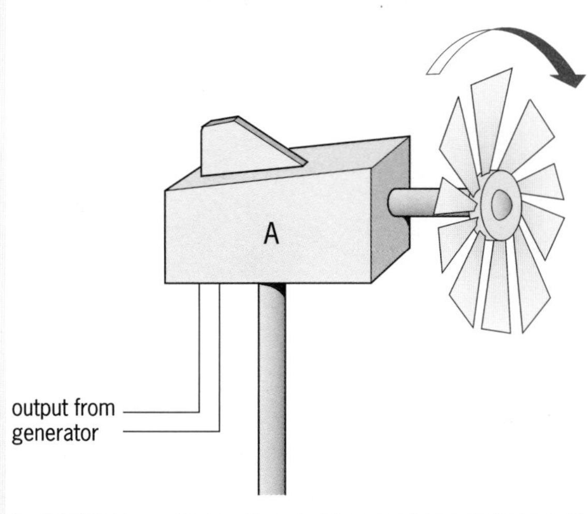

a) What do you think is inside the part marked A? Draw a sketch showing what you think is inside and explain how the movement of the blades can produce an electric current.
b) This table shows the power output of the generator at different speeds.

i) What affects the power output of the generator?
ii) Which of the factors seems to have the greatest effect on the power output?
iii) Someone suggested that the power output went up eight-fold when the wind speed doubled.

Draw a graph of power output against wind speed for a wind generator with a blade diameter of 5 m.

Use your graph to explain whether the statement was right or wrong.

3 Tests are now being carried out to find out whether freshwater oysters can be used to test for pollution in rivers. Oysters filter food from fresh water when their shells are open. At the first signs of pollution, the oyster shell closes. The more pollution, the faster the shell closes. In the trials a small permanent magnet is fitted to the lower shell of the oyster. A small coil is fitted to the upper shell. Any sudden change in the current through the coil triggers an alarm.

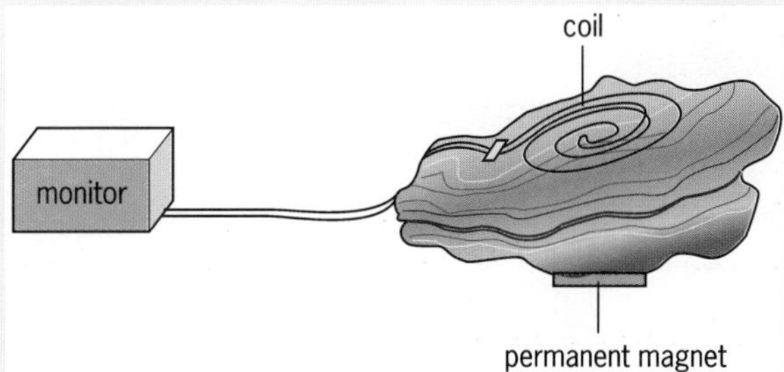

a) What will happen when the shell closes?
b) How will the system detect a sudden change to a higher level of pollution?

Blade diameter /m	Blade area /m^2	Power output/W at wind speed 2 m/s	4 m/s	6 m/s	8 m/s	10 m/s	12 m/s
1	0.8	0.001	0.008	0.02	0.06	0.13	0.23
2	3.1	0.004	0.03	0.1	0.27	0.53	0.92
3	7.1	0.009	0.07	0.26	0.62	1.2	2.1
4	12.6	0.02	0.14	0.46	1.1	2.1	3.7
5	19.6	0.03	0.2	0.7	1.7	3.4	5.8

2.18 Generating electricity

Generators are machines in which kinetic energy is transformed into electrical energy.

Power stations use large generators to supply the electricity which passes to our homes through the National Grid (see topic 2.19). Hospitals, factories and some shops have their own generators to supply emergency power in the event of a power cut. The dynamo on a bicycle is a generator which is driven by the wheels.

In 1994 a young girl appeared on television making enough electricity to light a small bulb by boiling water.

Many funfairs move around the country visiting villages and towns. They use their own generators to supply the electricity needed for the rides

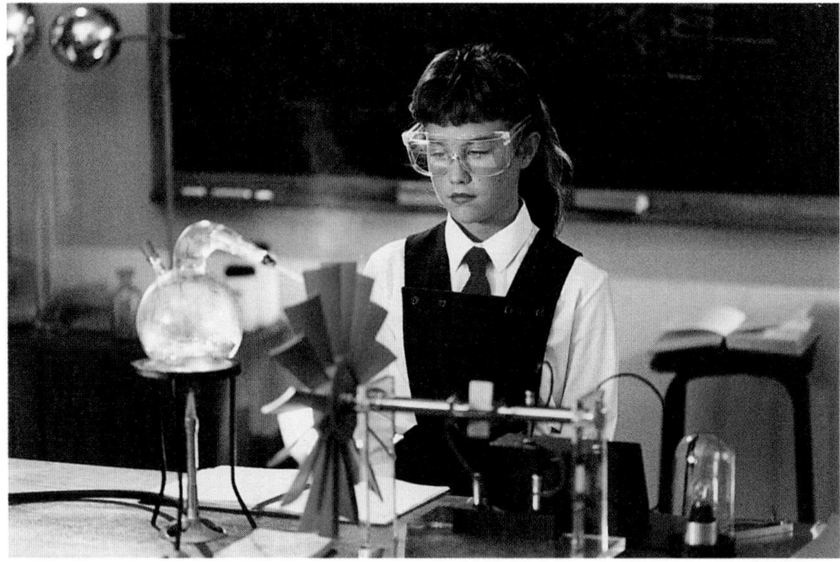

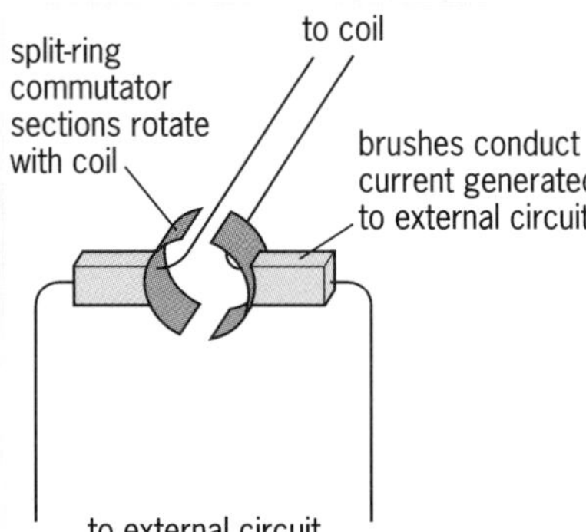

A direct current generator has a split-ring commutator (effectively a ring split into two sections). Every half-turn the sections pass from one brush to the other. The output is always in the same direction

The steam from the flask produced sufficient force to turn the small turbine (windmill) which turned a dynamo (a motor working in reverse) which produced the electricity.

heat energy ⟶ kinetic energy ⟶ electrical energy

Electricity is generated in power stations in much the same way, but on a much larger scale.

Any generator is basically a coil of wire which is made to rotate in a magnetic field. As the coil rotates it cuts through the magnetic field, and a current is induced in it. Generators can produce either direct current (d.c.) or alternating current (a.c.). The main difference between the two types of generator is in the structure of the commutator section shown right. Notice the similarities between the construction of a d.c. generator and the motor shown on page 85.

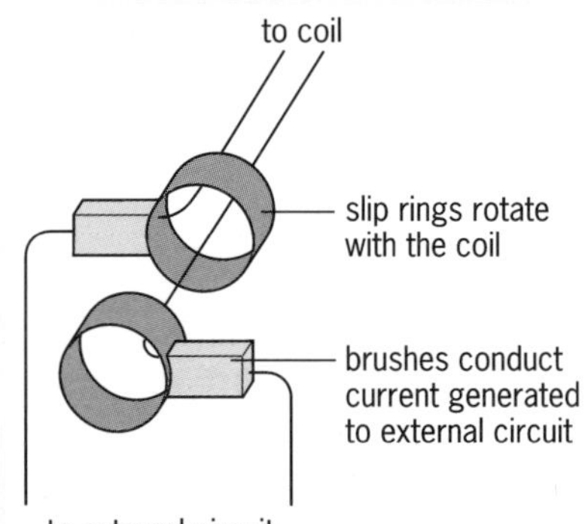

An alternating current generator has two full rings called slip rings. The brushes push against the rings as they turn. The output is a varying current which changes direction every half-turn of the coil

A simplified diagram of an a.c. generator helps us to understand why an alternating output is produced.

Power stations use a.c. generators which produce a large alternating voltage – the power supplied to your home is 230 volts a.c. The frequency (the number of complete cycles of the alternating voltage per second) is 50/s or 50 Hz.

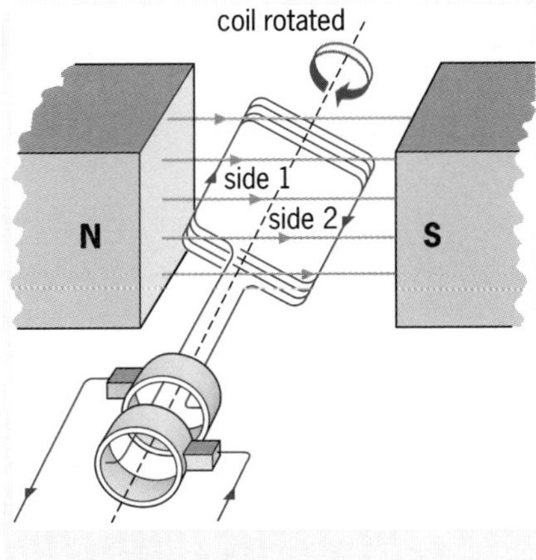

As the coil turns, side 1 moves up and side 2 moves down. A current is induced in the coil which is fed to the external circuit via the rotating slip rings and the brushes

As the coil moves into the vertical position it moves parallel to the magnetic field. The induced current is momentarily zero

Quarter of a turn later the coil is horizontal again but with side 1 moving down and side 2 moving up. The induced current is in the opposite direction in the external circuit

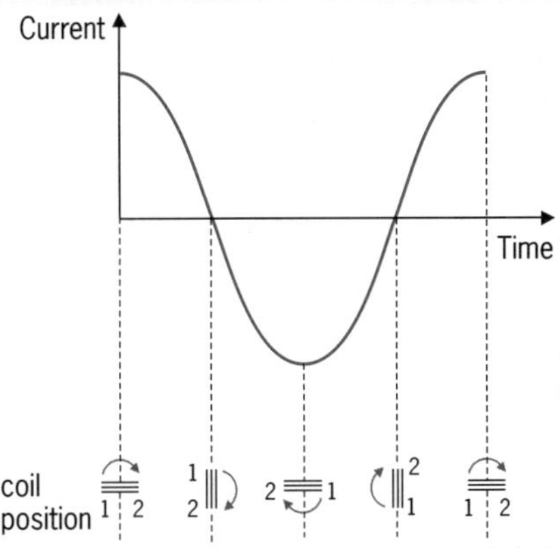

The size of the voltage produced by a generator depends on:

- the speed of the coil – the faster the coil moves, the greater the voltage,
- the strength of the magnetic field – the stronger the field, the greater the voltage,
- the number of turns on the coil – the more turns, the greater the voltage.

Most small-scale generators consist of several coils of wire wrapped around a soft iron core. They are made to rotate in the magnetic field of electromagnets.

★ THINGS TO DO

1 Make your own wind generator like the one illustrated here. The milliammeter will measure the current produced as the wind generator turns.

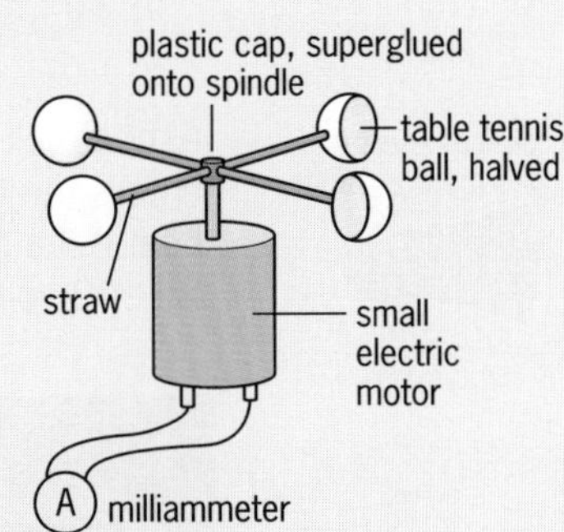

a) Make a table showing similarities and differences between a motor and a generator. How will the motor in your model act as a generator?

b) How do you think the current from this wind generator will depend on the speed of the wind? Add some drawings and explanation to support your answer.

c) Plan how you could test the idea you described in part **b**. If your teacher approves, carry out your tests and prepare a report.

d) Describe how you could calibrate the meter so that the scale showed the wind speed instead of the current.

2 **a)** Draw a flow chart showing the energy changes which take place when this bicycle dynamo is working.

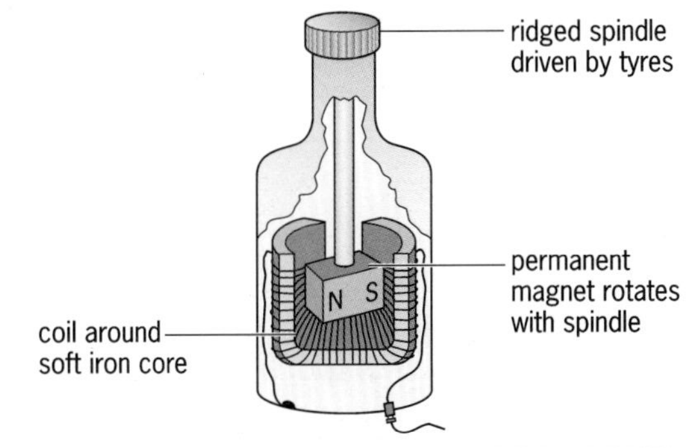

b) Make a list of similarities and differences between the way the dynamo works and how a power station generates electricity.

2.19

Electricity to your home

Millions of tons of coal are stored at this power station, ready to be burned. Other power stations may use gas, oil, or nuclear fuels to generate the electricity we need (see topic 1.15).

A coal-fired power station

The electricity which you use today could come from any power station – not necessarily the one nearest your home.

Overground and underground cables carry the electricity from power stations to houses, schools, offices and factories all over the country. The network of cables across the country is called the National Grid.

When an electric current flows through any cable, the cable warms up. Current flowing through the Grid is no exception – those cables also get warm. This means that some of the electrical energy (meant to be carried to consumers) is wasted – it is transferred *to* the cable (and then to the air) rather than *through* it.

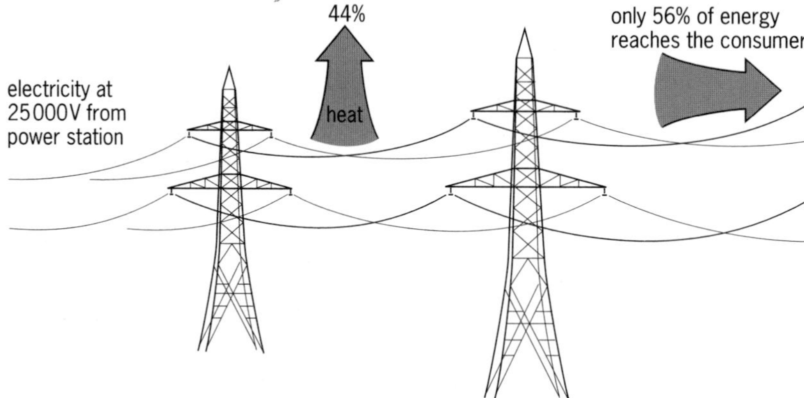

Almost half of the energy which enters the Grid would be lost as heat if the transmission voltage was 25 000 volts

To reduce the amount of energy lost, the voltage output from power stations is increased for transmission. Increasing the voltage decreases the current, and because the current is smaller, less energy is transferred to the cables as heat.

The voltage is changed by a **transformer**. A 'step-up' transformer increases the voltage to 400 000 V, reducing energy losses during transmission to about 1%.

Pylons carry cables which are at the dangerously high voltage of 400 000 volts

Throughout the National Grid, step-up and step-down transformers are used to increase and decrease the voltage as required. Eventually, before the electricity enters your home, a step-down transformer reduces the voltage to 230 V – the 'mains voltage'. Mains electrical appliances sold in this country are built to work at any voltage between 220 V and 250 V a.c.

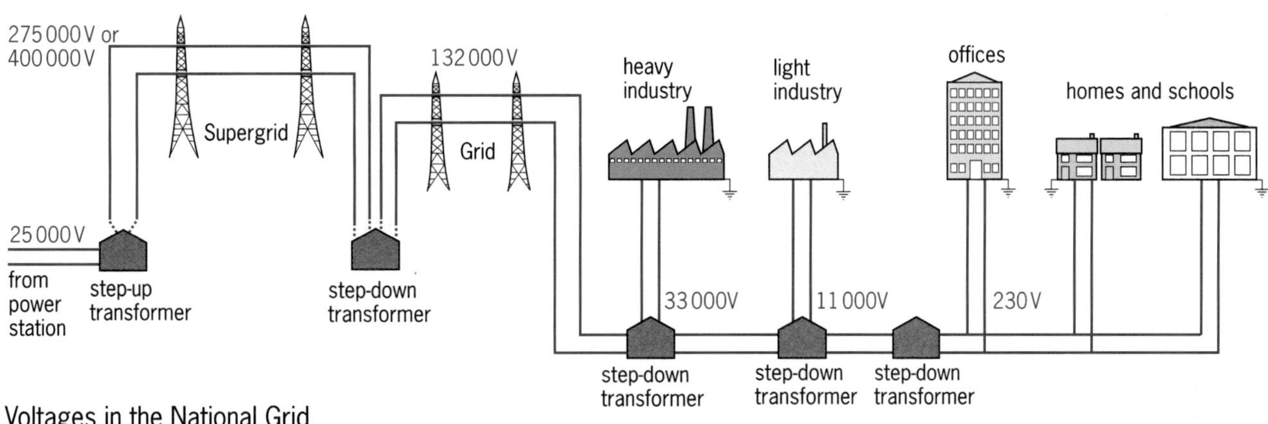

Voltages in the National Grid

★ THINGS TO DO

1 Hydroelectric power stations use water to turn the turbines which turn the generators to produce electricity. The water is stored behind dams, or in lakes high up in the mountains. The illustration shows one hydroelectric scheme in Scotland.

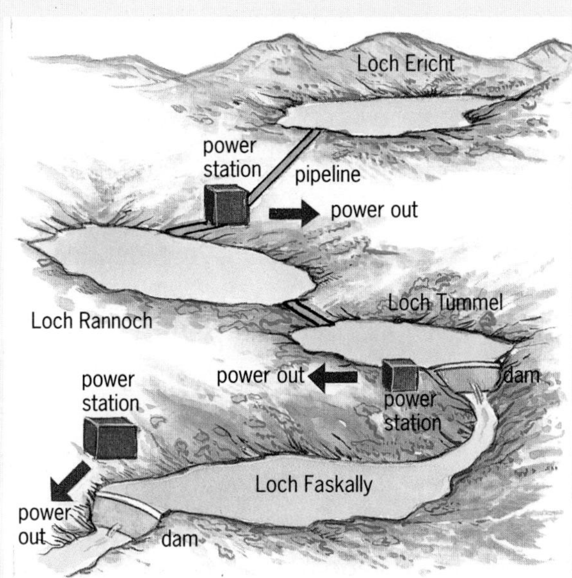

a) Why is this particular system of generating electricity so efficient?
b) What are the advantages of a hydroelectric power station over a coal-fired power station?
c) Why do you think we don't build more hydroelectric power stations?

2 The demand for electricity changes throughout the day and night. The graph on page 37 shows how the demand changes on weekdays during summer and winter.
a) Why do you think the demand is least before 6 a.m.?
b) Why does the demand show a peak at about 6.00 p.m.?
c) Draw another sketch graph showing what you think the demand would be like on a Sunday in summer. Add a brief description saying how the shape of your graph is different from the one for a weekday, and why it is different.

2.20 Transformers

Some children's toys, such as Scalextric racing sets and train sets, draw power from the mains supply. Exposed metal parts could endanger the lives of the children using them. To reduce the voltage (and current) to a safer level, a transformer is used. Transformers are used whenever we need to increase or decrease the voltage of a supply.

A laptop computer needs 17 V to work. A 'mains adaptor' can be used in the home or office, which reduces the mains voltage from 230 V to 17 V. It is a step-down transformer.

Similarly, a mains adaptor can be used to save the batteries of a personal stereo. It reduces the voltage from 230 V to 6 V.

In contrast, arc welders need very high voltages to join two pieces of metal. The 230 V mains supply is not high enough. A small step-up transformer increases the voltage from 230 V to 1000 V.

An arc welder requires a transformer to step up the mains voltage

What is inside a transformer?

A transformer consists of two coils wrapped around a soft iron core. The coil which receives the input voltage is the 'primary' coil. The coil which supplies the output voltage (from the transformer) is the 'secondary' coil.

If the number of turns in the primary and secondary coils are different then the output voltage across the secondary coil will be different from the input voltage across the primary coil. If, for example, the secondary coil has fewer turns than the primary, then the secondary voltage will be reduced (a step-down transformer). If the number of turns on the secondary is greater than the number on the primary coil, then the secondary voltage will be higher (a step-up transformer).

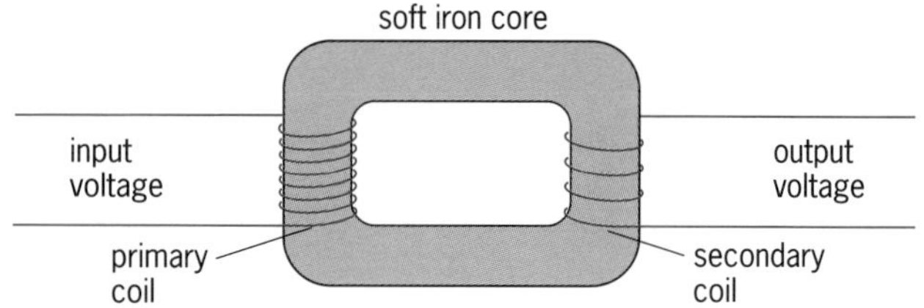

A step-down transformer

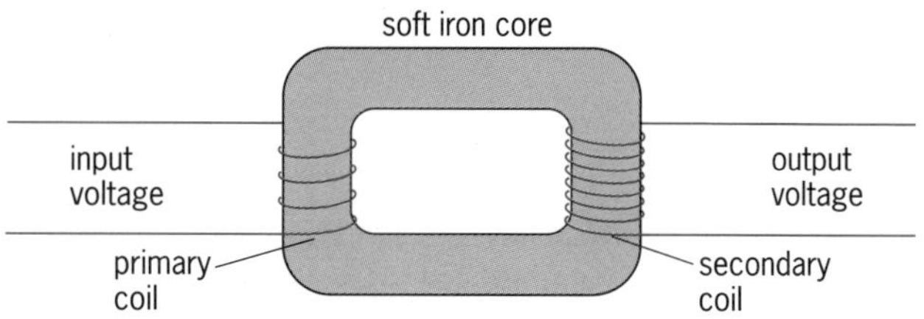

A step-up transformer

The two coils are shown on the symbol for a transformer which we use on circuit diagrams:

Calculating the output voltage

The output voltage depends on the number of turns on each of the coils:

$$\frac{\text{secondary (output) voltage}}{\text{primary (input) voltage}} = \frac{\text{number of turns on secondary coil}}{\text{number of turns on primary coil}}$$

Imagine, for example, that we have a transformer which has 960 turns on the primary coil and 16 turns on the secondary coil, and that the primary coil is connected to a 230 V a.c. supply. Then we can calculate the output from the secondary coil using the equation above.

$$\frac{\text{secondary voltage}}{230\text{ V}} = \frac{16}{960}$$

$$= 0.017$$

so the secondary voltage = 230 V × 0.017 = 3.9 V

This would be a step-down transformer – it has reduced the voltage from 230 volts to about 4 volts.

How a transformer works

Transformers only work when there is an a.c. (alternating current) supply to the primary coil. They do not work with a d.c. (direct current) supply, such as that produced by batteries.

An alternating current passes through the primary coil. As the current builds up in the primary coil, the magnetic field around the coil also builds up, cutting through the secondary coil. A current is induced in the secondary coil. As the current in the primary then begins to decrease, the magnetic field contracts, cutting through the secondary coil in the opposite direction. The induced current in the secondary coil is reversed. The output from the secondary coil will therefore be an alternating current.

The current in the secondary coil is therefore generated by electromagnetic induction.

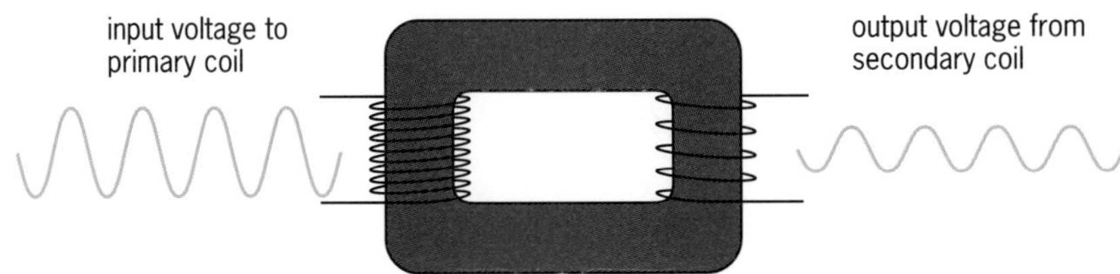

The regular changes in the mains voltage (it changes 50 times each second) across the primary coil generate a changing magnetic field which builds up and dies away every 1/50th of a second. As the magnetic field cuts through the secondary coil it generates an induced, alternating voltage with the same frequency (50 Hz) across the secondary coil

★ THINGS TO DO

1 What is the output of each of these transformers, assuming they are 100% efficient (i.e. there is no energy wasted)?

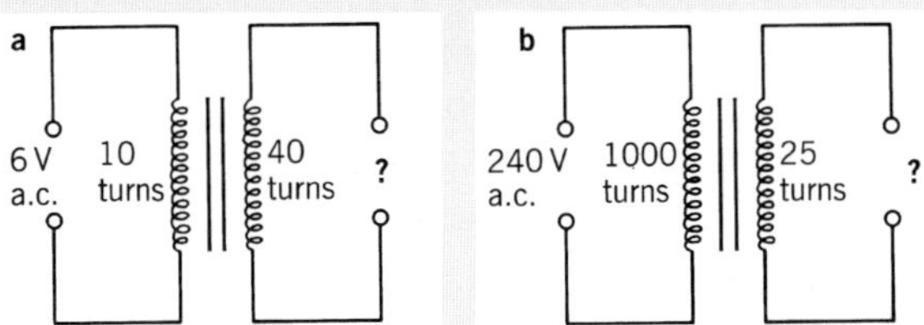

2 How many turns are needed on the primary and secondary coils of these transformers, assuming they are 100% efficient?

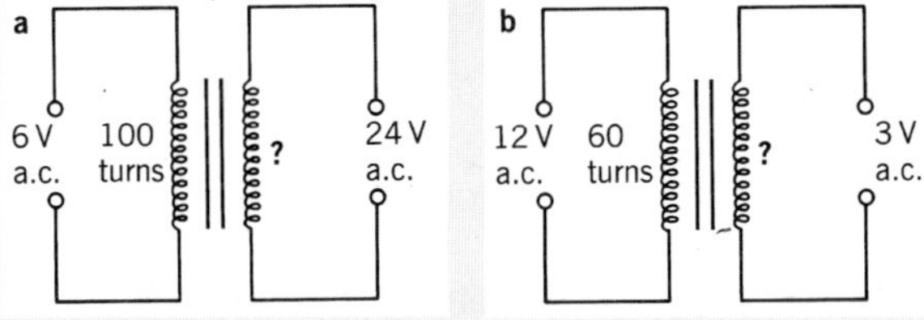

3 a) Draw what you think you would find inside the mains adaptor of a laptop computer.
b) The mains voltage is 230 V. The computer needs a 17 V supply. If the number of turns on the primary coil is 500, how many turns would be needed on the secondary coil to produce the required output voltage?

4 A large car factory needs 200 kW of power. This could be delivered through cables by:
a) a current of 200 A at a voltage of 1000 V, or
b) a current of 1 A at a voltage of 200 000 V.
Assuming the resistance of the cable is 2 ohms, calculate the power loss in the cables for each of the conditions described above. (You will have to use the information at the foot of page 78 to help you answer this question.)

Exam questions

1 a) Rods of glass, plastic and rubber can be charged by rubbing them with materials such as fur or silk.

Explain why it is **not** possible to charge rods of metal in the same way. (2)

b) Electrostatic charges have many commercial uses. Two important uses are in the spray painting of motor car bodies and in the removal of dust from chimney gases. The use of electrostatic charges in spray painting is shown in the diagram below.

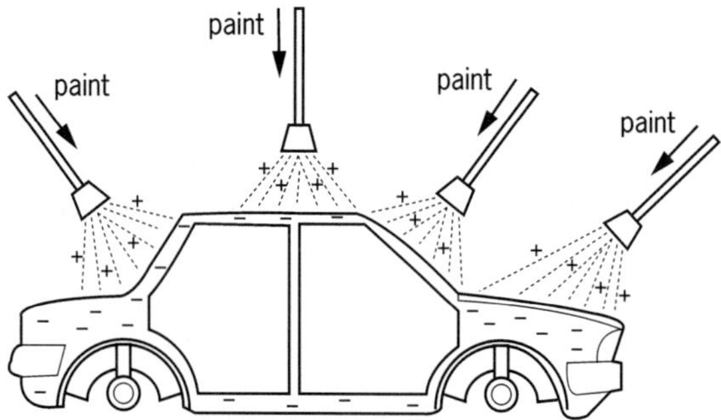

The spray of paint is given a positive charge and the car body a negative charge.

Explain why it is an advantage to give:

i) a charge of the same sign to all the paint droplets in the spray; (2)

ii) the car body a charge of the opposite sign to that of the droplets. (3)

c) Many chimney gases carry large quantities of dust. Much of this dust can be removed by electrostatic precipitators. The diagram below shows the construction of such a precipitator.

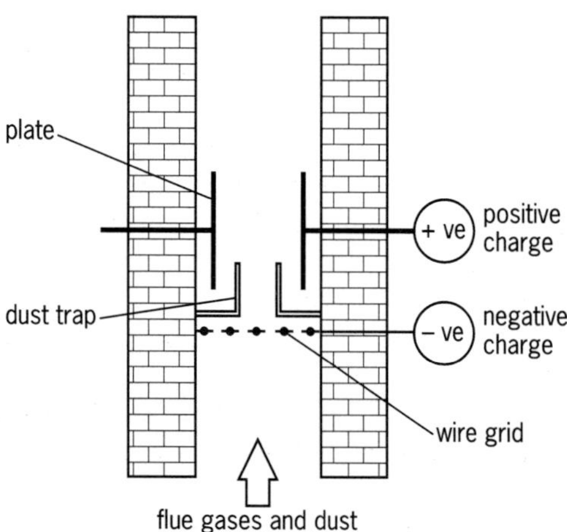

Use the diagram to help you to **explain** how the precipitator is able to remove dust from chimney gases. (3)

(SEG, 1994)

2 The diagram below shows an electric fence used to keep animals in a field.

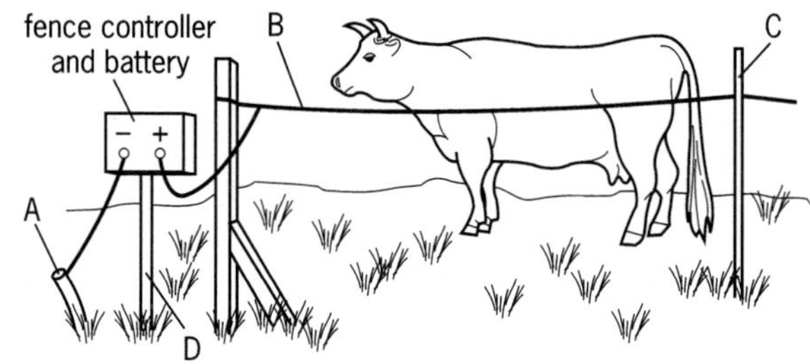

a) [Copy] the table below and enter the letters A, B, C and D in it to show whether those parts are made of conducting or insulating materials. (4)

Conductors	**Insulators**

b) What is the function of the stake A in the ground? (1)

c) What happens when the animal touches the fence? Explain your answer. (2)

d) Why should the animal be exposed to a small current only? (1)

e) Birds often land on electrical power lines. Explain why they suffer no ill effect. (1)

(ULEAC, 1994)

3 Margaret was doing an experiment to see how the temperature of water changed when a coil of wire carrying a current was placed in it.

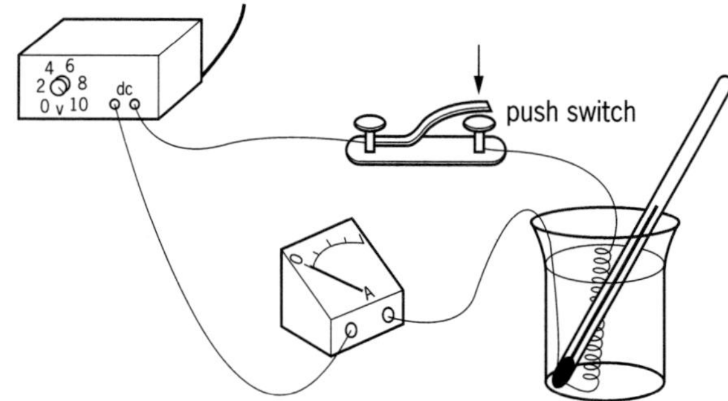

a) What would you expect to happen when the switch was closed? (2)

b) When Margaret visited a friend's house, she saw the following in the bathroom.

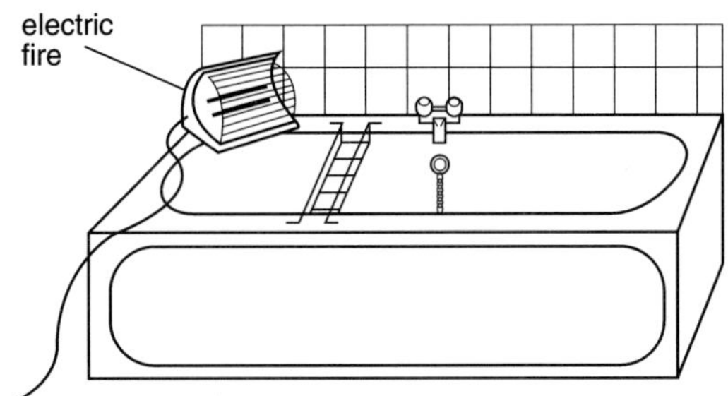

i) Why should electric fires **never** be used in bathrooms? (1)

ii) Explain your answer. (2)

c) If the current through an electric fire is too large the fuse blows.

Draw the circuit symbol for a fuse. (1)

(MEG, 1995)

4 The diagram shows part of a mains lighting circuit protected by a fuse.

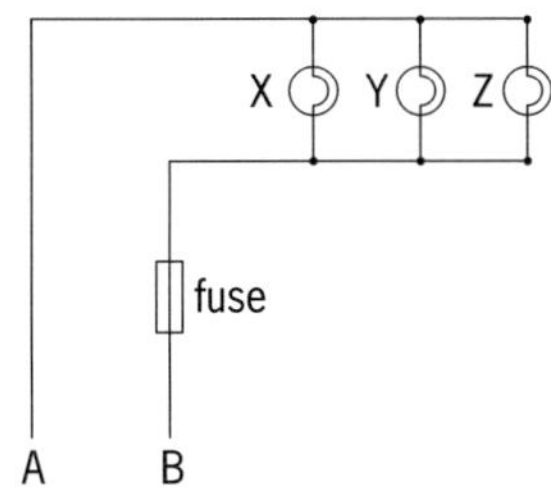

a) Which lead (**A** or **B**) is the live lead? (1)

b) [Copy] the circuit above and add to it, in the correct and safe position

i) a switch labelled S_1 which controls lamp **X** only,

ii) a switch labelled S_2 which controls lamps **Y** and **Z** only. (3)

c) A 5 A fuse is normally used in a household lighting circuit. Describe how it protects the circuit. (2)

(WJEC, 1995)

5 Daniel wanted to brighten his room so he used six 12 V bulbs and a variable power supply.

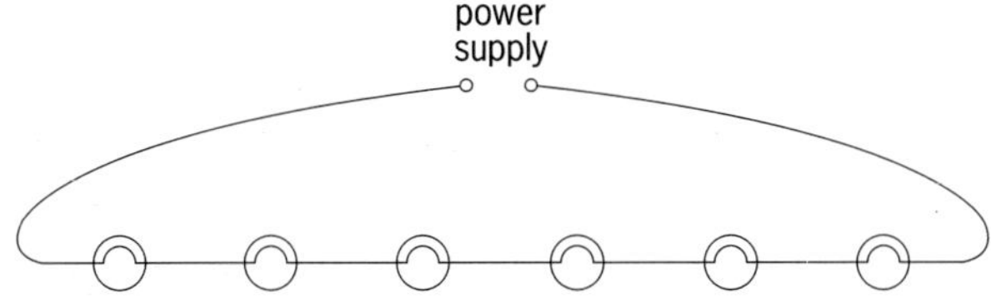

He was disappointed because the bulbs were very dim.

Suggest **two** changes he could make to his circuit to make these six bulbs brighter. (2)

(MEG, 1995)

6 The following diagram shows a flexible wire **AB** hanging between the poles of a powerful magnet. The switch is closed so that a current flows and the wire experiences a force at right angles to, and out from, the paper.

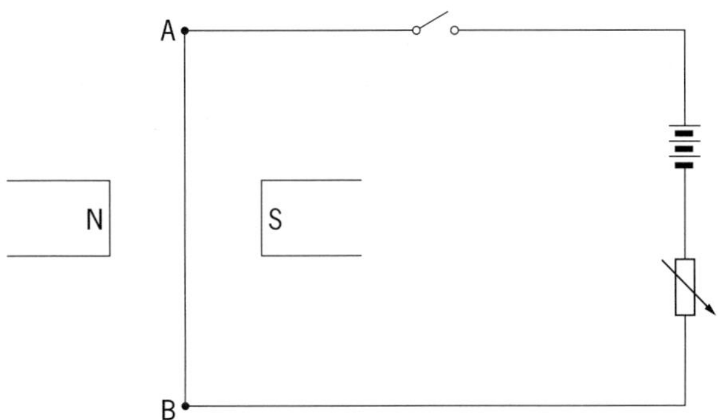

a) [Copy] the diagram and mark on it the direction of the current through the wire **AB** when the switch is closed. (1)

b) State what effect (if any) the following alterations would have on the force on the wire **AB**:

i) increasing the size of the current; (1)

ii) reversing the battery. (1)

(WJEC, 1995)

7 a) The diagram below shows a simple electromagnet in a circuit.

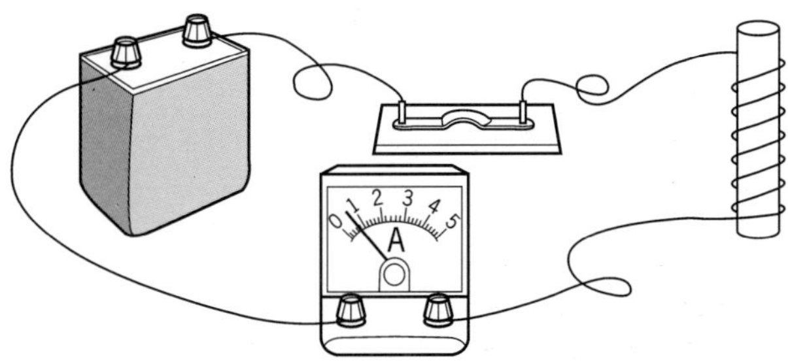

i) You want to measure the potential difference across the **electromagnet**.

Where should the voltmeter be connected? (1)

ii) Explain how you could find the resistance of the coil of the electromagnet. State any **formula** you would use. (3)

iii) You need to **control** the power of the electromagnet. What could you put in the circuit to do this? (1)

b) i) You want to use the parts of an electromagnet to make a **step-up** transformer. Explain how you could do this. (2)

ii) Why could the transformer **not** be used to change the voltage of a battery? (1)

c) The diagram below shows circuits used to start a motor car.

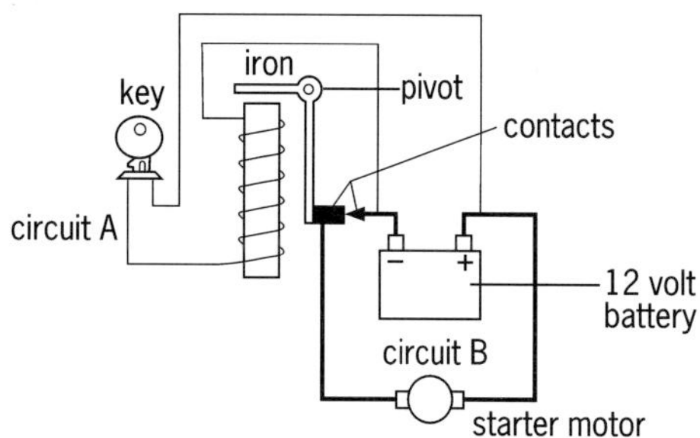

Explain how turning the key makes the current flow in the starter motor. (2)

(SEG, 1995)

8 The diagram shows a circuit for measuring the resistance of a coil of wire, which is kept at constant temperature.

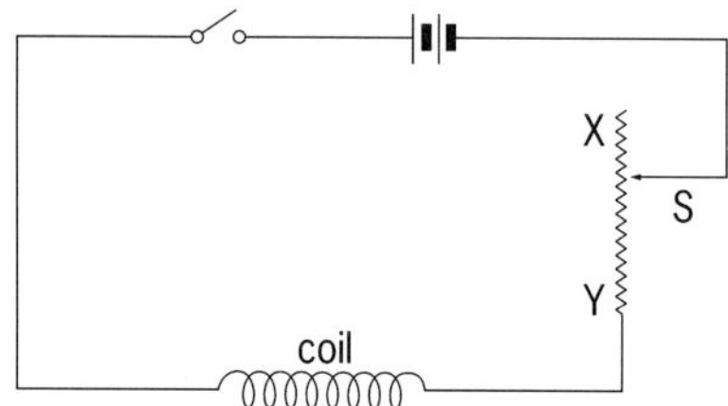

a) [Copy] the circuit above and add to it:
i) an ammeter, labelled A, to record the current through the coil; (1)
ii) a voltmeter, labelled V, to record the voltage across the coil. (1)
b) S is a sliding contact and **XY** is a resistance wire. When **S** is moved towards **X**, state what happens to the:
i) amount of resistance wire in the circuit and the total circuit resistance; (1)
ii) circuit current. (1)
c) The graph below shows how the current I through the coil changed as the voltage V across the coil was changed.

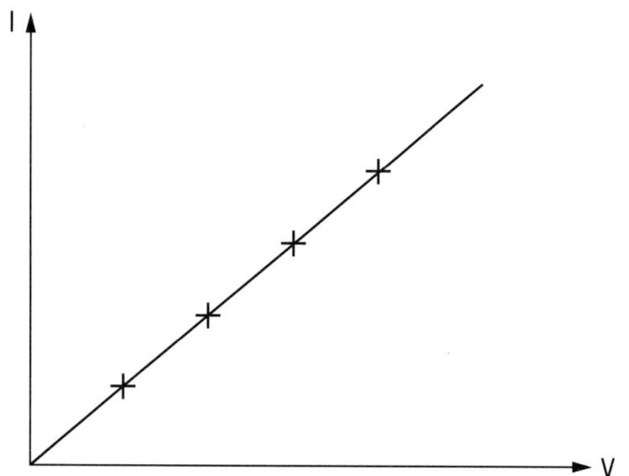

[Copy] the graph and sketch on it the line for a coil of greater resistance. (1)

(WJEC, 1995)

9 The diagram shows an electrical transformer. The transformer is designed to convert a mains voltage of 240 V to 12 V.

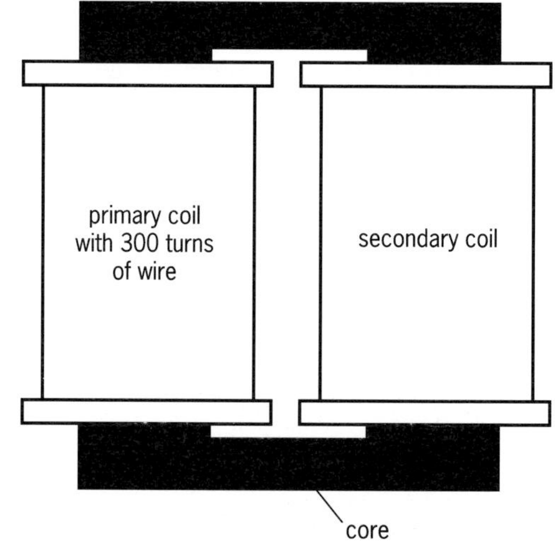

a) i) Why are the wires used for the coils thin and coated in plastic or lacquer? (1)
ii) How many turns of wire are there on the **secondary** coil? Show how you obtained your answer. (2)
b) Explain why the input to the primary coil must be a.c. and not d.c. (3)
c) The power input into the primary coil was 90 W, whilst the power output from the secondary coil was 80 W.
i) What is the **efficiency** of the transformer? (1)
ii) Suggest why a transformer has a high efficiency. (1)
iii) **Explain** why the efficiency of a transformer is **not** 100 per cent. (2)

(SEG, 1994)

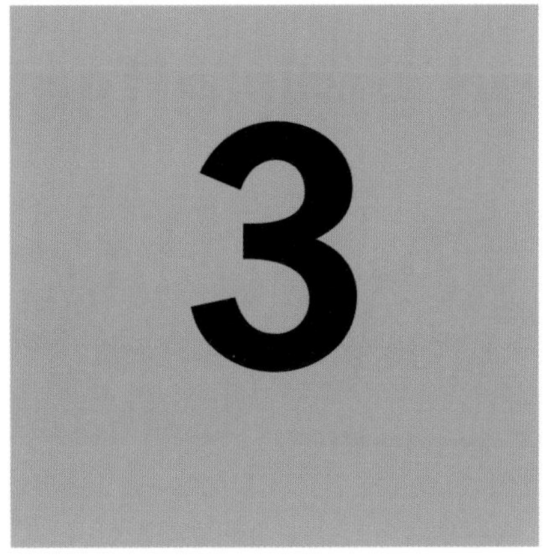

FORCES

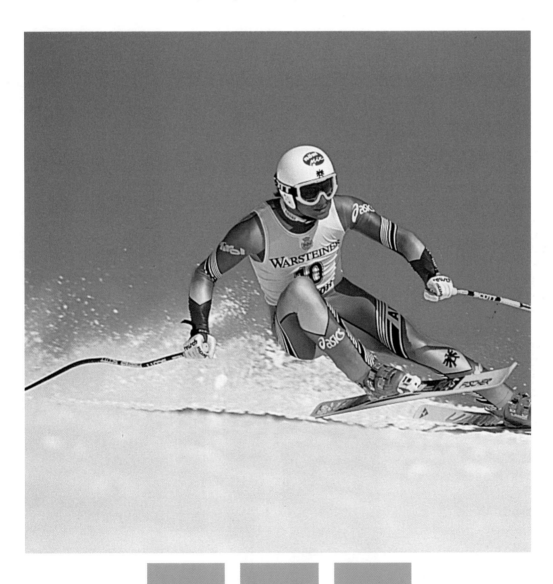

3.1 Forces and their effects

A force is needed to get something moving

A force can change the direction in which something is travelling

A force is needed to slow things down

A force can change the shape of materials

Forces are at work almost everywhere you look. You cannot see a force, but you will often see what is causing it and what effect it has. Some effects are barely noticeable; others are much more easily seen.

In each case the effect of the force depends on its size and the direction in which it acts.

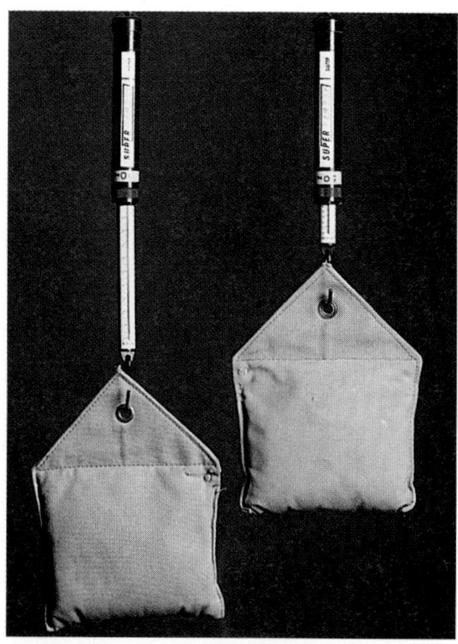

Two newtonmeters with different ranges

Measuring forces

Forces are measured in units called **newtons** (N). A larger unit, the kilonewton (kN), may be used for larger forces. 1 kN is another way of writing 1000 newtons.

Most forces in the laboratory can be measured with a forcemeter (or newtonmeter). Some forcemeters measure forces between 0 and 10 N; others may have different ranges. You must choose the one with the right range for the force you are measuring.

Forces can range from being very small to very large. The force needed to lift a can of Coke, for example, is only about 4 N. A much larger force – about 10 000 N – would be needed to lift a small car.

The size of the force determines what it can, or cannot, do. In some cases it is very important that the forces are big enough to do the job for which they are intended.

A force of about 10 million newtons is needed to launch this rocket. If a smaller force were exerted by the engines, the rocket would remain on the ground

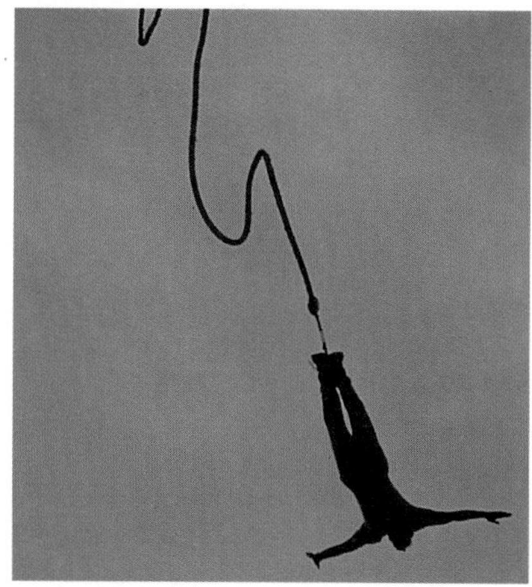

The force exerted by the bungee cord must stop the person falling before she reaches the ground. If the force is too small to stop her, she would hit the ground

The direction of a force

The *direction* of a force also affects what happens. The upward force on the stationary rocket, for example, makes it begin to move faster (accelerate) in that direction. The upward force exerted by the bungee cord (acting in the opposite direction to the falling body) causes the jumper to slow down. In both cases, the size and direction of the forces affect the motion of the objects on which they are acting.

A force which acts on a moving object can also change the direction in which it is moving.

If, for example, one of these bumper cars is struck by another *from the side* then its direction will change. It will be pushed (from its original path) in the direction of the force exerted on it by the other car.

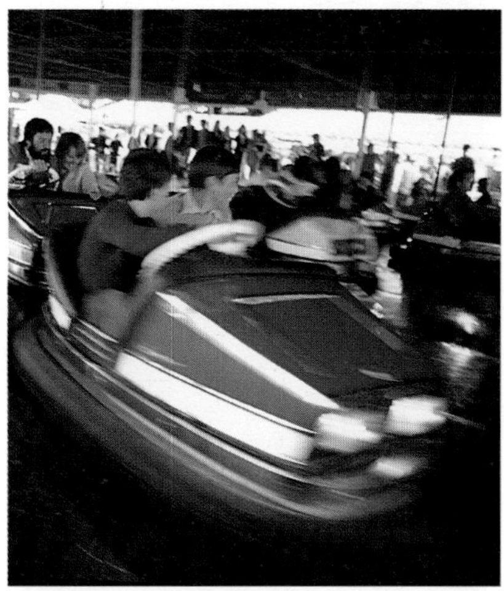

The force of one car on another can change their direction

★ THINGS TO DO

1 Use a stretched elastic band to make a toy car move along the floor. Measure the size of the force exerted by the elastic on the car, and how far the car travels.

What do you think affects how far the car travels? Make a note of your ideas, including a reason for each one.

Test your ideas and prepare a report of your investigation.

2 Think of some forces which you could measure, such as the force needed to pull a book across the bench at a steady speed. For each one, estimate the value of the force you think will be needed, then measure it using a forcemeter.

Make a table showing what you do, your prediction and the size of the force you measure.

3 Copy this table and complete each column.

What happens	What the effect is	What causes the force	What would happen if the force were bigger
Someone stands on a diving board			
Someone kicks a football			
Someone sits on a cushion			
Someone holds a bag of groceries in mid-air			

4 The following values match the forces needed for the jobs illustrated. Which force is needed to do each job?

10 000 N 10 N 300 N 3 N 3 000 000 N

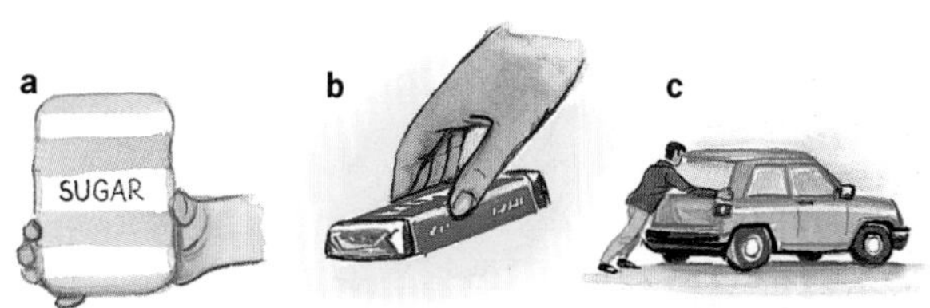

3.2 Gravity

Parachutists are pulled to the Earth by gravity

One force which affects everything and everybody is the force called **gravity**. The Earth's gravity tends to pull everything, including things which are far out in space, towards its centre.

Water is pulled down the plughole; leaves are pulled to the ground; a ball is pulled back to the ground. Without gravity none of these things would happen.

Gravity is perhaps more than you expect. *Every object*, in fact, *pulls on every other object* with a gravity force. You and the person sitting next to you are pulling on one another, although the force is far too small to have any effect on you or your neighbour!

What affects the size of the gravity force?

The size of the gravity force between two objects depends on:

- the mass of each object – the bigger the mass, the bigger the force, and
- how far they are apart – the further they are apart, the smaller the force.

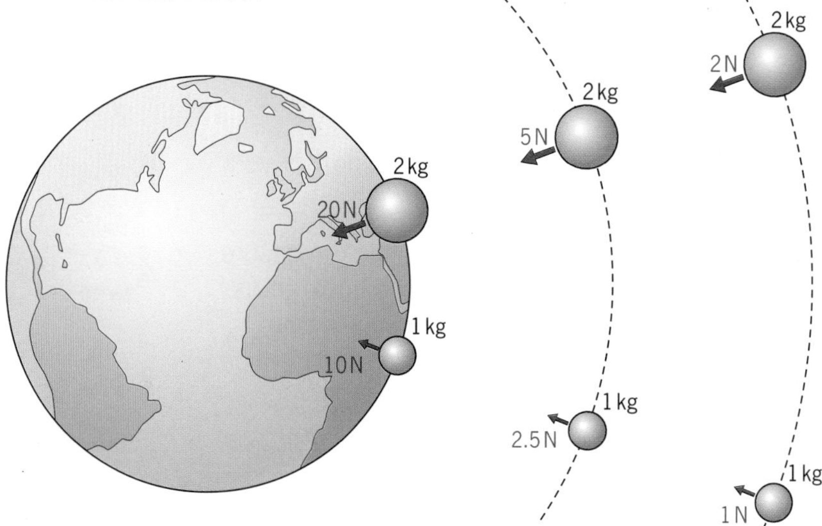

The pull of the Earth's gravity on an object depends on the mass of the object and on its distance from the Earth

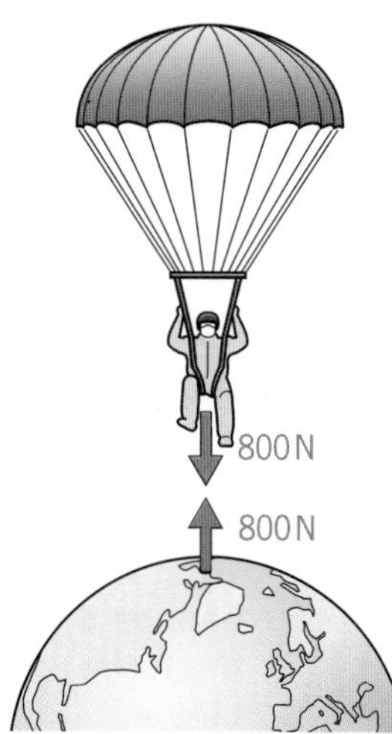

The Earth and the parachutist pull on one another with the same gravity force – about 800 N. That force is big enough to make the parachutist fall but is *not* big enough to make something as massive as the Earth move

Gravity forces only become noticeable when one or both of the objects has a huge mass. The Earth is so massive (it has a mass of about six million, million, million, million kilograms) that it exerts a gravity force which is large enough to make other things move towards it. It is important to remember that the objects pull on each other equally – the same pulling force acts on each of them. Imagine, for example, the gravity forces between the parachutist and the Earth. The Earth pulls on the parachutist, but the parachutist is also pulling on the Earth.

The Earth's gravity

At the Earth's surface, each kilogram of matter is pulled down with a force of 10 newtons (10 N). This value (10 newtons per kilogram) is the **gravitational field strength** of the Earth.

A bag of sugar, for example, has a mass of 1 kilogram (1 kg) but its weight is 10 newtons (10 N). **Weight** is a force – it is the *force due to gravity*.

To change mass into weight:

weight (N) = mass (kg) × gravitational field strength (N/kg)
= mass (kg) × 10 N/kg (on Earth)

Gravity is different elsewhere

The same bag of sugar on the Moon would only weigh 1.66 newtons. It would be the same size and the same shape – it would contain the same amount of matter and have the same mass. Its weight would be only 1.66 N (one-sixth of its 'Earth weight') because the Moon's gravitational field strength is only one-sixth of that of the Earth.

This table shows the weight of a 1 kg bag of sugar, if we measured it on the surface of the Moon and some of the planets.

Place	Mass/kg	Gravitational field strength/ N/kg	Weight/N
Earth	1	10	10
Moon	1	1.66	1.66
Venus	1	9	9
Mars	1	4	4
Jupiter	1	26	26
Neptune	1	14	14

Because the gravitational field strength is different, the sugar's *weight is different*, even though its *mass is constant*.

★ THINGS TO DO

1 The masses of some items of shopping are shown. Calculate the weight in newtons of each item (on Earth).

2 Measure or calculate your own weight on Earth. Make a chart showing what your weight would be on the Moon and on each of the planets listed in the table above.

3 This recipe is for making gingerbread on Earth. Write the recipe out again, showing the quantities you would have to use on Mars. Explain any similarities or differences between the 'Earth' recipe and the 'Mars' recipe.

3.3 The shape of things

Forces can change the shape of materials. The shape of this diving board depends on the size and direction of the forces which are acting on it.

The type of material also affects how much it bends. A steel diving board (with the same length, thickness and width) would not bend as much as a wooden board if the same force acted on it.

The dimensions of the board will also have an effect. A thicker board of the same material would not bend as much as a thinner board.

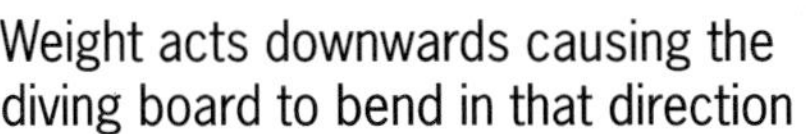

Weight acts downwards causing the diving board to bend in that direction

A heavier object (a bigger force) causes the diving board to bend more

Plastic and elastic materials

When the diver leaves the diving board it 'springs' back to its original shape. Materials which do this are said to have **elastic** properties. This does not mean they are made from the material we call elastic. The word 'elastic', used in this sense, describes how the material behaves when a force acts on it. Steel, wood and many other materials, including glass, show elastic behaviour to some extent, although larger forces may leave the materials permanently distorted or broken.

Other materials, such as plasticine, do not regain their shape after being deformed. This sort of behaviour is described as **plastic** behaviour. Once again, this does not mean that the object is made from plastic. Here the word 'plastic' describes the behaviour of a material that does not regain its shape when it is deformed.

The material used to make this bottle has elastic properties. It returns to its original shape after use

The material used to make this tube has plastic properties. Its shape remains changed after use

Springs

This machine, called a Bullworker, is used to exercise muscles. When the ends are pushed inwards, the spring inside it is compressed. The bigger the force, the more the spring is compressed. If the force is gradually reduced, the spring expands until it regains its original shape. The spring is showing that it has elastic properties.

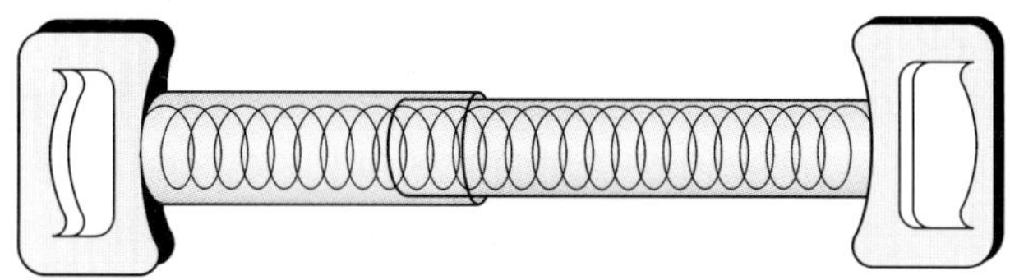

Section through a Bullworker showing the spring coils

Opposing forces

When the spring in the Bullworker is compressed it 'pushes back' on the arms. The more it is compressed, the bigger is the 'pushing back' force. Similarly, when a rubber band is stretched between your thumbs it exerts a force which tries to pull your thumbs back together. Materials with elastic properties exert a 'restoring' force in the opposite direction to the force which is stretching or compressing them. These pairs of forces help us to understand the behaviour of springs.

When a weight is suspended from a spring, for example, the spring stretches until the upward (restoring) force of the spring is equal to the weight. The forces are equal, but act in opposite directions. They are said to be in **equilibrium**. If more weight is added, the downward force increases. The spring stretches until the (restoring) force is once again equal to the weight.

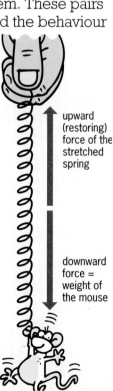

upward (restoring) force of the stretched spring

downward force = weight of the mouse

A spring in equilibrium

Hooke's Law

Imagine measuring the extension (the amount by which the spring stretches) of a spring when different loads are hung from it.

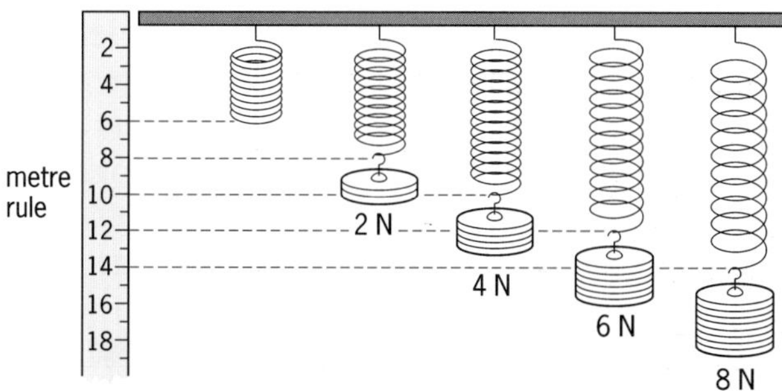

A graph of extension against load will be a straight line up to a point called the **elastic limit**.

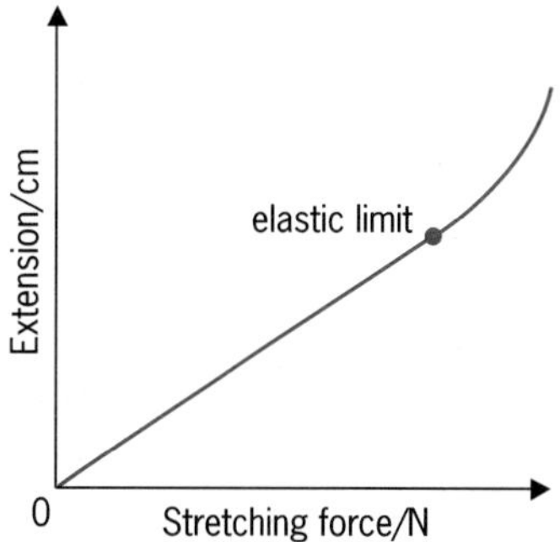

This straight line shows us that *the extension is directly proportional to the load on the spring*. That means the extension will double if the force doubles; it will treble if the force trebles, and so on. This relationship is known as **Hooke's Law**.

Up to a limit

If the force on a spring is too large, the spring becomes permanently stretched – it does not return to its original shape.

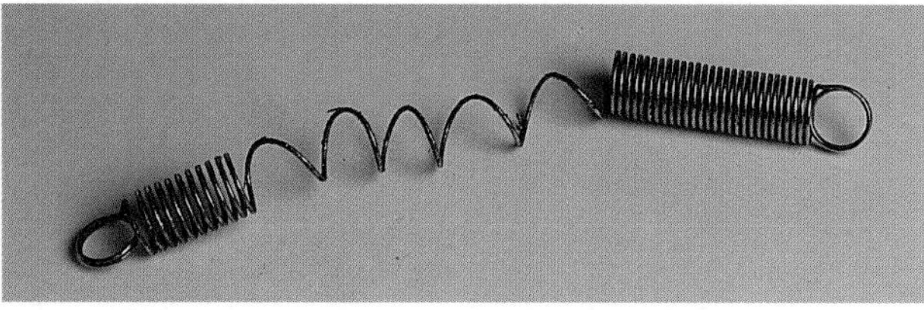

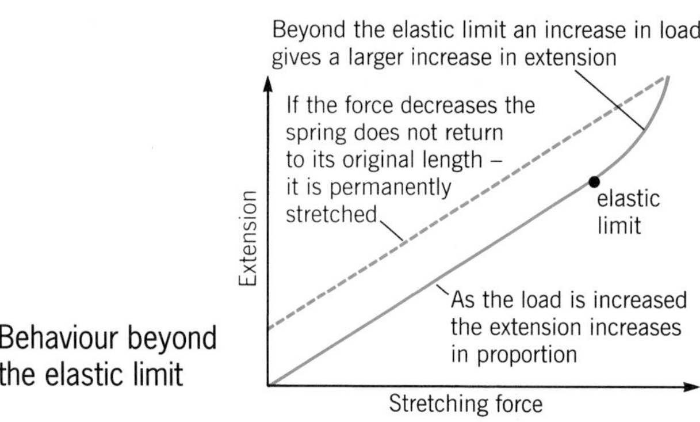

Behaviour beyond the elastic limit

There must therefore be a point at which the behaviour of the spring stops being 'elastic' and becomes 'plastic'. That point is the elastic limit. A spring stretched beyond the elastic limit becomes permanently damaged – it remains stretched when the load is removed. You can see from the graph that, beyond the elastic limit, small increases in the load result in larger increases in the extension.

Other materials with elastic properties behave in a similar way. If, for example, the steel of a car door receives a small push, it bends slightly, then 'springs back' when the force is removed. If the force is too big the elastic limit is exceeded and the steel panel remains permanently bent.

Under tension

Many modern bridges are supported by thick cables which also show elastic behaviour. The cables exert forces in different directions on different parts of the structure. The cables are all under **tension** – each experiences forces which pull it in opposite directions, effectively trying to stretch it.

The metal cables A and B shown in the diagram below support the central section of the bridge. The total downward force of the weight of the bridge and the people is balanced by the upward forces of the cables on the bridge. The cables pull inwards on the upright wooden poles. To balance these forces, the poles are pulled outwards by metal cables C and D, which are fixed into the ground. The upright poles in fact support the whole weight of the bridge and need to be the strongest part of the structure.

The forces on a simple suspension bridge. Cables A, B, C and D are under tension

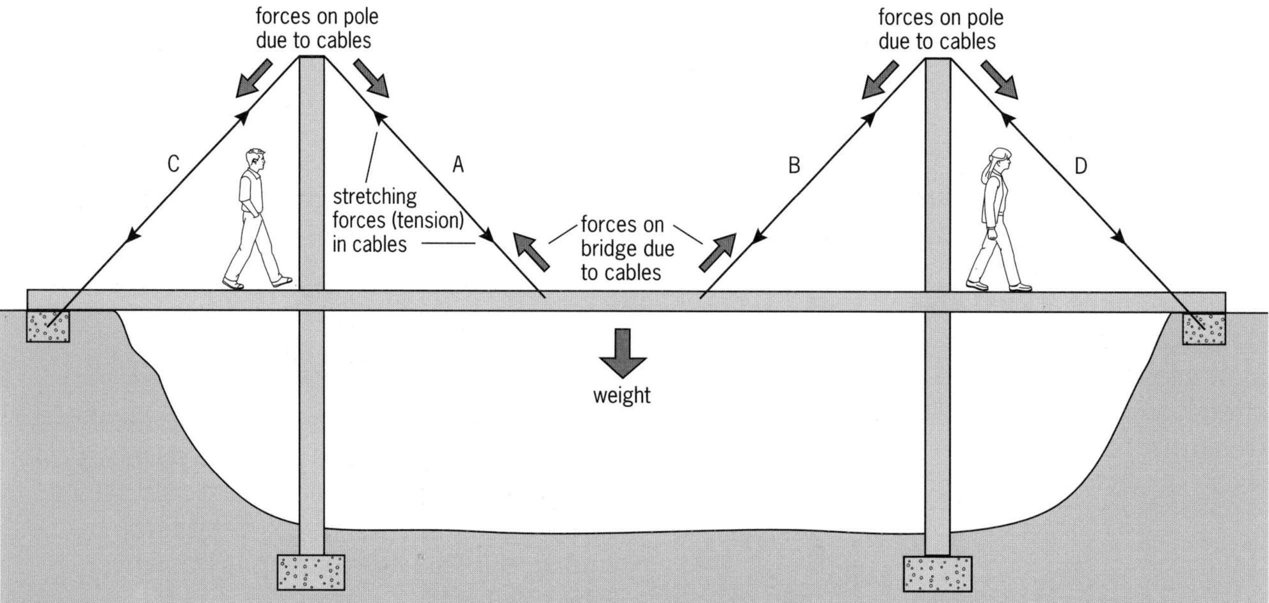

Whilst the structure on the opposite page may seem very simple, the same principles apply to the construction of much larger suspension bridges such as the one shown here.

All parts of this bridge are acted on by equal and opposite forces – it is in equilibrium

★ THINGS TO DO

1 When a force acts on a spring it stretches. The amount by which it stretches is called the extension.

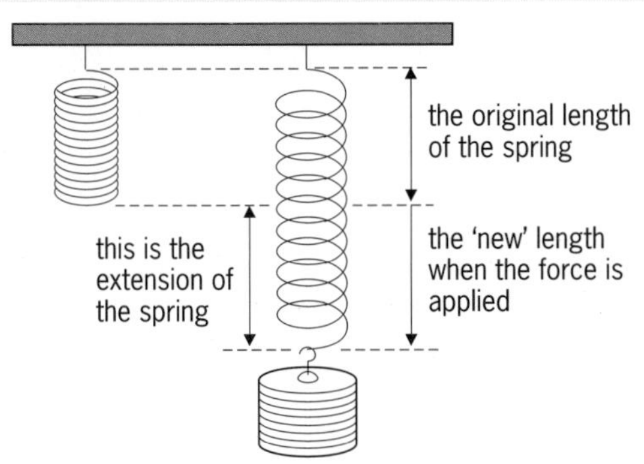

a) Carry out an experiment to show how the extension of a spring depends on the force which acts on it. Include a graph as part of your results section.
b) What is the value of the force which would cause the spring to exceed the elastic limit?

2 Try repeating the experiment with (i) a rubber band, (ii) a bungee used to hold luggage on cars, (iii) a strip of polythene. Compare the results with those for your spring. What can you say about the behaviour of these materials compared with that of the spring?

3 Find out whether the same relationship applies in the case of a spring being squashed. Is the amount by which it is compressed proportional to the force acting on it?

4 These graphs were drawn by some students who tested springs.

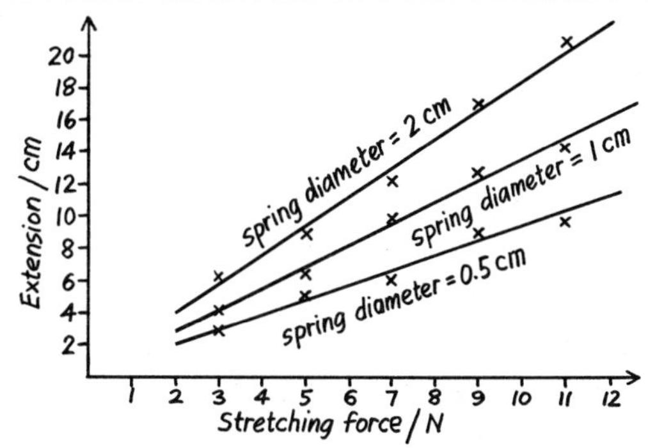

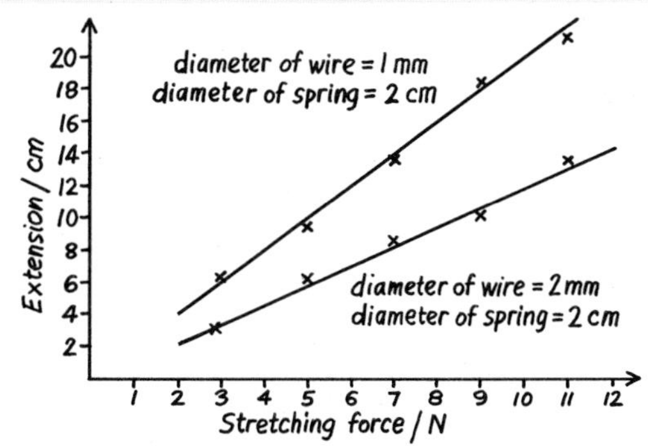

a) Describe briefly, but accurately, what you think the students did for each test.
b) What conclusions can be drawn from the graphs?
c) A motor-bike manufacturer found that the springs they were using for the suspension were too 'soft' – they compressed and stretched too easily. What could they do to make the springs harder to compress?

3.4 Stronger structures

Struts and ties

Sometimes we must take steps to increase the strength of supporting structures. This hanging basket and its contents, for example, may be so heavy, particularly after watering, that they bend the horizontal part of the bracket.

To prevent this an extra section – a **strut** – is added which gives the horizontal part of the bracket more support. The strut is under **compression** – it experiences forces which try to compress it.

The strut forms a triangle with the vertical and horizontal parts of the bracket. Triangular sections such as this are very strong. The bracket is an example of a **structure** – an arrangement of parts which are joined together in such a way that they support one another.

Struts are often used in conjunction with **ties** – parts of a structure which are under tension. The struts and ties ensure that *at any point*:

- any downward-acting forces are balanced by upward forces,
- any outward-acting forces are balanced by inward-acting forces.

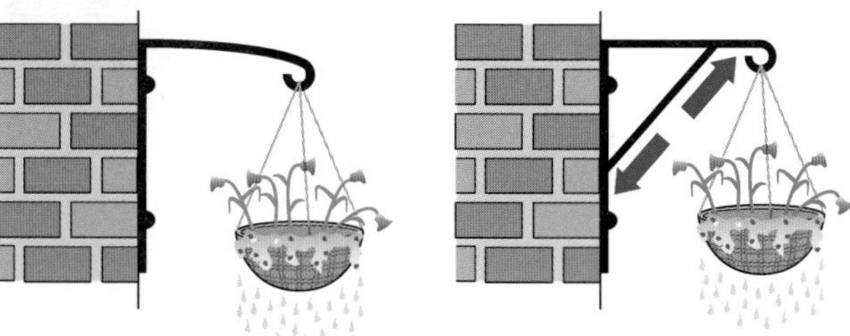

A supporting structure is made stronger with a strut

Scaffolding consists of struts and ties which hold the whole structure strongly together

Reaction forces

For anything to remain in equilibrium there must be equal and opposite forces acting on it. The weight of the bridge shown here is supported by the vertical pillars. These, in turn, are supported by the ground. The ground must therefore exert an upward force on the pillars which 'balances' their downward force on the ground. This type of force is called a **reaction** force (or just 'the reaction'). The same ideas apply in all situations where forces are acting. The 'restoring' force of a spring is, in fact, a reaction to the force which is compressing or stretching it. We can summarise this by thinking that *whenever a force acts there will be a reaction force in the opposite direction.* The bigger the force, the bigger the reaction.

The pillars of these bridges are under compression, due to the action of the weight of the bridges and the reaction of the ground

A particle view

In a solid material the particles are held a fixed distance apart by small forces which act between them – **a**.

When the solid is compressed, the particles in it are pushed closer together – **b**. As this happens, the forces of repulsion between the particles increase. If the compressing force is removed, the material will regain its original shape as the particles push back to their 'natural' distance apart.

When the solid is stretched (placed under tension) the particles are pulled further apart than normal – **c**. As this happens, forces of attraction between the particles come into play, pulling the particles back together. If the stretching force is removed, the material will return to its original shape. In both cases, the forces which return the material to its original shape are exerted by the particles of the material itself.

If the force applied to the solid is too big, however, it will be permanently distorted.

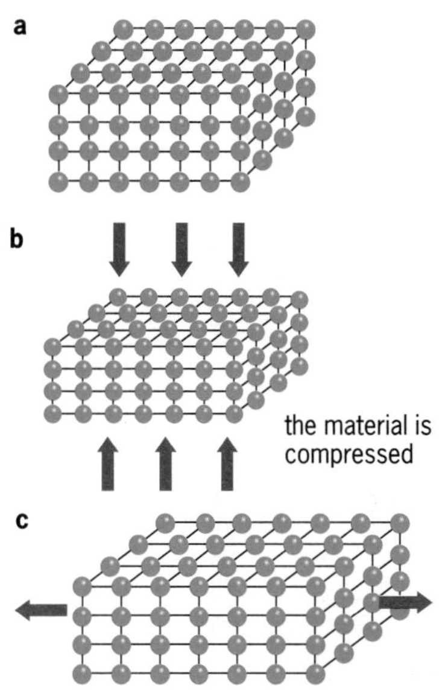

Particles of a solid material

What happens when beams bend

Horizontal concrete beams bend when forces act on them, although the amount is so small that you do not notice it. When a beam bends, the material on the underside is stretched (put under tension) and the material at the top is compressed.

Concrete is strong under compression but weak under tension. Concrete beams are therefore weaker (and more likely to break) on the underside where the particles are under tension. To overcome this, steel rods are often placed in the concrete on the underside. Steel is strong in compression *and* tension. The rods therefore strengthen the concrete beam where it would otherwise be weak.

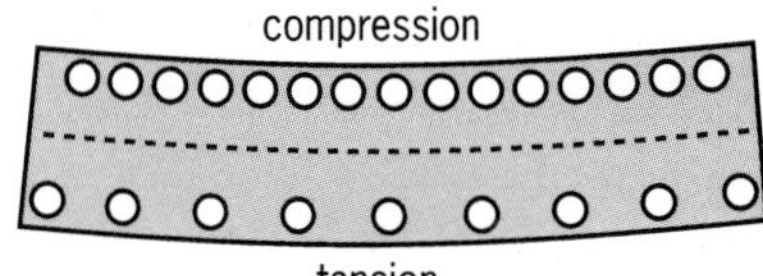

Particles in a bent beam

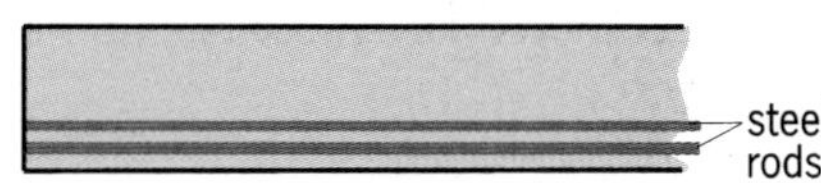

Reinforced concrete beam

★ THINGS TO DO

1 Metal beams (or girders) are used in many large structures although they may not be visible. There will, for example, be a beam above the windows and doors of your home, supporting the weight of the walls above. Beams are made in different shapes such as those shown here.

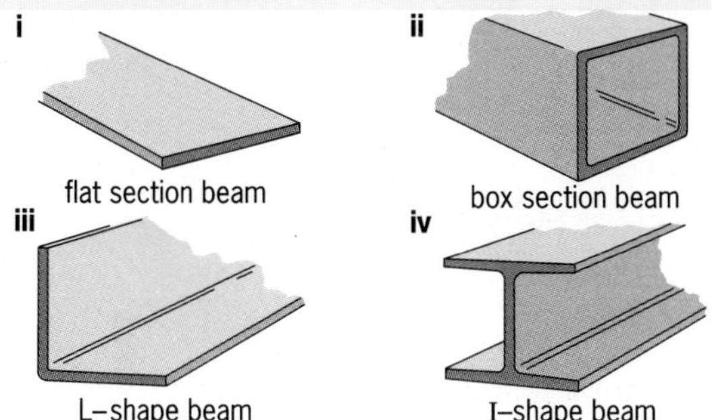

Make your own beams from card. Carry out tests to find out which will be best to use:
a) above a door, where the weight of the wall above is supported on each side,
b) as a vertical beam supporting the horizontal parts of a structure.

2 Draw diagrams of:
a) a laboratory stool,
b) a garden swing.
On each diagram draw arrows showing the direction of any forces which act on the structure. Add the words *under tension* and *under compression* where they are appropriate.

3.5 Pressing problems

Skiers do not sink into powdery snow

When you stand on soft snow you sink into it. If you were to stand on skis, your would not sink so far, although your weight would not change. The reason is that your weight is now spread over a much larger area.

Imagine that the weight of this skier is 900 N.

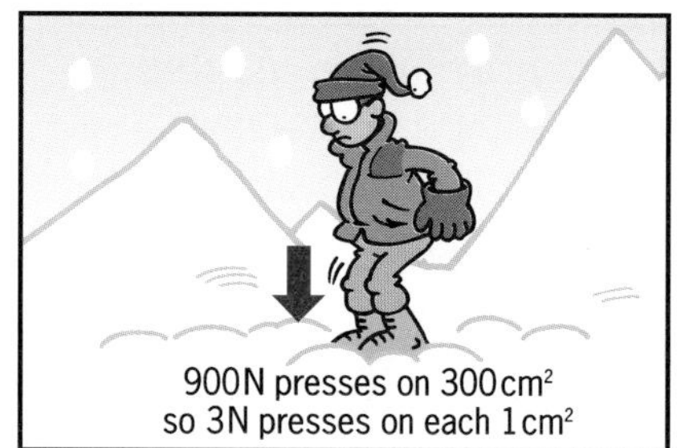

900N presses on 300cm²
so 3N presses on each 1cm²

There is less force on each square centimetre when wearing skis, so the skier does not sink so far into the snow

Increasing the area on which the weight acts has decreased the force acting on the unit area or the **pressure** on the snow.

Calculating pressure

The standard unit of pressure is the **pascal** (Pa). 1 Pa is equivalent to a pressure of 1 N/m^2 (1 newton of force acting over an area of 1 square metre). Pressure can be calculated using the equation:

$$\text{pressure (Pa)} = \frac{\text{force (N)}}{\text{area (m}^2\text{)}}$$

Imagine, for example, a large box weighing 1000 N resting on the floor. When the box rests on its larger side its weight is spread over twice the area, so the pressure which it exerts on the floor is halved.

The weight of the box (1000 N) is spread over an area of 0.25 m^2 (1 m × 0.25 m)

$$\text{pressure} = \frac{\text{force}}{\text{area}} = \frac{1000\text{ N}}{0.25\text{ m}^2}$$

The pressure is 4000 Pa (or 4 kPa)

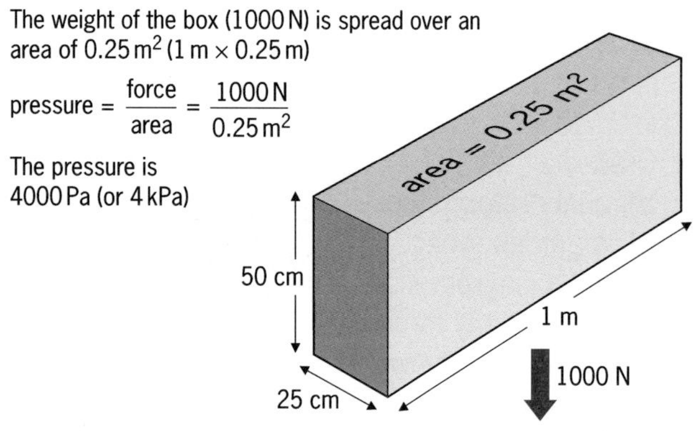

If the box is placed on its larger side, then the weight is spread over a bigger area — 0.5 m^2 (1 m × 0.5 m)

$$\text{pressure} = \frac{\text{force}}{\text{area}} = \frac{1000\text{ N}}{0.5\text{ m}^2}$$

The pressure is 2000 Pa (or 2 kPa)

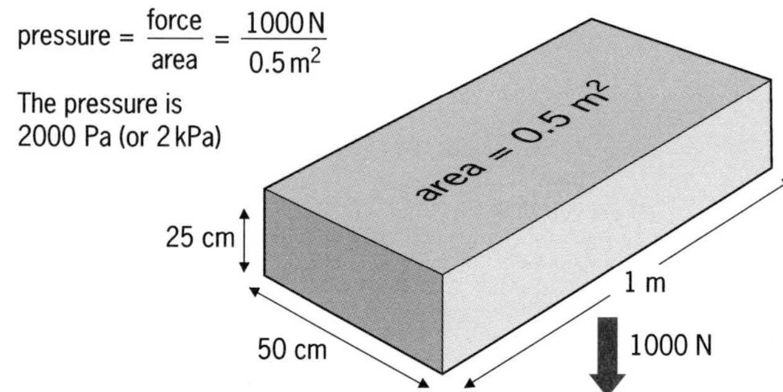

Pressure in liquids

Anything immersed in a liquid experiences pressure on it due to the weight of the liquid above it.

Divers know that the high pressure they experience in deep water can affect their ability to think clearly. The effect is called nitrogen narcosis and is caused by dissolved nitrogen forming in the blood.

To prevent problems associated with nitrogen narcosis, deep-sea divers breathe a mixture of helium and oxygen

The connection between pressure and depth can be seen in the laboratory using the apparatus shown here. When the can is filled with water, water spurts from the tubes, pushed out by the pressure of the water at that level. The deeper the tube, the further the water travels as it leaves the tube.

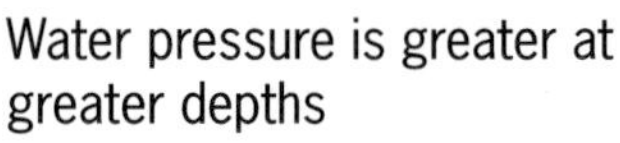

Water pressure is greater at greater depths

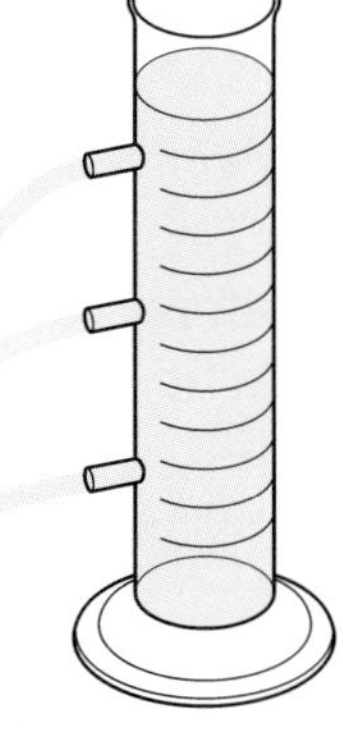

The pressure at any point in a liquid depends on:

- the depth of the liquid at that point – the greater the depth, the greater the pressure, and
- the density of the liquid – the greater the density, the greater the pressure at any level.

The pressure acts in all directions

In fluids (liquids and gases) the pressure at any point acts in all directions (unlike the pressure which your weight exerts on the ground which only acts downwards). You can understand why if you imagine a cardboard box filled with marbles being pressed down. The marbles behave in a similar way to the particles of a fluid.

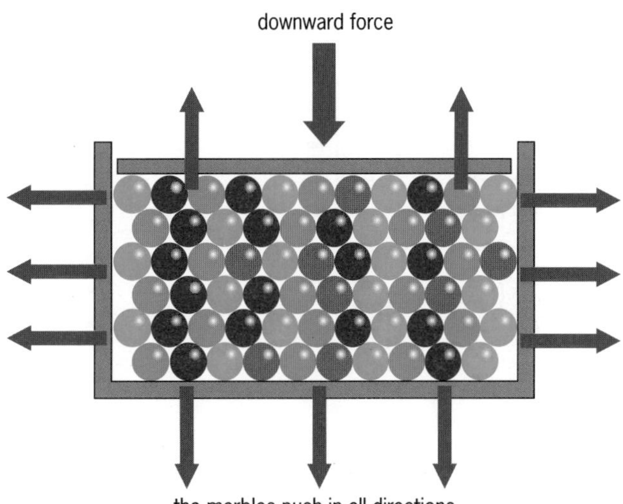

Fluid particles, like marbles, exert pressure in all directions

Submarines must be carefully designed to withstand the high pressures which will act on them when submerged. At a depth of 1000 metres there would be a pressure of about 10.5 million Pa (N/m^2) on each part of the hull of a submarine – sufficient to crush most things. (That is the same as resting about 90 adult elephants on the area of your chest – and you know what that would do!)

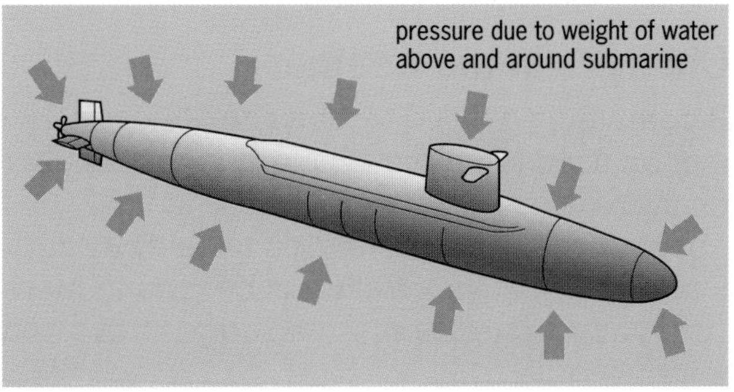

Submarines experience the pressure of water when they are submerged

Under pressure from the air

The weight of the air exerts a pressure on the surface of the Earth and everything on it. The pressure is called **atmospheric pressure** and is about 101 kPa (101 000 N/m^2). Because air is also fluid (the particles can 'flow'), the pressure is exerted in all directions and increases with depth (i.e. it decreases as you get higher above the Earth's surface).

The effects of atmospheric pressure can be seen in the experiment illustrated.

a

An empty can is under pressure from the air outside and inside. The air pressure on the inside is equal to the pressure on the outside of the can

b

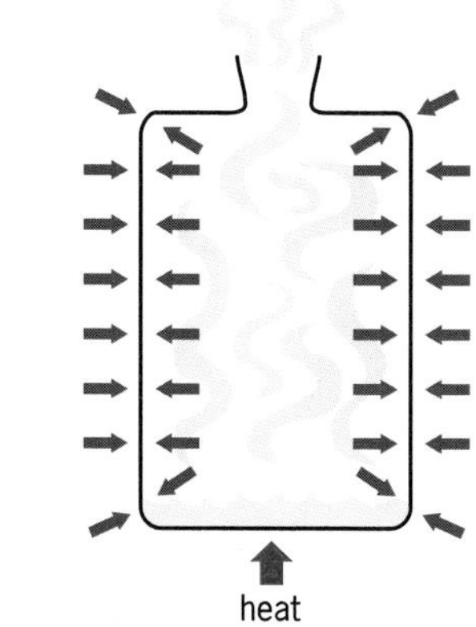

A small amount of water is placed in the can and boiled. The can fills with steam, driving out the air

c

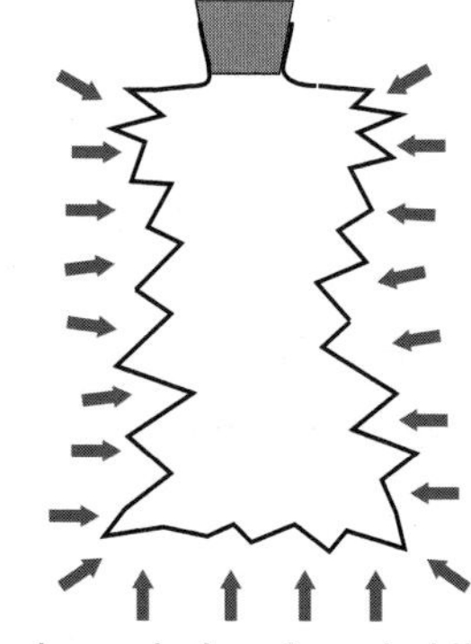

The can is sealed and cooled. The steam condenses, leaving a vacuum inside the can (an empty space). The pressure of the air outside crushes the can

In flight

Our bodies function properly at normal atmospheric pressure. At high altitudes, where atmospheric pressure is lower, we find it difficult to breathe and the circulation of blood is affected.

Long-distance passenger airliners fly at a height of about 12 000 m. At this height atmospheric pressure is only a fraction of its value at the surface. The inside of an aircraft is 'pressurised' so that the pressure is similar to that on Earth. Even so, your ears may 'pop' due to changes in pressure during take-off and landing.

Changes in the weather

Barometers are used to measure atmospheric pressure. They can be used to predict changes in the weather – slight changes in atmospheric pressure indicate that the weather is about to change. In general, if the atmospheric pressure falls, it indicates that the weather is becoming more unsettled; rising atmospheric pressure suggests the weather is improving.

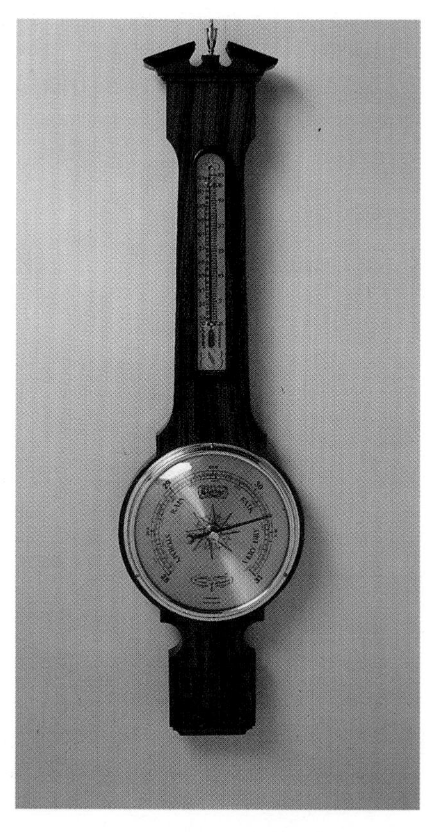

You may have a barometer in your home

★ THINGS TO DO

1 Write a sentence or two about how pressure is involved in each of these photographs.

2 Copy and complete this table. Include appropriate units.

	Weight or force	Area on which it acts	Pressure
Table lamp	40 N	200 cm^2	
Car resting on tyres	8000 N	400 cm^2 (0.04 m^2)	
Child on sledge		100 cm^2	4 N/cm^2
Pressing drawing pin	50 N		5000 N/cm^2

3 Early diving machines were little more than a bell-shaped piece of metal designed to trap air which the diver could breathe. The problem was that they filled up with water as they moved deeper below the surface.

A group of pupils set up this apparatus to 'model' a simple diving bell. They intended finding out how the amount of air in the bottle depended on the depth of the bottle below the surface.

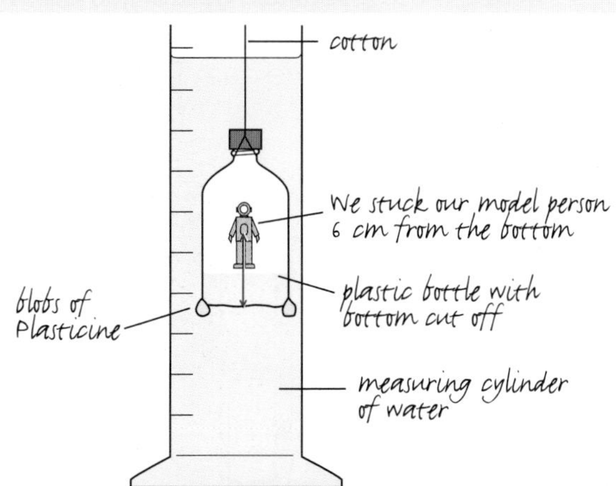

Plan how *you* would use this apparatus to investigate the effects of depth on pressure. Before you start predict what you think will happen, with some reasons for your prediction. If your teacher approves your plans, carry out the investigation and prepare a report.

4 An altimeter is an instrument used for measuring height. It works by measuring atmospheric pressure but the scale is calibrated to show height above sea level. This table shows how atmospheric pressure and height are related.

Height/km	**Pressure**/kPa
0	101
5	64
10	36
20	22
30	12
40	8
50	3

a) Plot a graph of atmospheric pressure against height above sea level.
b) Most long-distance aircraft fly at a height of 12 km. What will be the atmospheric pressure at that height?
c) At what height will the atmospheric pressure be halved compared with its value at sea level?
d) What will be the pressure at the top of Mount Everest, 9000 metres above sea level?

3.6 Under pressure

Child undergoes emergency eye surgery after tyre explodes

A 7-year-old child underwent an emergency operation last night after he tried to inflate his bicycle tyre at a local garage. The child had connected his tyre to the air supply normally used for car tyres. As air entered the tyre the pressure became so great that the tyre exploded, scattering lumps of torn rubber. One of these pieces struck him directly in the eye, bursting the surface. A hospital spokesperson said he was now in a stable condition following the operation.

The air inside a bicycle tyre is really millions of tiny molecules spread out through the space inside the tyre. The molecules are constantly moving, often at speeds of about 300 metres per second. They change direction regularly as they collide with one another and with the inner surface of the tyre. It is impossible to predict the direction in which they will travel – their movement is random.

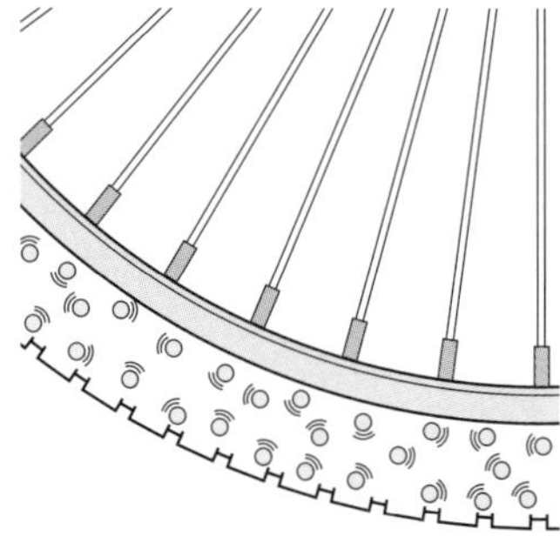

Random motion of air molecules inside a tyre

Each time the molecules hit the inner surface of the tyre they exert a small force (rather like someone running into you). Because there are millions of molecules moving in all directions, pressure is exerted in all directions over the inside of the tyre and on the rim of the wheel.

The average pressure depends on the rate at which molecules strike the tyre – the more often they strike it, the higher the pressure. The pressure will therefore depend on:

- the temperature of the air in the tyre – at higher temperatures the molecules move faster, and so strike the walls more often;
- the amount of air in the tyre – the more air molecules in the tyre, the more collisions occur per second at any given temperature.

A safe limit

Tyres are made to withstand certain pressures. If the pressure becomes too great, the tyre could burst.

Bicycle tyres should normally be inflated to a pressure of about 0.25 MPa (250 kPa)

How does the volume affect the pressure of a gas?

If you put your finger over the end of a bicycle pump (to stop the molecules escaping) and push on the plunger you will find it more and more difficult to push down. Eventually you will be unable to squash the gas further – the pressure of the gas on the piston is then equal to the pressure that the piston is exerting on the gas. They are balanced.

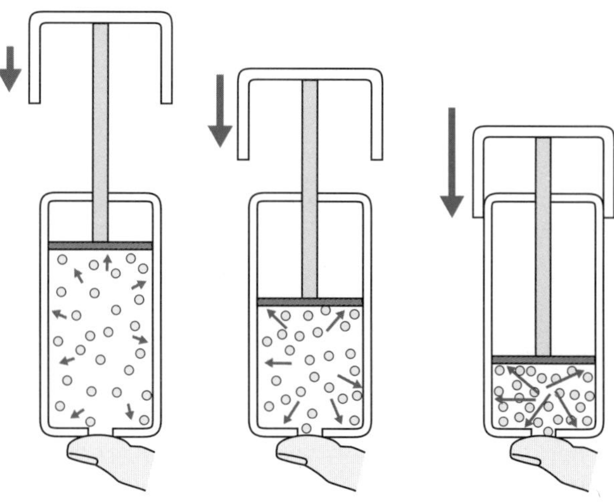

As you push the plunger in further, the pressure of the air inside increases

As the pump is pushed in, the molecules are pushed closer together. Because the molecules are travelling at the same speed, but in a smaller volume, they collide with the walls more often, and so they exert a greater pressure. If the handle is released, the pressure of the gas may push the plunger back out. The volume of the gas then increases, and the pressure decreases.

There is a simple mathematical connection between pressure and volume. Assuming the temperature of the gas does not change, if the pressure is halved, the volume doubles. If the pressure is doubled, the volume is halved. Another way of expressing this relationship is to say that *for a fixed mass of gas, at constant temperature, the pressure is inversely proportional to the volume*. This can be written in the form of an equation:

$$\text{pressure} \times \text{volume} = \text{a constant value}$$

★ THINGS TO DO

1 A pupil did a test to find out how the pressure affected the volume of air in a bicycle pump. She measured how much the plunger went down when different weights were put on it. Her results are shown.

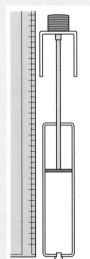

Area of piston = 4 cm^2

Weight on pump / N	Distance moved by plunger / cm
5	2.8
10	5.0
15	6.9
20	8.3
25	9.5

a) Make another table showing (i) the pressure of the piston on the air and (ii) the volume of the air in the pump.
b) Draw a graph showing the connection between the pressure on the air and its volume.
c) Make a note of any connection you can see between the pressure on the air and its volume. Explain why the volume of the air changes in the way that it does.
d) What happens to the volume of air when the pressure doubles? What happens when it trebles? Write a sentence describing a mathematical relation between the pressure and the volume.

2 If the pressure in car tyres is too high or too low, the car may not steer properly. Tyres could also wear more quickly than normal. A tyre pressure gauge can be used by motorists to test the pressure of the air inside their tyres.

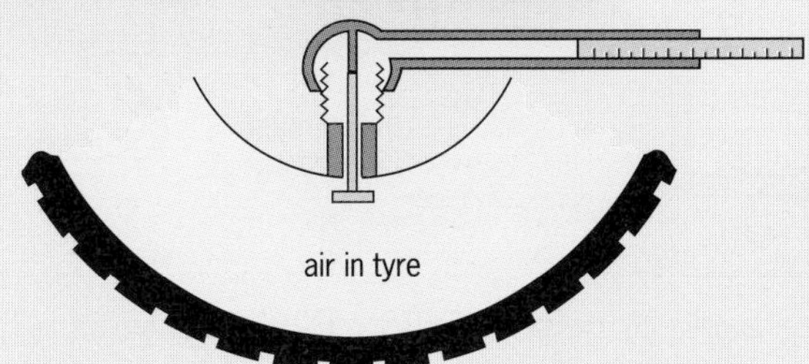

The valve in a tyre, and the inside of the pressure gauge

a) Discuss how you think the pressure gauge works. Why does it give a higher reading when more air is pumped into the tyre? Why does it give a lower reading if some air escapes?
b) What will happen to the pressure of the air inside the tyre after the car has been travelling for several miles?
c) Explain your answers to **a** and **b** in terms of the movement of the air molecules inside the tyre.

3.7 Transferring forces

There are times when we cannot apply forces at the point where they are needed. When you need to slow down a bicycle, for example, you pull on the brake levers on the handlebars. They each pull on a cable which in turn moves the brake block against the wheel. The force has been transferred from the handlebars to the wheels by the levers and cables.

In a car, a fluid, such as light oil, is used to transfer the force from the brake pedal to the brake shoes through a system of pipes. Systems such as this which transfer forces using fluids are called **hydraulic systems**.

GIANT

▶ Bicycle braking system

Hydraulic car brakes ▼

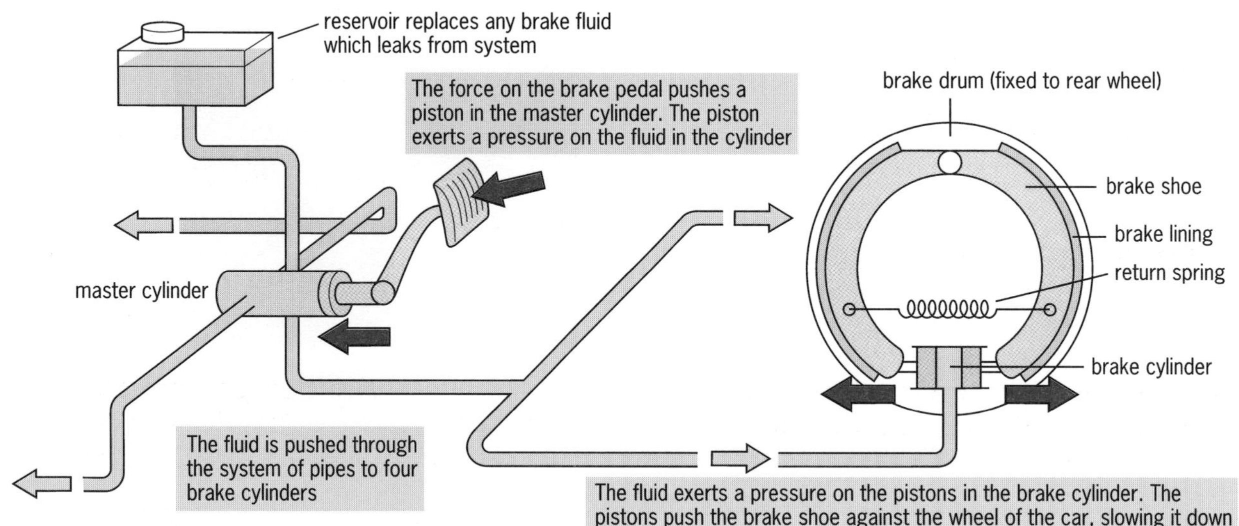
reservoir replaces any brake fluid which leaks from system
The force on the brake pedal pushes a piston in the master cylinder. The piston exerts a pressure on the fluid in the cylinder
brake drum (fixed to rear wheel)
brake shoe
brake lining
return spring
master cylinder
brake cylinder
The fluid is pushed through the system of pipes to four brake cylinders
The fluid exerts a pressure on the pistons in the brake cylinder. The pistons push the brake shoe against the wheel of the car, slowing it down

The basic principle of all hydraulic systems is that *the pressure is the same throughout the system.* Imagine, for example, a force of 400 N exerted on a master cylinder of cross-sectional area 2 cm^2; the cross-sectional area of the brake cylinder is 4 cm^2.

You can see from the calculation below that the force on the brakes is *twice* the force exerted by the brake pedal on the master cylinder. The system is a **force multiplier** – the hydraulic system increases the size of the applied force.

In the first (the 'master') cylinder

$$\text{The pressure on the fluid} = \frac{\text{force}}{\text{area}}$$

$$= \frac{400\,\text{N}}{2\,\text{cm}^2} = 200\,\text{N/cm}^2$$

In the brake (the 'slave') cylinder

The pressure which the fluid exerts on the piston in the brake cylinder is *exactly the same*, i.e. 200 N/cm^2. By re-arranging the equation (pressure = force/area) we can calculate the force which the fluid exerts on the piston.

$$\text{Force} = \text{pressure} \times \text{area}$$

$$= 200\,\text{N/cm}^2 \times 4\,\text{cm}^2 = 800\,\text{N}$$

The hydraulic jack

The large force needed to raise a car can be transferred by applying a much smaller force using a hydraulic jack. The idea is the same as for the brake system shown opposite – that the pressure throughout a fluid is the same at all points.

A hydraulic jack may be used to lift a car from the ground when a tyre needs changing.

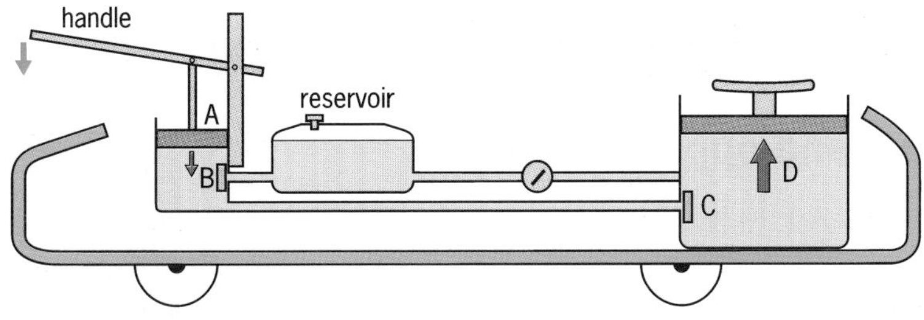

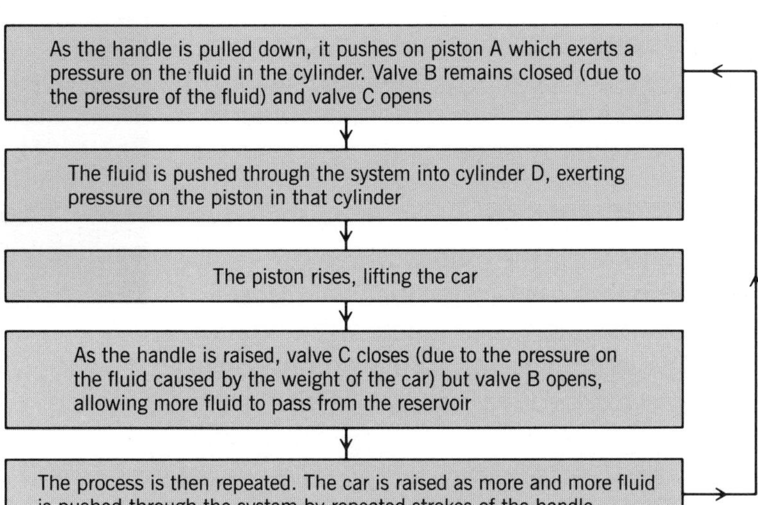

As the handle is pulled down, it pushes on piston A which exerts a pressure on the fluid in the cylinder. Valve B remains closed (due to the pressure of the fluid) and valve C opens
The fluid is pushed through the system into cylinder D, exerting pressure on the piston in that cylinder
The piston rises, lifting the car
As the handle is raised, valve C closes (due to the pressure on the fluid caused by the weight of the car) but valve B opens, allowing more fluid to pass from the reservoir
The process is then repeated. The car is raised as more and more fluid is pushed through the system by repeated strokes of the handle

How a hydraulic jack works

★ THINGS TO DO

1 Large hydraulic systems may be used to raise cars in garages.
a) Calculate the force that must be applied to the master cylinder to lift a car weighing 10 000 N using the hydraulic system shown below.
b) How many times bigger is the force on the slave cylinder compared with that on the master cylinder?

2 The handle of the lift system is a lever pivoted at the end. Plan and carry out a test to find out how the force applied to piston A depends on the distance from the pivot to the point where the piston is connected.

Write a full account of your investigation. Add a section as if to a manufacturer, suggesting how the position of the pivot affects how well the handle acts as a force multiplier.

3 Describe two ways in which the system could be re-designed to:
a) raise the same load using a smaller force,
b) raise the same load through the same height with a smaller movement of the handle.

4 Most hydraulic systems use oil to transfer the forces.
a) Why is oil a good fluid to use?
b) Why would air not work effectively in a system such as the one below?

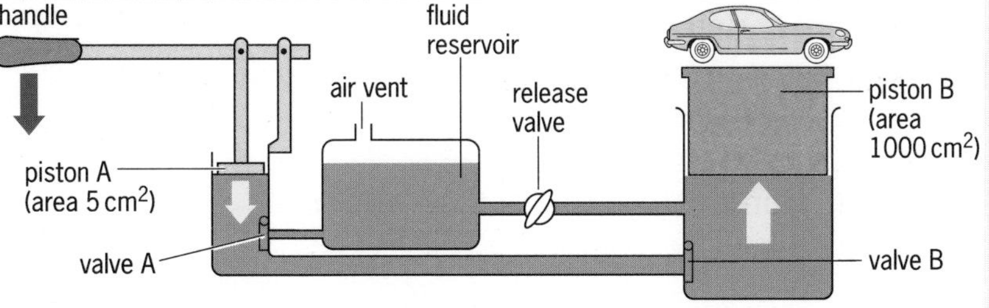

When the handle is pushed down, piston A moves down and transmits pressure to the fluid in the system; valve B opens and the fluid transmits pressure to piston B which rises

3.8

Forces and movement

Equal and opposite forces

The two teams in the photograph are pulling in opposite directions. If the forces are equal then the teams will not move. The two forces effectively 'cancel one another out' – they are 'balanced', or in **equilibrium**.

When balanced forces act on a stationary object it does not move. (We shall see later that balanced forces keep a *moving* object travelling at a steady speed.)

Unbalanced forces

If the force towards the right suddenly increases so that it is bigger than the force towards the left, then both teams will begin to move to the right. The forces are now 'unbalanced'. The 'extra' force exerted by the team on the right causes the movement.

Stationary objects begin to move when unbalanced forces act on them. They will begin to move in the direction of the 'extra' force.

Bungee jumping

As the jumper leaves the platform, her weight is the only force acting so she begins to fall towards the ground. The bungee cord runs loose behind her – **a**. As the cord tightens it exerts an upward force on the jumper. The more it stretches, the bigger the force. Soon the upward force will be bigger than the downward force of the jumper's weight. The forces on the bungee jumper – her weight and the force of the bungee cord – are then unbalanced – **b**. There is 'extra' force in an upward direction (against the motion of the jumper) so she slows down and eventually stops.

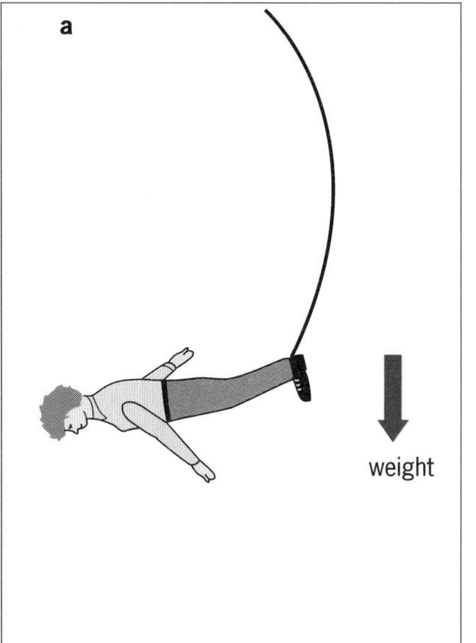

The bungee cord is slack so there is no upward force

b

force from bungee

weight

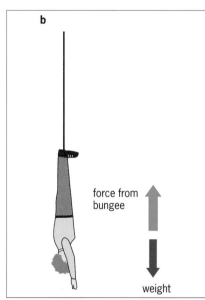

When the cord tightens the jumper continues to fall but slows down

If there are unbalanced forces acting on a moving object, and the 'extra' force is in the opposite direction to the movement, then the object will slow down and eventually stop.

A quick push

Imagine a sledge moving down a hill at a steady speed.

There are opposing forces acting – the weight of the sledge and the person on it acts down the slope, and friction (between the sledge and the snow) acts up the slope. If the two forces are balanced the sledge moves downhill at a steady speed.

If there are balanced forces acting on a moving object, it moves at a steady speed.

If, however, someone runs up behind the sledge and gives it a push, the same two forces still act on the sledge but now they are unbalanced – the downward force is bigger than the upward force (due to the 'extra' force provided by the pusher). The sledge will speed up, or 'accelerate', for as long as the extra force acts on it.

If there are unbalanced forces acting on a moving object, and the 'extra' force is in the same direction as the movement, then the object will speed up.

★ THINGS TO DO

1 The illustrations show the forces acting on different things.

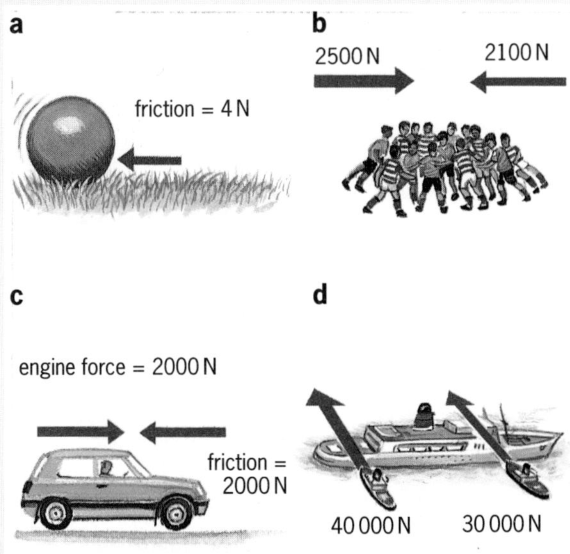

For each one describe the forces acting on the object (including their relative size and direction) and say how they will affect the motion of the object. Draw a diagram if it helps.

2 Use some elastic and weights to model a bungee cord and the 'jumper'. Find out how the amount by which a bungee cord stretches (before stopping the downward motion) depends on:

a) the height from which the person falls, and

b) the weight of the person.

Draw two graphs using the results of your investigation.

Use your results to describe any safety calculations which the organisers of a bungee jump should make, and say how graphs similar to your own would help.

3 Submarines can rise or sink lower in water. On the sides of a submarine are large tanks (ballast tanks). The tanks can be filled with water, or can contain some water and some air. Describe how you think the rise or fall of the submarine is controlled. Use ideas about forces in your answer.

3.9 Friction and movement

These wide tyres of soft rubber are ideal for gripping the ground – the force of friction will be large

Friction is a force which acts between solid surfaces as they move over one another, and when objects move through gases or liquids.

Without friction there would be no 'grip' between surfaces, which would mean feet and wheels would just slip over the ground.

What causes friction?

If a book on a table is given a short, sharp push it will move across the table. Eventually it will slow down and stop, so there must be a force acting against the movement (see topic 3.8). This force is friction, caused by the roughness of the two surfaces. Even surfaces which feel quite smooth are 'rough' when seen through a microscope.

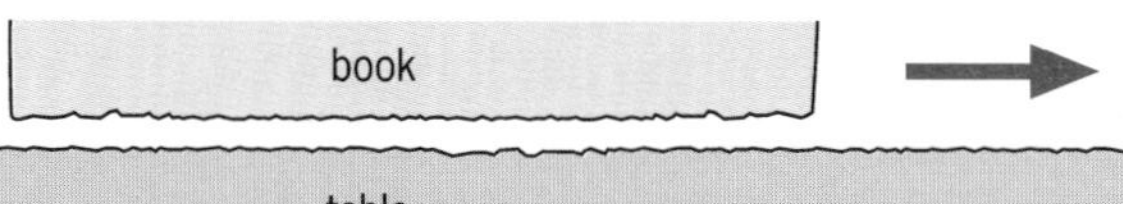

As the book moves across the table, the humps and hollows on one surface tend to 'grip' those on the other. This causes the force of friction which slows down the book

These soles are designed to grip the ground. The friction force will prevent the runner's feet from 'slipping away' under him

Reduced friction

Water, snow and ice all reduce the grip between the ground and our feet or our tyres.

When there is water or ice on a road, the humps and hollows of the rough road surface are levelled out. The reduced friction causes cars and other vehicles to skid, as the tyres are unable to grip the ground.

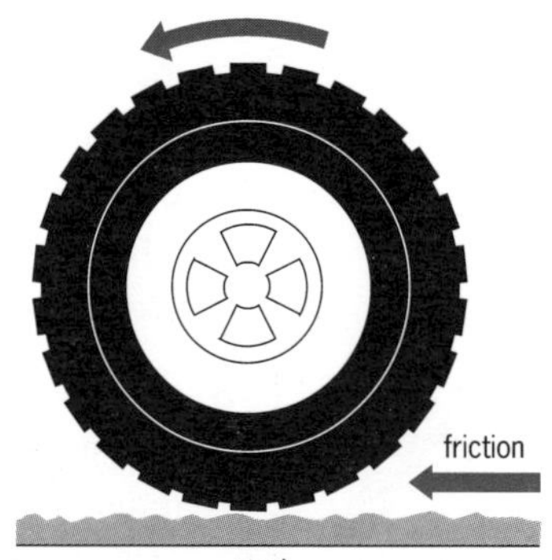

The tyre grips the road. The frictional force enables the car to move

On an icy road there is less friction. The wheel spins, so the car may not move, or may skid

Ice helps reduce friction so you slide easily – at times this can be fun!

Reduced friction also makes it more difficult to stop a car. The brakes stop the wheels moving, but if there is not enough grip between the tyres and the road the car will slide forward.

Frictional drag

Moving objects experience a frictional 'drag'. An increased force is needed to keep them moving. The drag can cause:

- surfaces to wear,
- a temperature rise at the surface,
- the moving object to slow down.

Friction between the sides of a ship and the water slows it down

Friction between the air and a space shuttle re-entering the Earth's atmosphere generates intense heat, particularly on the underside of the shuttle. Space shuttles are designed to be re-used so are covered with heat-resistant tiles to protect the craft and its crew

To understand why friction slows things down we need to think about the forces which are involved. Imagine, for example, what happens as you cycle along a flat road. There are two main forces at work, acting in opposite directions – the force which you exert, driving the bicycle forward, and friction. The friction is caused by the air molecules 'brushing' against you and the bicycle as you move along.

The friction creates a drag in the opposite direction to movement and so it tends to slow you down.

If you need to slow down more quickly, you could apply the brakes. The 'extra' friction between the brake blocks and the wheels means that the force opposing the movement is greater, so you slow down faster.

If there was no friction then once something was moving it could keep on moving forever. Space probes travel millions of miles through space without using engines because there is no friction to slow them down.

As you pull away, the forward force is greater than friction so you speed up – **a**. The faster you go, the greater is the force of friction – **b**.

Eventually the forward force and friction are balanced – **c**. You travel at a steady speed.

If you stop pedalling, then friction is the only force at work – **d**. This is in the opposite direction to the movement so you slow down and eventually stop

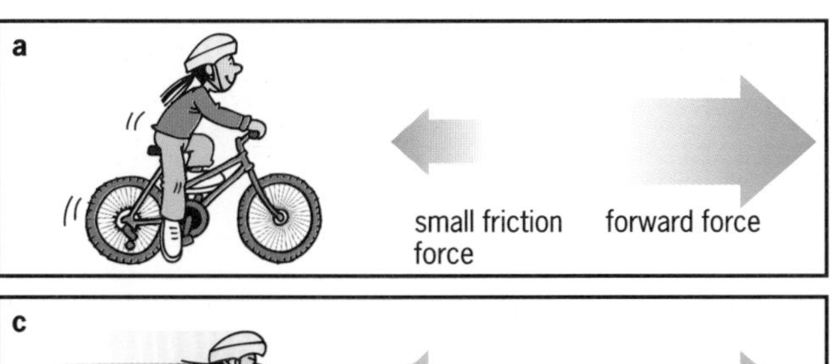

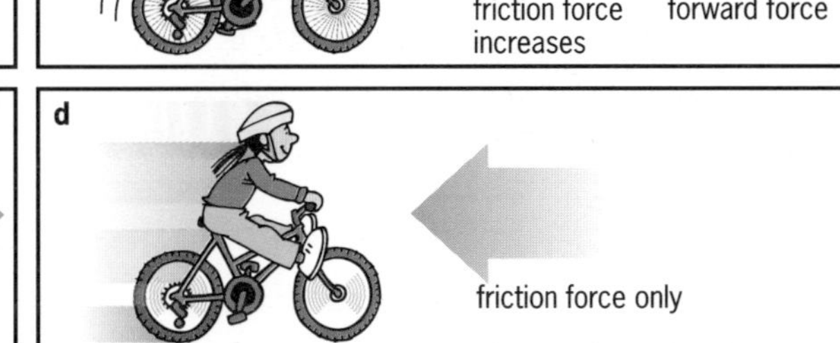

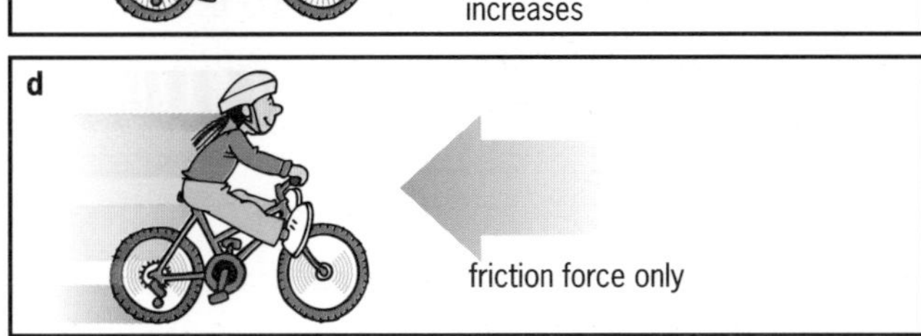

Streamlining

Some marine animals have a shape which is adapted to reducing frictional 'drag' between them and the water. This helps them move quickly through the water, improving their ability to catch prey or escape predators.

Car manufacturers have tried to copy this natural 'streamlining' in their design of cars, to reduce friction (or 'air resistance'). By doing so:

- the top speed can be increased, and
- less fuel is needed to maintain a particular speed.

The cars are therefore more efficient – they travel further for each litre of petrol used.

The 'streamlined' shape of this shark minimises friction

Terminal velocity

Friction has a big effect on the motion of 'sky-divers' as they fall through the air.

As a sky-diver leaves the aircraft, he initially speeds up, or accelerates, because there are unbalanced forces acting – his weight is greater than the frictional drag force – **a**.

As his speed increases, the frictional drag due to the air increases. 'Spread-eagling' himself increases his surface area, and further increases the frictional drag – **b**. The increased drag reduces the rate at which he accelerates.

The frictional drag force increases until it becomes just equal to the weight of the sky-diver. The forces are now balanced – **c**. From this point, the diver falls at a constant speed. This speed is called the **terminal velocity**.

When the parachute opens there is a sudden increase in the frictional force – **d**, due to the extra drag between the parachute and the air. This causes the sky-diver to slow down (because the frictional force is now greater than his weight). As he slows down the frictional force decreases until it is again equal and opposite to his weight. He then continues to fall to the ground at a constant (and safe) speed.

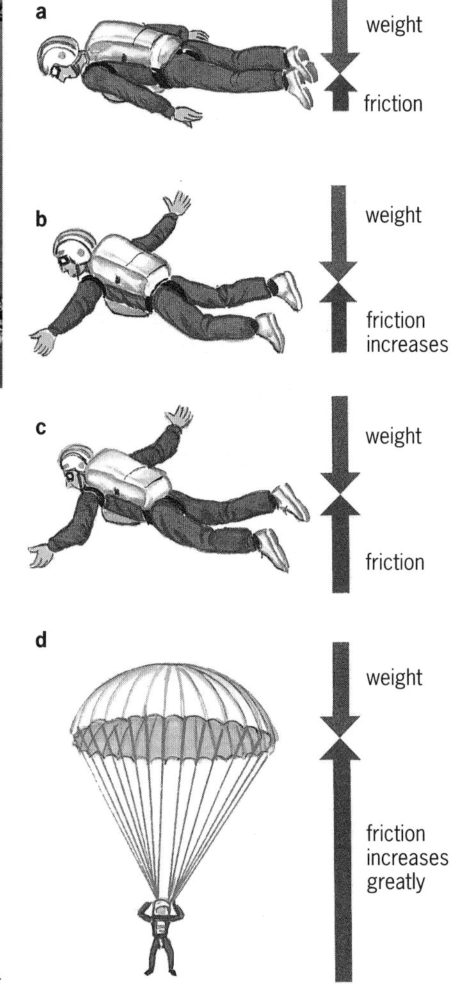

★ THINGS TO DO

1 Write a sentence or two describing how frictional forces are at work in these photographs.

2 Make a list of situations you have seen or discussed where:

a) friction acts to slow things down (such as the grip between the brakes and wheels of a bicycle),

b) low friction forces allow things to happen (such as sliding on ice),

c) friction forces cause wear and tear on materials (such as wear on carpets),

d) steps are taken to reduce friction forces (such as oiling the axles on a bicycle),

e) friction forces make things heat up (such as when you rub your hands together).

3 The chart below shows the stopping distances for a car travelling at different speeds.

a) What do you think the stopping distance will be for a car travelling at 70 km/h?

b) What is the connection between stopping distance and speed?

c) Draw what you think the chart would look like for icy roads. Explain any similarities and differences between your chart and the one shown here.

d) What other factors could affect the stopping distance of a vehicle?

4 Sandpaper can be bought in several different grades – 20, 40, 60, 80 and 100. Compare the surfaces of these grades of sandpaper. Do you think there is any connection between the frictional force exerted by the sandpaper and the grade number? Make a note of your predictions, including your reasons.

Plan an investigation to test your idea, including any safety precautions you should take.

When your teacher has approved your plan, carry out the investigation and prepare a detailed report of your findings.

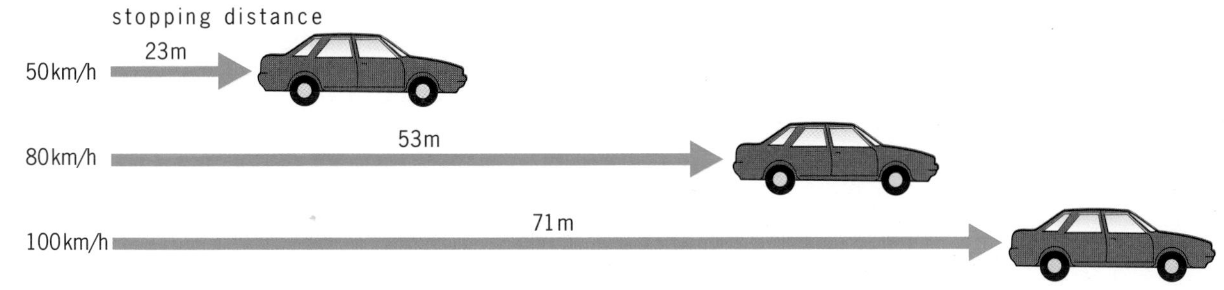

3.10 Speed

The three-toed sloth is the slowest animal on Earth. It travels about 2 metres each minute. A tortoise is faster – it travels about 4.5 metres each minute

A world-class sprinter is much faster, travelling at about 600 metres each minute during a race

Even a sprinter is slow compared with the fastest car in the world. It covered a distance of about 15 000 metres each minute during its record-breaking run

To describe the movement of something accurately we need to know about its **speed**. Speed is the rate at which an object covers distance. If, for example, a car is travelling at a steady speed of 50 kilometres per hour (50 km/h), then it will cover a distance of 50 kilometres in a time of one hour. Notice that *distance* and *time* are linked by the word *speed*.

Light is the fastest thing known. It travels at about 18 000 million million metres each minute!

Distance, time and speed

Consider a cyclist and a jogger moving along a road at different speeds. The bicycle in the illustration below is travelling at twice the speed of the jogger, so it travels twice as far in the same time. Another way of looking at this is to say that the jogger takes twice the time to cover the same distance as the bicycle.

Speed, distance and time are connected by the equation:

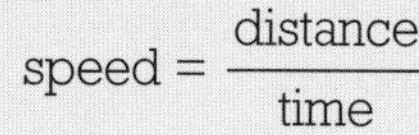

$$\text{speed} = \frac{\text{distance}}{\text{time}}$$

There are many units which can be used for speed, depending on the units in which the distance and the time are measured.

One second after starting the jogger is 2 metres along the road. The bicycle is 4 metres along. It has travelled 2 metres further than the jogger

After 2 seconds the jogger has travelled 4 metres. The bicycle has travelled 8 metres. It has travelled 4 metres further than the jogger

After 3 seconds the jogger has travelled 6 metres. The bicycle is now 12 metres from the start – it has travelled 6 metres further than the jogger

Average speed

Most moving objects do not travel at the same steady speed for any length of time – their speed changes throughout any journey. A car, for example, slows down as it approaches traffic lights and roundabouts, and speeds up as it leaves them. Whilst we could describe its speed at any instant during the journey, it is far more convenient to think in terms of the *average* speed over the whole journey:

$$\text{average speed} = \frac{\text{total distance covered}}{\text{total time taken}}$$

It follows that the actual speed at some times will be higher than the average; at other times it will be lower than the average.

Velocity

When something is moving it moves in a particular direction. Speed describes only how quickly it moves. A more accurate way of describing the movement is to include speed and direction. The **velocity** of a moving body is the speed at which it is moving in a particular direction.

Imagine, for example, two trains travelling towards one another, both at 60 km/h. The speed of each train is the same but their velocities are different because they are moving in different directions.

★ THINGS TO DO

1 Wind up a clockwork toy and let it move across the floor. Calculate its average speed.

2 Copy and complete this table.

Speed/m/s	**Distance**/m	**Time**/s
30	15	
50		5
	20	4
15		3

3 At the end of a 100-metre race, three runners finished in the positions shown. The lines across the track are one metre apart.

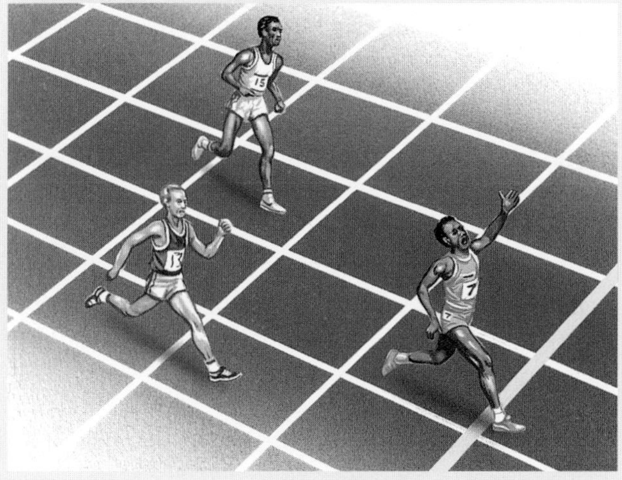

a) Which runner must have had the highest average speed? Explain your answer.
b) Someone said that the second runner had reached the highest speed. Could this have been right? Explain your answer.
c) The illustration shows the first runner crossing the final 100-metre line. The time was 10.00 seconds. What was the winner's average speed?
d) What was the average speed of the third-placed runner?

4 This chart shows the speed of cars measured along a 100-metre section of road outside a school.

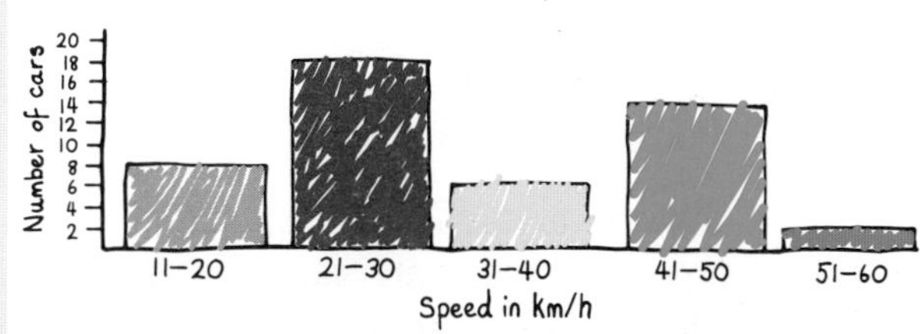

a) Describe how you think the pupils measured the speed of the cars.
b) How many cars were travelling at speeds of between 41 and 50 km/h?
c) The speed limit on the road is 50 km/h. How many cars were breaking the speed limit?

3.11 Distance–time graphs

A graph is a useful way to show the motion of any moving object.

Imagine, for example, a squirrel moving at a steady speed from the base of a tree towards some nuts. It then stays in the same position for a while, eating the nuts, before returning to the tree at the same speed. A graph can be plotted with distance on the vertical axis and time on the horizontal axis.

The graph is a *distance–time graph* showing how the squirrel moved on its journey.

Calculating speed from the graph

The speed of the squirrel can be calculated from the distance–time graph. Consider the first section of the graph.

The squirrel starts at point A. 3 seconds later it has travelled 6 metres from its starting point. It has therefore travelled a distance of 6 metres in 3 seconds. Using the equation:

$$\text{speed} = \frac{\text{distance}}{\text{time}}$$

$$\text{speed of squirrel} = \frac{6\,\text{m}}{3\,\text{s}}$$

$$= 2\,\text{m/s}$$

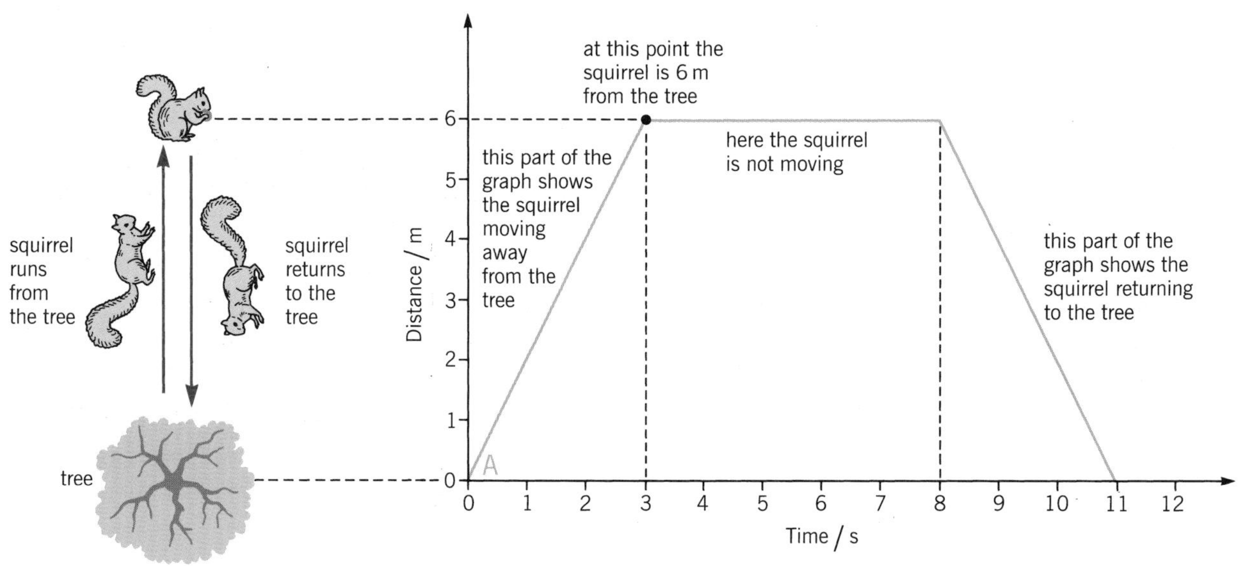

squirrel runs from the tree
squirrel returns to the tree
tree
Distance / m
Time / s
at this point the squirrel is 6 m from the tree
this part of the graph shows the squirrel moving away from the tree
here the squirrel is not moving
this part of the graph shows the squirrel returning to the tree
A
0
1
2
3
4
5
6
7
8
9
10
11
12

★ THINGS TO DO

1 Use a clockwork toy again. Draw a sketch graph (one without units) showing what you think the distance–time graph for the toy would look like. Add a sentence or two saying why you think the graph will look like that.

a) Now plan how you could test your prediction. Carry out your experiment and draw a distance–time graph using your 'proper' results.

b) Add a note describing how the graph from your experiment compares with your original sketch graph.

c) Calculate the maximum speed of the clockwork toy from your graph.

2 These distance–time graphs show the movement of each of the things listed below:

- a maggot crawling along the ground,
- a car moving along a road,
- a yo-yo moving up and down,
- dad sitting in the chair.

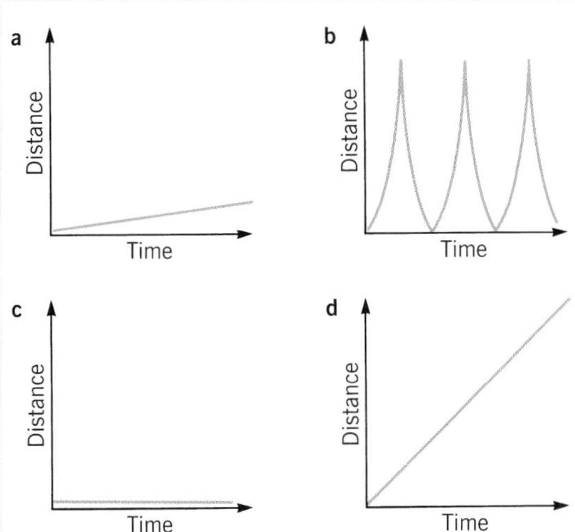

Match the graphs to the moving objects and add a reason for each choice.

3 The distance–time graphs below show the movement of **a** a cross-channel ferry and **b** an aeroplane for a 60-minute period during their journeys.

Calculate the speed of the ferry and the aeroplane from the graphs.

4 A train (A) leaves King's Cross station at 11.00 a.m. and travels at an average speed of 90 km/h. At 12.00 a second train (B) leaves, and travels at an average speed of 120 km/h on the same line.

Time	Train A	Train B
	Distance travelled from station/km	**Distance travelled from station/km**
11.00	0	—
12.00		0
1.00		
2.00		
3.00		
4.00		
5.00		

a) Copy and complete the table above showing the distance travelled by each train at times during the journey.

b) Plot your results for train A on a graph which has distance on the vertical axis and time on the horizontal axis.

c) Plot your results for train B on the same axes.

d) At what time will train B catch up with train A?

e) How far from King's Cross will they meet?

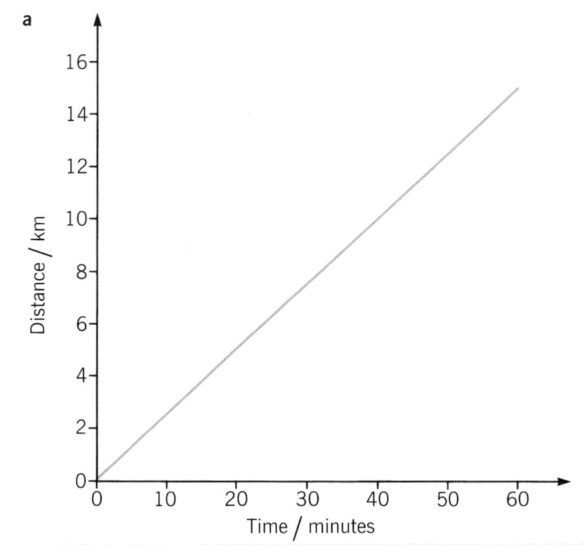

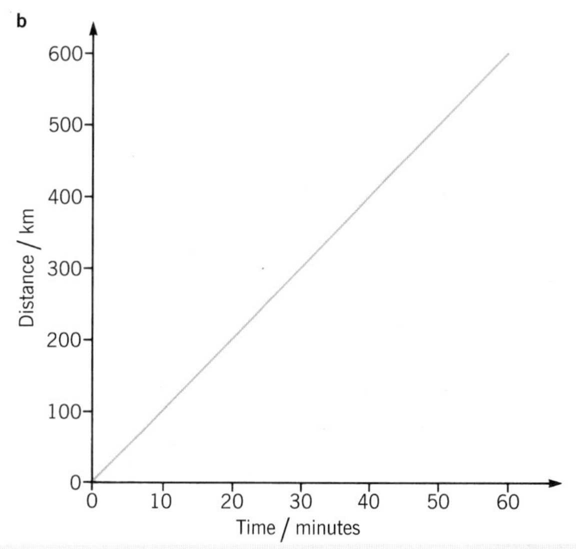

3.12 Acceleration

Starting from rest these dragsters can reach speeds of up to 400 km/h in just a few seconds

During a normal journey cars speed up and slow down as road conditions change

When the velocity of a moving object changes we say it is 'accelerating'. **Acceleration** is the rate at which the velocity of something changes. For objects moving in a straight line, it is the rate at which the speed changes. (In other circumstances the acceleration may be due to a change in direction.)

Consider the motion of a bus as it moves away from a bus stop.

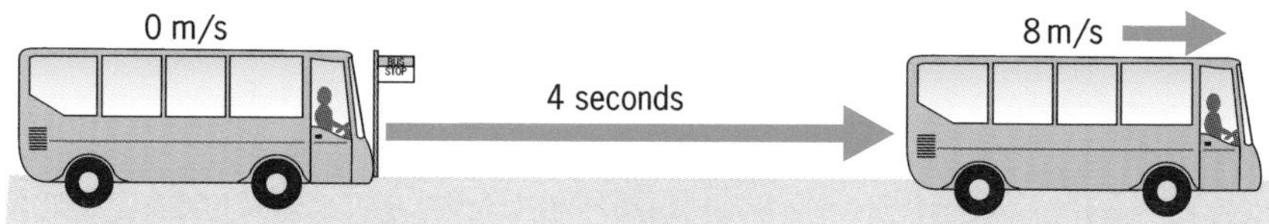

As the bus pulls away from rest, it accelerates

As the bus accelerates its speed increases from 0 to 8 m/s. It takes 4 seconds for this change to occur. Assuming its speed changes by the same amount each second, then it must change by 2 m/s every second. We say its acceleration is 2 m/s/s. Another way of writing this is 2 m/s^2.

If you consider the speed of the bus each second you can see what this means more clearly. You can see that the distance travelled by the bus during each one-second interval increases. It travels further (in the same time interval) because its average speed is greater.

How the speed of the bus changes each second

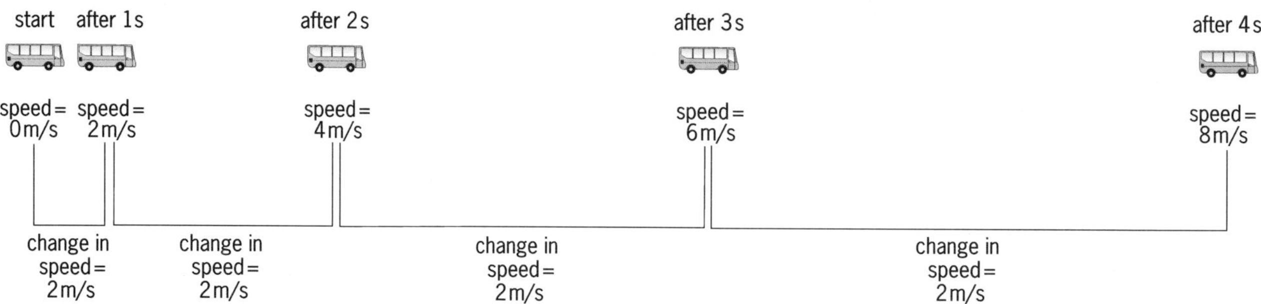

Calculating acceleration

The acceleration of a moving object can be calculated using the equation:

$$\text{acceleration (m/s/s)} = \frac{\text{change in velocity which takes place (m/s)}}{\text{time taken for the change in velocity (s)}}$$

Imagine, for example, a car starting from rest and reaching a speed of 40 m/s after 8 seconds.

Change in velocity = 40 m/s (from 0 m/s to 40 m/s)
Time taken for this to happen = 8 s

$$\text{So acceleration} = \frac{\text{change in velocity}}{\text{time taken}} = \frac{40\text{ m/s}}{8\text{ s}}$$

$$= 5\text{ m/s/s (or 5 m/s}^2)$$

Slowing down

When things slow down their speed decreases. This is still acceleration (although you might also see the word 'deceleration' used). Imagine a curling stone slowing down as it moves in a straight line over the ice.

Here the speed is decreasing by 1 m/s each second. To show that the speed is decreasing the acceleration is given a negative value. The acceleration is therefore written as –1 m/s/s or –1 m/s^2.

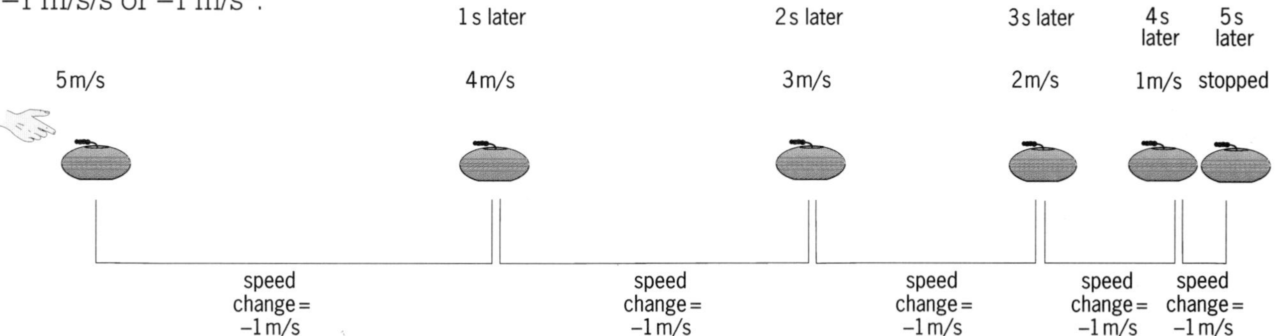

How the speed of the curling stone changes each second

★ THINGS TO DO

1 Calculate the acceleration of the following. In each case show your working clearly.
a) A bus which starts from a bus stop and which, 5 seconds later, is travelling at 30 m/s.
b) A Formula One car which speeds up from 35 m/s to 87 m/s in 4 seconds.
c) A car travelling at 15 m/s which stops in 3 seconds.
d) A parachutist who slows down from 30 m/s to 10 m/s in 5 seconds as the parachute opens.

2 Things which fall freely through the air all have the same acceleration of 10 m/s^2. This is the acceleration due to gravity. The National Westminster Tower in London is 183 m high. Someone calculated that if they dropped a coin from the top it would take 6 seconds to reach the ground.
a) What would be the speed of the coin when it reached the ground?
b) Why would the coin actually take longer than the calculated value?

3 The figures here show the times for different cars to reach 90 km/h from rest on a test track.

Car A	9.2s
Car B	7.1s
Car C	5.4s
Car D	12s
Car E	4s

a) Which car has the greatest acceleration? Explain how you arrive at your answer.
b) If they all started in line, and accelerated for 30 seconds, how would they appear after 15 seconds? Draw a sketch.

3.13 Speed–time graphs

To provide a check that drivers of heavy vehicles are meeting the law, a 'tachometer' inside the vehicle produces a paper chart – a 'tachograph' – showing the speed of the vehicle throughout its journey. The tachograph is an example of a *speed–time graph* – a chart showing how the speed changed with time.

The actual speed of the vehicle at any time can be found from this tachograph

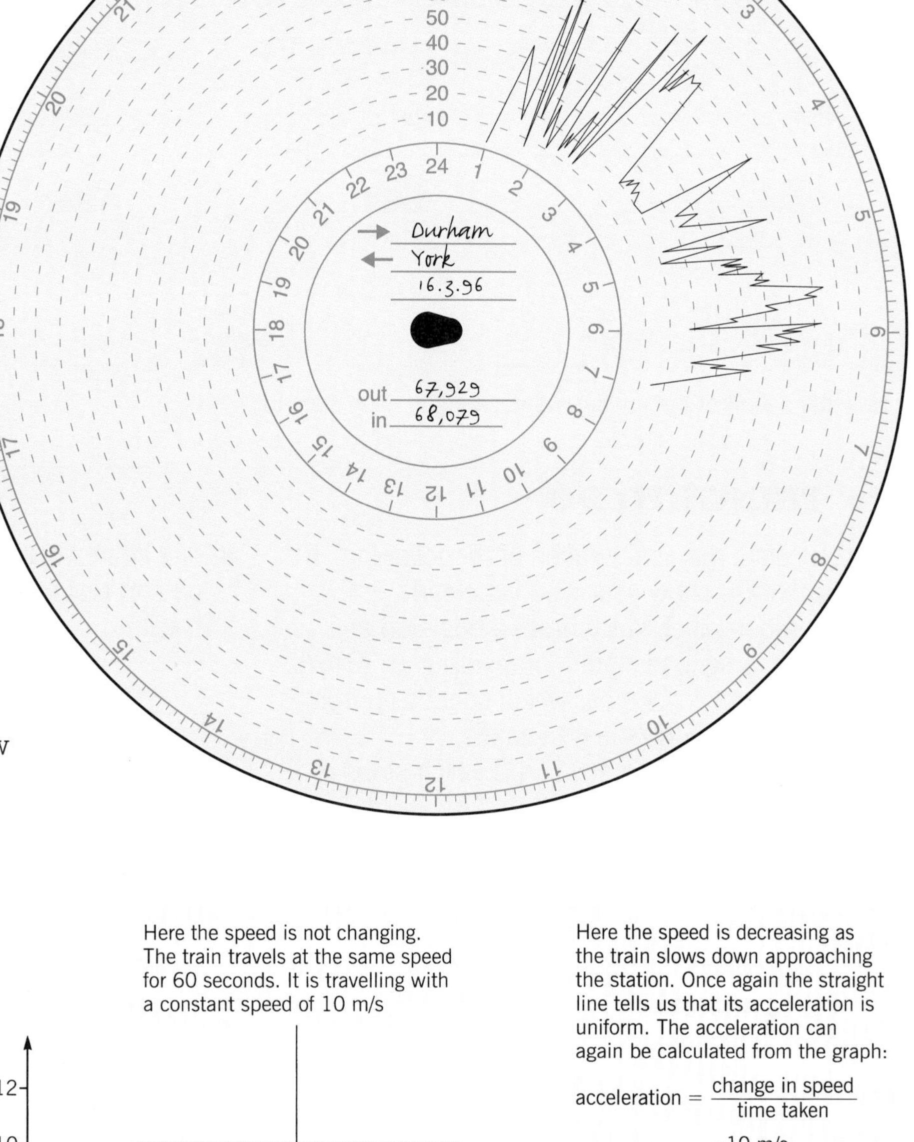

In any 24-hour period a driver must:

- not exceed a speed of 96 km/h
- have a rest period of 11 consecutive hours
- have a break of 45 minutes after 4.5 hours of driving without a break
- not drive for longer than 9 hours

Drivers of all heavy vehicles must obey laws which govern the time for which they can drive, and their maximum speed

The speed–time graph below shows how the speed of an underground train changed between stations.

You can see that the speed over this section increases. The straight line tells us that the speed increases by equal amounts in equal intervals of time. This is *uniform acceleration.* The acceleration can be calculated using the equation:

$$\text{acceleration} = \frac{\text{change in speed}}{\text{time taken}}$$

$$= \frac{10 \text{ m/s}}{20 \text{ s}}$$

$$= 0.5 \text{ m/s/s}$$

(or 0.5 m/s^2)

Here the speed is not changing. The train travels at the same speed for 60 seconds. It is travelling with a constant speed of 10 m/s

Here the speed is decreasing as the train slows down approaching the station. Once again the straight line tells us that its acceleration is uniform. The acceleration can again be calculated from the graph:

$$\text{acceleration} = \frac{\text{change in speed}}{\text{time taken}}$$

$$= \frac{-10 \text{ m/s}}{40 \text{ s}}$$

$$= -0.25 \text{ m/s/s}$$

(or -0.25 m/s^2)

Note the minus sign, showing that the speed is decreasing

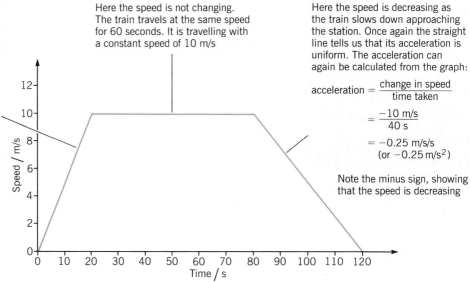

Speed / m/s: 0, 2, 4, 6, 8, 10, 12

Time / s: 0, 10, 20, 30, 40, 50, 60, 70, 80, 90, 100, 110, 120

The chart and graph opposite represent changes in the speed of the lorry and the train over a period of time. Any change in speed means that the velocity must be changing (although the direction *may not* change). Graphs such as this are described, more generally, as *velocity-time graphs.*

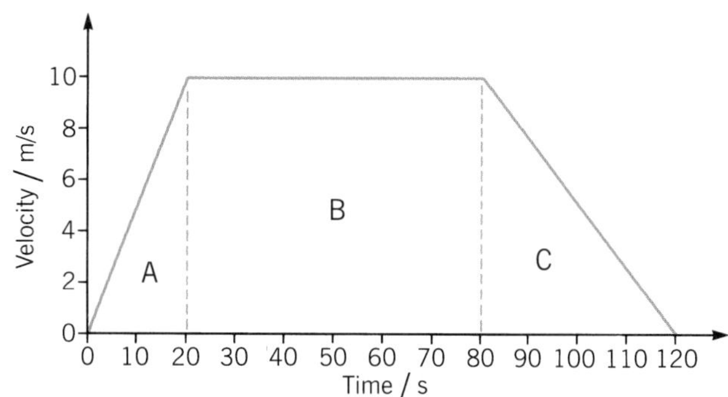

Distance from velocity–time graphs

The area under a velocity–time graph is equal to the distance travelled during a journey. Calculating this area often involves calculating the area of several rectangles and triangles.

Area of a rectangle = length × height
Area of a triangle = ½ × length × height

The velocity–time graph shown here is a smaller version of the graph shown opposite. To find the distance travelled during the journey we have to calculate the area under the whole graph.

The total area under the graph is:

(area of section A) + (area of section B) + (area of section C)
= 100 + 600 + 200
= 900

The distance travelled during the journey is therefore 900 m.

Area of section A = ½ × length × height
= ½ × 20 × 10
= 100

Area of section B = length × width
= 60 × 10
= 600

Area of section C = ½ × length × height
= ½ × 40 × 10
= 200

★ THINGS TO DO

1 This graph shows the speed of an athlete during a race.

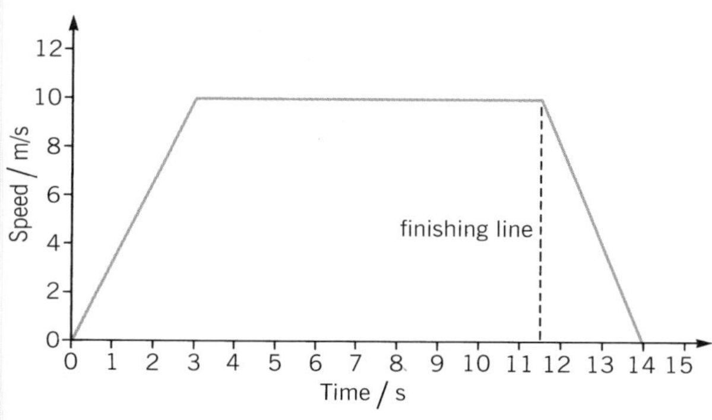

a) What is the acceleration of the athlete over the first 2 seconds?
b) How long after starting does the athlete begin to slow down?
c) Calculate the acceleration of the athlete after crossing the finishing line.
d) What was the race distance?
e) What was the average speed of the athlete during the race?

2 A dragster car accelerates uniformly from rest and reaches a speed of 85 m/s in 10 seconds. It then travels at this speed for 5 seconds. A parachute then opens, slowing the car (uniformly) to a stop in 30 seconds.
a) Draw a velocity–time graph for the dragster. From your graph:
b) Calculate the acceleration of the car in the first 5 seconds.
c) Calculate the acceleration as it slowed down.
d) Calculate the distance travelled during the journey.

3.14 Forces and acceleration

On a level road, if you stop pedalling you will slow down and eventually stop. The only force is friction, acting against your movement. Friction is fairly small, so the 'slowing down force' is quite small

Experience tells you that the harder you pull on the brakes of a bicycle, the faster you stop. The reason behind this is that there is increased friction between the brake blocks and the wheels, creating a bigger unbalanced force in the opposite direction to the movement.

The opposite effect is also very apparent. When a golf club hits the ball, the ball accelerates. The harder the ball is hit, the bigger the force and the greater the acceleration.

In general, the acceleration depends on:

- the size of the force – the bigger the force, the greater the acceleration (assuming the mass is constant), *and*
- the mass of the object – the greater the mass, the smaller the acceleration (assuming the same force is applied).

Calculating the effects of force on acceleration

The connection between force and acceleration is given by the equation:

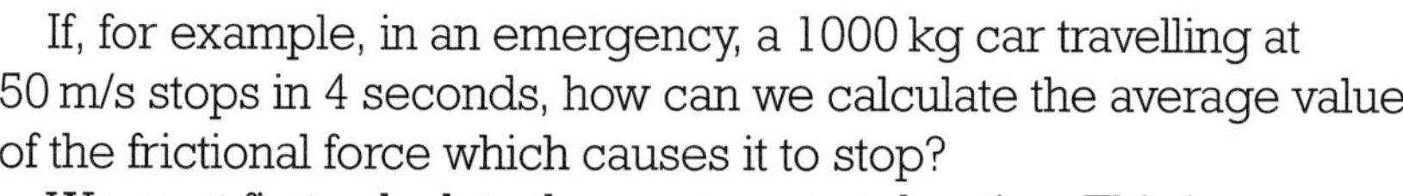

$$\text{force (N)} = \text{mass (kg)} \times \text{acceleration (m/s}^2\text{)}$$

When you pull on the brakes an 'extra' frictional force is applied as the brake blocks rub against the wheels. The force against your movement increases, and you slow down faster – your deceleration is greater

If, for example, in an emergency, a 1000 kg car travelling at 50 m/s stops in 4 seconds, how can we calculate the average value of the frictional force which causes it to stop?

We must first calculate the average acceleration. This is calculated using the equation (see page 128):

$$\text{acceleration} = \frac{\text{change in velocity}}{\text{time taken}}$$

Because the velocity decreases by 50 m/s, the change in velocity is written as –50 m/s in the calculation:

$$\text{acceleration} = \frac{-50\text{ m/s}}{4\text{s}}$$

$$= -12.5\text{ m/s}^2$$

We can now calculate the average force needed:

$$\text{average force} = \text{mass} \times \text{acceleration}$$

$$= 1000\text{ kg} \times -12.5\text{ m/s}^2$$

$$= -12\,500\text{ N}$$

The minus sign indicates that the force acts in the opposite direction to the movement. The minus sign can be omitted when stating the 'value' of the force.

The average value of the frictional force which slows down the car from 50 m/s to a stop in 4 seconds is therefore 12 500 N.

The acceleration due to gravity

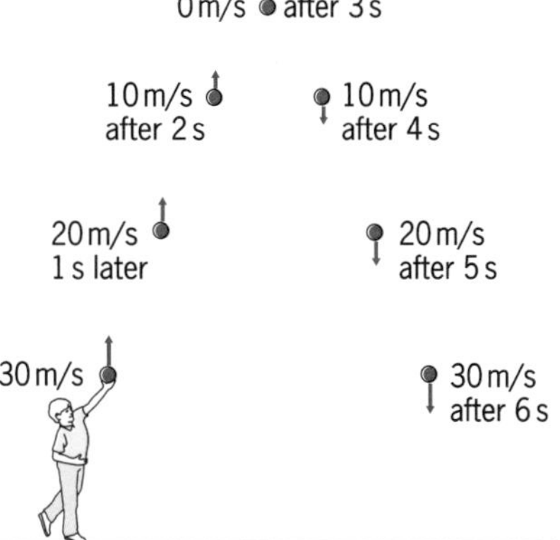

On Earth, all objects moving vertically upwards experience an acceleration of $-10\ \mathrm{m/s^2}$ (note the minus sign indicating that they are slowing down). When objects fall vertically, they experience an acceleration of $+10\ \mathrm{m/s^2}$. The value $10\ \mathrm{m/s^2}$ is the value of the **acceleration due to gravity**.

If something is thrown upwards it slows down because the force of gravity (the weight) acts against its motion. Eventually it will stop, and then begin to fall. As it falls it will accelerate because the force of gravity acts in the same direction as the movement. The illustration alongside shows how the velocity changes as an object rises and falls.

Everything falls at the same rate

Perhaps surprisingly, the value of the acceleration due to gravity does not depend on the weight of the object. Imagine, for example, a 10 N (1 kg) stone and a 1000 N (100 kg) stone being released above the ground.

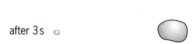

The acceleration of anything $= \dfrac{\text{force}}{\text{mass}}$ (from force = mass × acceleration)

The force on each stone is its weight,

so the acceleration of the smaller stone $= \dfrac{10\ \mathrm{N}}{1\ \mathrm{kg}} = 10\ \mathrm{m/s^2}$

and the acceleration of the larger stone $= \dfrac{1000\ \mathrm{N}}{100\ \mathrm{kg}} = 10\ \mathrm{m/s^2}$

Both stones will therefore have the same acceleration of $10\ \mathrm{m/s^2}$ – the acceleration due to gravity.

★ THINGS TO DO

1 Calculate the force exerted in each of the following situations:
a) A 50 g dart striking a dart board and slowing from 5 m/s to a stop in 0.1 s.
b) A 100 000 kg rocket accelerating from rest and reaching a speed of 300 m/s after 30 seconds.
c) A 1500 kg car slowing from 30 m/s to a stop in 4 seconds.

2 A 60 kg cyclist travelling at 4 m/s stops pedalling and slows to a stop in 10 seconds on a level road. Calculate the frictional force on the bicycle and cyclist.

3 Some modern cars have 'crumple zones' built into their design. In an accident these areas crumple rather than remaining rigid. Other cars have 'impact-absorbing bumpers' which are designed to do a similar job.

Explain how crumple zones and impact-absorbing bumpers affect what happens to the car and its occupants during an accident.

3.15 Kinetic energy

When things are given a push they begin to move – they accelerate. Energy is transferred to them – energy associated with movement. This is called **kinetic energy**.

As the people push on the car it begins to move. Chemical energy released in the muscles of the people pushing the car is transferred to the car as kinetic energy – its kinetic energy increases as it accelerates

The car is now moving at a steady speed so there is no change in its kinetic energy. Yet the people are still transferring energy to it. Under these conditions the two forces acting on the car – friction and the push provided by the people – must be balanced

When the people stop pushing, the only force acting on the car is friction so it slows down. Its kinetic energy decreases as energy is transferred to the air, the ground and the moving parts. When the car stops it will have no kinetic energy

Kinetic energy and work

To get the car moving and to keep it moving, work must be done on it by the people pushing. As the car begins to move its velocity increases and hence its kinetic energy increases. The work done on the car is transformed into kinetic energy and heat energy (as friction is overcome). When the car is moving at a steady speed there is no gain in kinetic energy. The work done by the people pushing the car is used entirely to overcome friction.

Calculating kinetic energy

The kinetic energy of a moving object depends on:

- the mass of the object – larger objects have more kinetic energy than smaller objects moving at the same velocity,
- the velocity of the object – faster-moving objects have more kinetic energy than slower objects with the same mass.

The bus has more kinetic energy because it has a larger mass

The kinetic energy, mass and velocity of an object are related by:

$$\text{kinetic energy (J)} = \tfrac{1}{2} \times \text{mass (kg)} \times [\text{velocity (m/s)}]^2 = \tfrac{1}{2} mv^2$$

Imagine, for example, a hockey ball moving across a field at a steady speed of 20 m/s. If the mass of the ball is 400 g (0.4 kg), then

$$\begin{aligned}\text{kinetic energy of the ball} &= \tfrac{1}{2} mv^2 \\ &= \tfrac{1}{2} \times 0.4\,\text{kg} \times (20\,\text{m/s})^2 \\ &= 80\,\text{J}\end{aligned}$$

Energy transfers

Any change in the speed of a moving object must be accompanied by a change in its kinetic energy. As we saw in the *ENERGY* section, energy cannot just appear or disappear – it must always be transferred to or from something else, or into a different form.

On a roller-coaster there is a regular interchange of energy from kinetic to gravitational potential energy (see page 18) and back to kinetic. The changes in motion depend on the size and direction of the forces acting on the roller-coaster car during its journey.

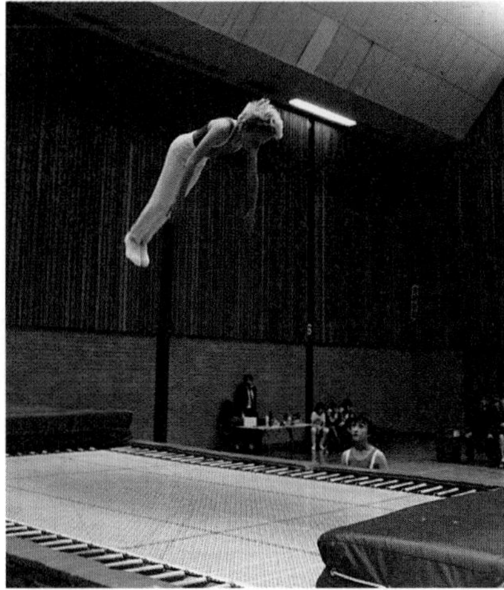

When the gymnast lands on the trampoline the springs will stretch, slowing him down. The kinetic energy of the gymnast will be transferred to the springs as elastic potential energy

Work is done on the cars (by an electric motor) which draws them to the top of the slope. Energy is transferred to the cars (and the passengers) as gravitational potential energy:

electrical energy ⟶ gravitational potential energy

As a car moves down the slope its gravitational potential energy decreases (because it is losing height). Its kinetic energy increases (because it is gaining speed). Neglecting friction, we can say that the gravitational potential energy lost by the car is equal to the kinetic energy gained by the car:

gravitational potential energy ⟶ kinetic energy

As the car rises, it gains gravitational potential energy. Because it is slowing down it loses kinetic energy. The kinetic energy lost is equal to the gravitational potential energy gained (again assuming we ignore energy 'lost' due to friction):

kinetic energy ⟶ gravitational potential energy

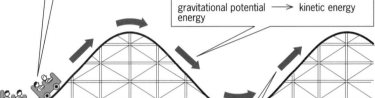

Energy transfers on a roller-coaster ride

★ THINGS TO DO

1 Calculate the kinetic energy of:
a) a 20 000 kg aeroplane moving at a speed of 150 m/s,
b) a 0.01 kg snake moving across the ground at a speed of 0.5 m/s,
c) a 50 kg cheetah moving at 8 m/s.

2 Copy and complete this table.

Mass /kg	Velocity /m/s	Kinetic energy /J
20		9000
	10	140 000

3 Set up a piece of wood so that it forms a slope down which you can roll a toy car or a trolley. Draw three sketch graphs predicting how you think the speed at the bottom of the slope depends on the angle of the slope. Add a brief explanation supporting your sketches.

Plan and carry out an investigation to test your predictions.

4 A 'pile driver' is used to drive steel beams into the ground. This pile driver has a mass of 100 kg and is raised through 8 m by the engine. It is then released and falls, striking the beam below.

a) Calculate the potential energy which is gained as the pile is raised (see page 18). Take $g = 10$ N/kg.
b) Calculate its kinetic energy as it hits the beam after falling (assuming no energy is 'lost').
c) Calculate the speed at which it strikes the beam.

3.16 Projectiles

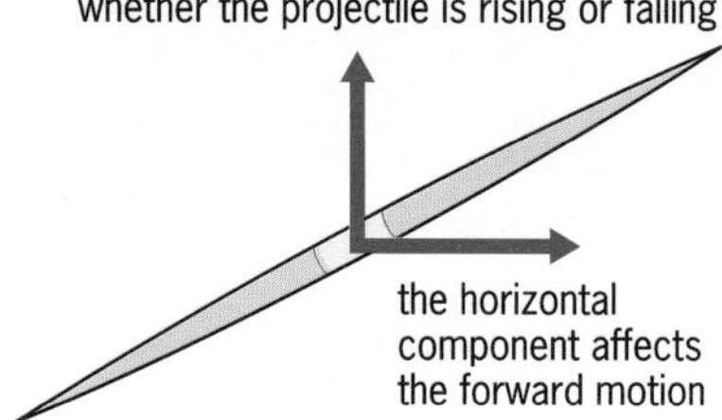

the vertical component affects the motion in the vertical plane, whether the projectile is rising or falling
the horizontal component affects the forward motion

Projectile motion

A javelin is a **projectile**, launched by the thrower's arm. Other projectiles include a bullet, a rocket, a badminton shuttle, a tennis ball and a football. Anything that is launched upwards and in a forward direction is a projectile.

The motion of a projectile can be considered to consist of two parts which are quite independent of each other. One part is the vertical motion – whether, and how, it is travelling up or down. The second part is the horizontal motion – how it travels in relation to the ground. These two parts are called the 'vertical component' and the 'horizontal component'.

Forces on a projectile

Once the javelin leaves the thrower's hand there are no horizontal forces acting on it (if we assume that friction is negligible over these short distances and with such an aerodynamic projectile). Its velocity across the ground (the horizontal component) will therefore be constant from the time it leaves the thrower's hand to the time it strikes the ground.

Science plays a big part in helping javelin throwers to achieve longer distances. The javelin itself must be as aerodynamic as possible, so that the effects of friction are minimal, and the javelin must be thrown in just the right way so that it travels as far as possible

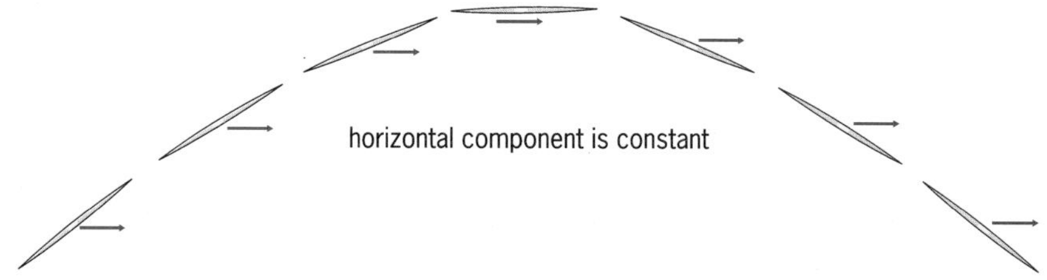

horizontal component is constant

The horizontal component of the javelin's velocity remains constant

Gravity, however, affects the vertical component of the javelin's velocity. Gravity slows down the vertical motion when the javelin is rising – the vertical component of the velocity decreases. At the highest point of the motion the vertical component is zero – the javelin is neither moving up nor down. The weight of the javelin then causes it to accelerate towards the Earth, and the vertical component of the velocity increases.

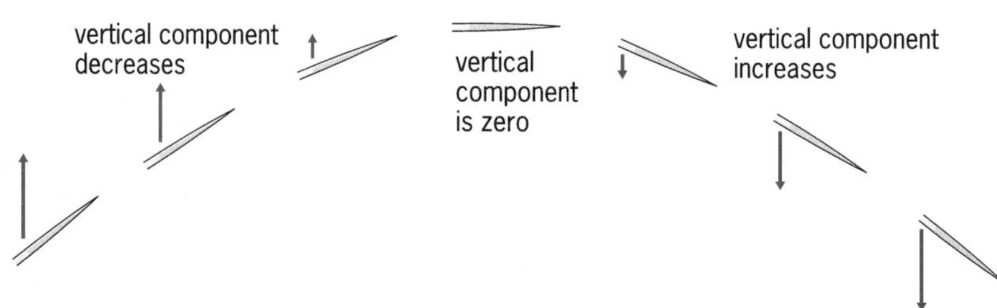

vertical component decreases
vertical component is zero
vertical component increases

The vertical component of the javelin's velocity decreases to zero as it rises and then increases as it falls

It follows that to get the javelin to travel as far as possible, it should stay in the air for as long as possible.

Trajectories

The path of a projectile is called its 'trajectory'. Although the basic shape of the trajectory is the same for all projectiles, the height reached and the distance travelled ('range') will be different. Those factors depend on the launching force and the angle at which the projectile is launched.

All projectiles follow a parabolic trajectory

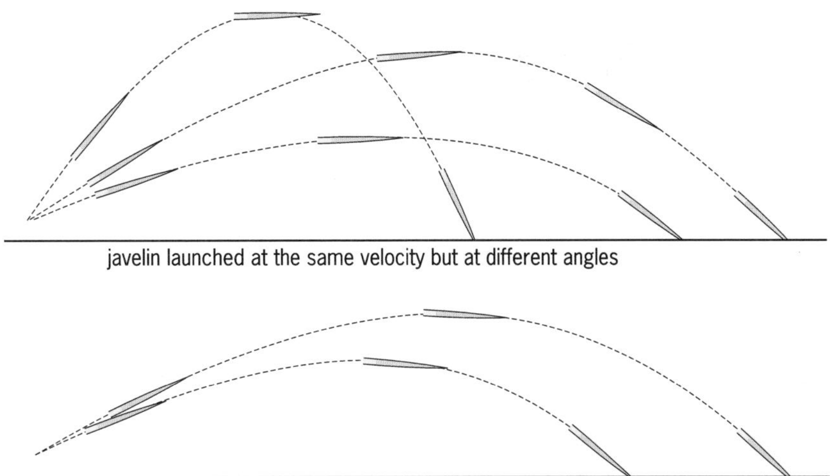

javelin launched at the same velocity but at different angles
javelin launched at the same angle but with different velocities

★ THINGS TO DO

1 Someone suggested to a javelin thrower that the angle at which the javelin left his arm (relative to the ground) was more important than the force with which it was thrown.

Carry out a series of tests to find out how each of these factors affects the horizontal distance travelled by a (safe) projectile in the laboratory.

Prepare a report which could be used by javelin throwers to analyse their techniques, but make sure your report mentions any differences which may be expected between your 'model' and the real event.

2 This table shows the distance travelled by a rocket designed to carry a grappling hook. Such a rocket is often used by coastguards to fire a rope onto cliffs.

Angle of projection	**Horizontal range**/m
10°	13.1
15°	20
20°	25.5
25°	30.6
30°	34.6
35°	37.6
40°	39.4
45°	40

a) Draw a graph of range against angle of projection.
b) What relationship can you see between the angle of projection and the range?
c) How far would the grappling hook travel if it were launched at an angle of 32°?
d) On one rescue the coastguard had to send a line to some children trapped on a rock which had been surrounded by the incoming tide. Calculate the minimum angle at which the rocket must be fired to reach the children.

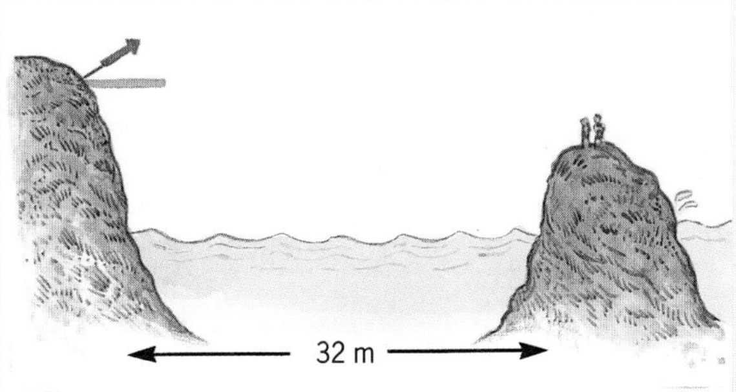

e) Describe any other factors which could affect how far the rocket would travel. For each one explain how the motion of the rocket would be affected.
f) Make sketches of what you think the graph of distance against angle of projection would look like if (i) the wind was blowing in the opposite direction, and (ii) a heavier grappling iron was carried by the rocket.

3.17 Moving in a circle

A force is needed to make a fairground car move round the loop

In topic 3.14 we saw that an unbalanced force acting on an object moving in a straight line causes the object to accelerate. The object either speeds up or slows down, depending on the direction in which the force acts. When a force acts in a different direction to that in which the object is moving, it still causes acceleration but now the direction of the object changes. The velocity changes, although the speed may not.

As one of these fairground cars enters the circular part of the track, there is an unbalanced force exerted by the rails on the car. The force is towards the centre of the circle and changes the direction of the car so that it travels round the circular track. The velocity of the car has been changed by the force.

At the point where the car leaves the circular section, the forces on the car are once again balanced, so it travels in a straight line once more. The ride illustrates one of Newton's Laws of Motion – that *a moving object will continue to move in a straight line unless some unbalanced force acts on it.*

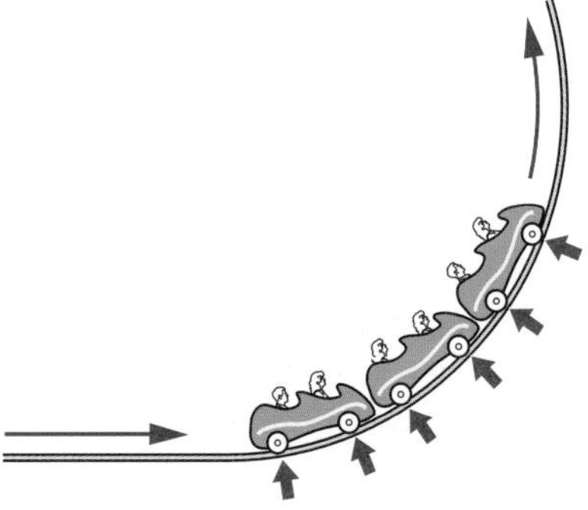

The straight line motion is changed into circular motion by the force exerted on the car by the curved track

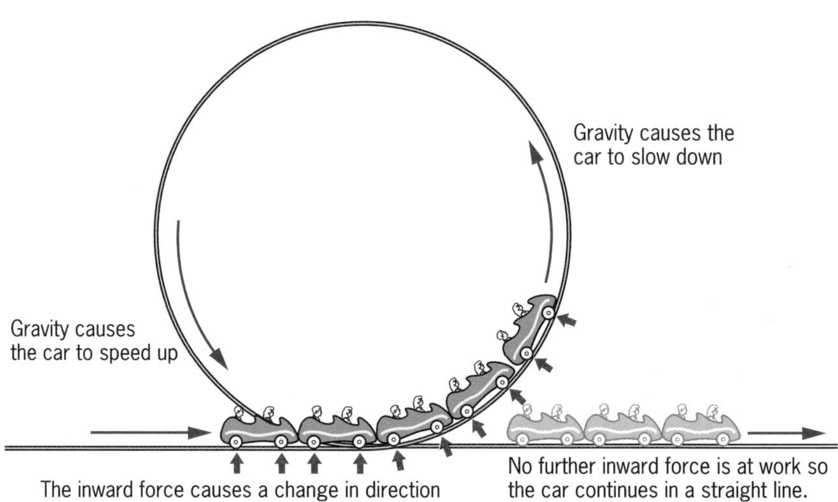
Gravity causes the car to slow down
Gravity causes the car to speed up
The inward force causes a change in direction and the car begins to follow a circular path
No further inward force is at work so the car continues in a straight line. Friction may then slow the car down

The car 'loops the loop' and then continues in a straight line again

Centripetal force

The force acting on any object moving in a circle is a **centripetal force** – a force which always acts towards the centre of the circle in which movement takes place.

The value of the centripetal force is given by the formula:

$$F = \frac{mv^2}{r}$$

where m is the mass of the object, r is the radius of the circle and v is the speed of the object.

From this equation you can see that the faster the object moves, the bigger the force needed to keep it moving in a circle.

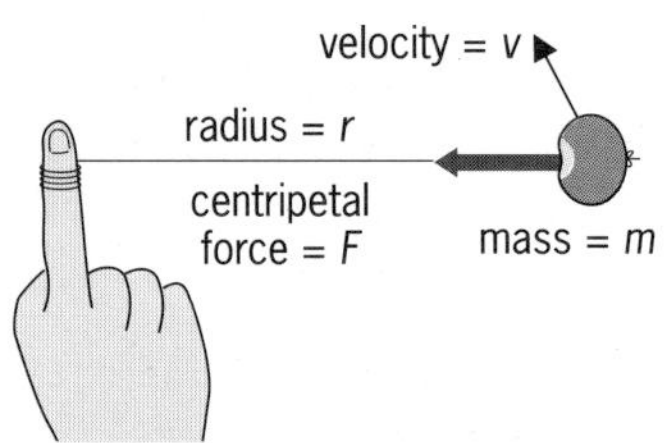
velocity = v
radius = r
centripetal force = F
mass = m

Tension in the string provides the centripetal force for this conker

Dry clothes

The drum in a spin-drier moves at between 800 and 1200 revolutions per minute – the spin speed. The wall of the drum exerts a force on the clothes which keeps them spinning. Drops of water in the clothing pass through spaces in the cloth, eventually reaching the wall of the drum. The wall, however, has holes in it. Water next to a hole has nothing to exert the force needed to keep it moving around and so it escapes from the drum.

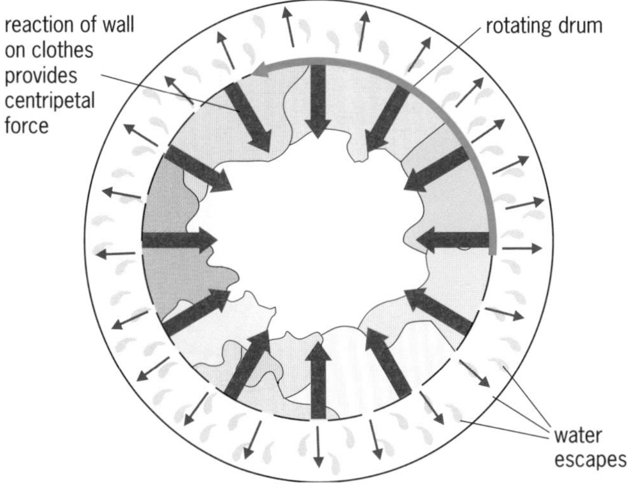

Section through a spin-drier

More fun at the fair!

Imagine the forces acting on the people in this fairground ride. When the ride first starts, the cage is horizontal and the people inside it are standing vertically. The cage then begins to spin. As it spins the people feel the cage behind pressing on them – it is providing the force which keeps them moving in a circle. (If it was not there they would move in a straight line.) At just the right speed, the cage begins to lift into the vertical position. Then the people are 'lying' parallel to the ground. Why don't they fall flat on their faces at the top of the ride?

★ THINGS TO DO

1 Describe two everyday examples of straight-line motion being changed into circular motion. For each one suggest what provides the centripetal force needed to bring about the acceleration.

2 Machines which fire 'clay pigeons' change their circular motion into straight line motion. Describe two other examples of a change such as this.

3 In 1968 the USA launched a manned space probe which orbited the Moon before returning to Earth.

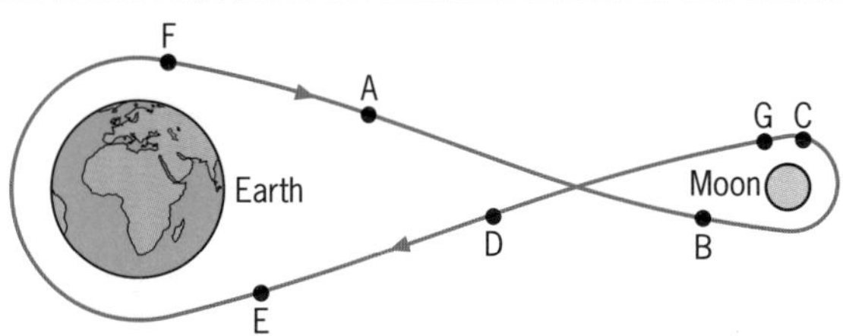

Path of the space probe

a) Describe the forces acting on the space probe, and their effect on its motion, at points A, B, C, D and E.
b) Small booster rockets were fired to move the rocket from Earth orbit at point F and from Moon orbit at point G. Why were they needed?

3.18 In orbit

Our knowledge of forces, and their effects, has played a big part in the exploration of space. On 12th April 1961 a Russian cosmonaut, Yuri Gagarin, was the first person to travel into space. He orbited (travelled around) the Earth once – in just 1 hour 28 minutes. Since then there have been many more ambitious manned space flights, including a Moon landing in 1969.

Unmanned space probes have been launched which have travelled throughout the Solar System, sending back information and close-up pictures of the planets. Thousands of unmanned satellites now orbit the Earth.

Manned space stations have orbited the Earth since 1971. People can live and work for many months in these space stations, carrying out experiments in 'weightless' conditions. The Russian space station, *Mir*, is the largest structure orbiting the Earth.

Space shuttles can dock with *Mir*, carrying food and other supplies

An early idea

The possibility that an object could be launched into orbit around the Earth was suggested by Isaac Newton over 300 years ago. He suggested that if something was fired horizontally from a high point on Earth, it would follow a parabolic path. The faster it was fired, the further it would travel.

If it could be fired fast enough, Newton suggested, the object would travel 'beyond the edge' of the Earth, as shown by path C. Rather than continuing into space from point D, the Earth's gravitational pull would hold the projectile at exactly the same distance from the surface – it would fall, but at exactly the same rate as the Earth's surface was 'falling away' from it (because of its curvature). Eventually it would return to its firing position, having completed one orbit of the Earth.

That early 'thought experiment' helps us to explain how a satellite is launched into Earth orbit.

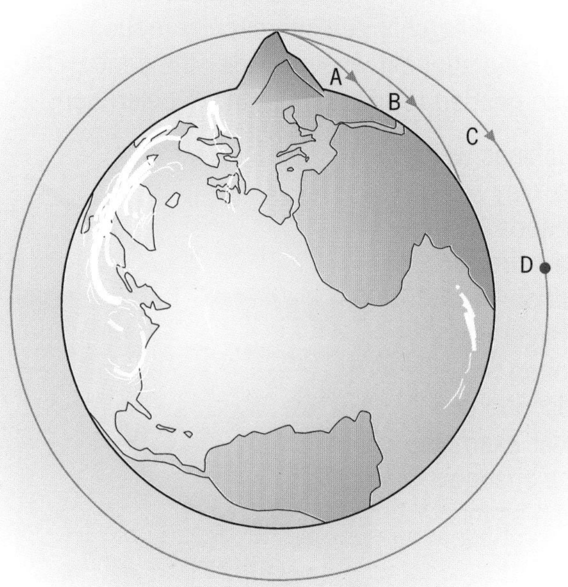

In theory a projectile fired at high speed would not fall to the ground but would orbit the Earth ($v_C > v_B > v_A$)

Lift-off

Satellites and space shuttles are launched using powerful rockets which can provide the force needed to lift them against the Earth's gravity (see page 102).

Most rockets consist of three stages, which fall away as they are no longer needed. In combination with a reduced fuel load (as it is used up), this means that the mass of the rocket decreases greatly, so smaller forces are needed to maintain the acceleration. As the rocket rises, its guidance system slowly turns it until it is moving at 90° to the Earth's surface.

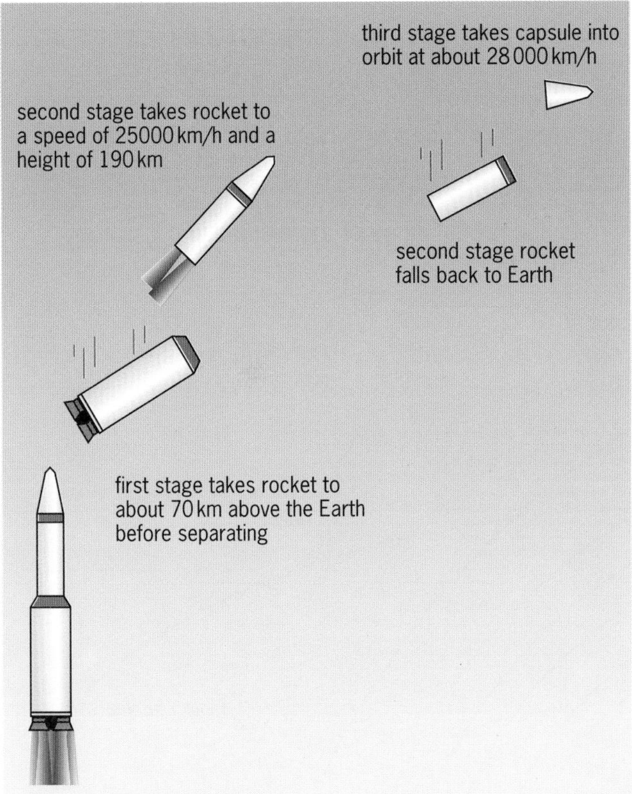
third stage takes capsule into orbit at about 28 000 km/h
second stage takes rocket to a speed of 25000 km/h and a height of 190 km
second stage rocket falls back to Earth
first stage takes rocket to about 70 km above the Earth before separating

Lifting a satellite into orbit

The satellite is eventually released, travelling at just the right speed to keep it in the intended orbit.

The satellite has not escaped from Earth's gravity. It is, in fact, falling all the time, at exactly the same rate as the Earth's surface falls away from it, so it stays at the same height.

The satellite is moving in a circle, so its direction is constantly changing (although its speed is not). The satellite must therefore be accelerating (see page 138). The force which produces this acceleration is gravity.

Speed and gravity

Speed and gravity both play a part in making sure that satellites and space shuttles stay in orbit. They must travel at just the right speed to stay in a particular orbit. If they travel too slowly they will fall back towards the Earth. If they travel too fast they will be carried out of their orbit and follow a straight line path through space.

Communications satellites are released at just the right speed to maintain their intended orbit, 36 000 km above the Earth

As we saw on page 102, the gravitational force between two objects gets smaller as they get further apart.

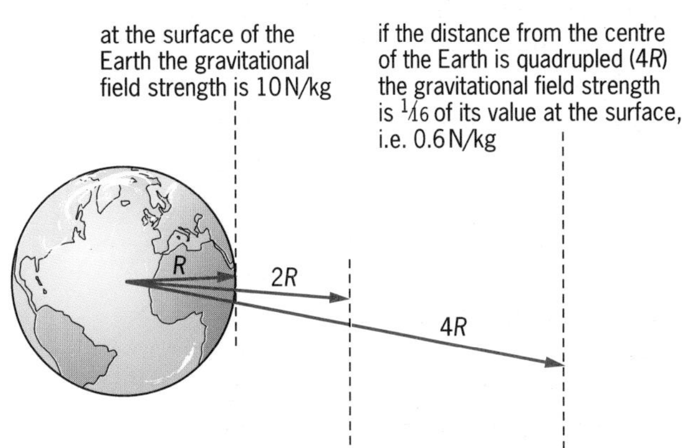
at the surface of the Earth the gravitational field strength is 10 N/kg
if the distance from the centre of the Earth is quadrupled (4R) the gravitational field strength is 1/16 of its value at the surface, i.e. 0.6 N/kg
R
2R
4R
when the distance from the centre of the Earth is doubled (2R) the gravitational field strength is 1/4 of its value at the surface, i.e. 2.5 N/kg

Each time the distance is doubled the gravitational field strength becomes ¼ of its original value

The gravitational force between a satellite and the Earth therefore decreases as the distance between them increases. In high orbits the force is smaller, and the satellite will stay in orbit at a lower speed. In low orbits the force is bigger, and a higher speed is needed to keep the satellite in orbit.

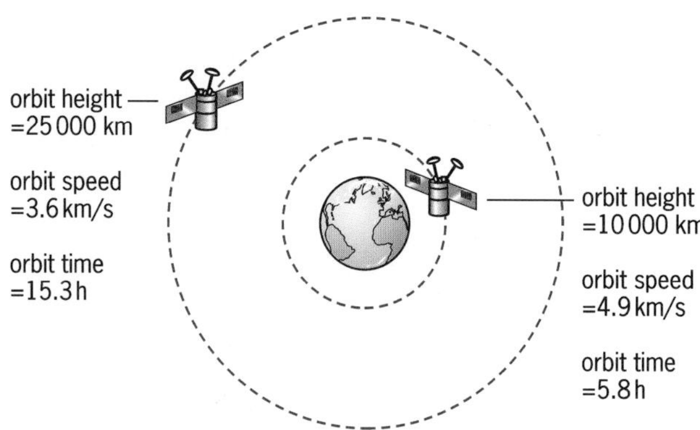

The speed at which satellites are placed in orbit is carefully calculated to make sure they will continue to orbit at that height

Well held

The Sun contains about 99% of all the matter in the Solar System. Its huge mass exerts a gravitational force large enough to keep the planets in orbit. The orbits are not quite circular – more like squashed circles (or 'ellipses') with the Sun fairly close to the centre. The planets all travel around the Sun in the same direction. One planet, Pluto, has a very elliptical orbit which cuts inside the orbit of Neptune, so there are times when it is closer to the Sun than Neptune.

As you can see from the illustration, the time taken for each planet to orbit the Sun depends on its distance from the Sun. The further away the planet is (i.e. the bigger the orbit) the slower it travels and the further it has to travel to complete one orbit.

Orbits and orbital times of the planets in our Solar System (not to scale)

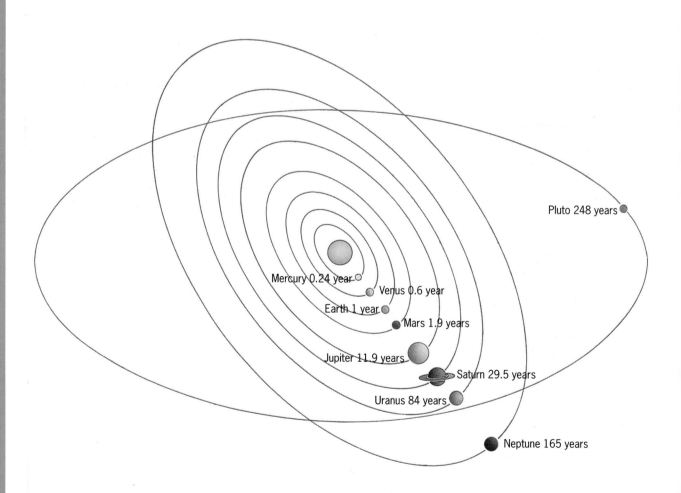

Pluto 248 years
Mercury 0.24 year
Venus 0.6 year
Earth 1 year
Mars 1.9 years
Jupiter 11.9 years
Saturn 29.5 years
Uranus 84 years
Neptune 165 years

★ THINGS TO DO

1 This table shows some information about the planets in the Solar System.

Planet	**Distance from Sun/** millions of km	**Average surface temperature/**°C	**Time to spin once on its axis**	**Time to travel once around the Sun**/years
Mercury	58	350	1416 h	0.24
Venus	108	460	5832 h	0.6
Earth	150	15	24 h	1
Mars	228	–25	24 h 37 m	1.9
Jupiter	779	–120	9 h 56 m	11.9
Saturn	1427	–180	10 h 20 m	29.5
Uranus	2670	–200	10 h 50 m	84
Neptune	4496	–220	15 h 50 m	165
Pluto	5906	–240	154 h	248

a) Choose *one* of the planets and describe how day and night would be different from on Earth.

b) i) Draw a graph of surface temperature against distance from the Sun. What general pattern does the graph show?

ii) Imagine that another planet had been found which was 3500 million kilometres from the Sun. Use the graph to predict what its surface temperature might be.

iii) If the Earth's surface temperature were 50 °C lower or 50 °C higher then living things would not be able to survive. How far from the Sun would the Earth have to be to have these surface temperatures?

c) i) Draw a graph of orbit time against distance from the Sun. What general pattern does it show?

ii) Suppose another planet was discovered 5000 million km from the Sun. How long would it take to orbit the Sun? Write a note for other people, describing how they could use your graph to find out.

2 Use your research skills to collect as much information as you can about each of the planets in the Solar System. You may be able to use the library, CD Rom or other computer information systems.

Design your own computer database containing information about the planets.

You could also use a word processor to produce an instruction booklet so that other people can use your database.

3 A space probe travels at a speed of about 28 000 km/h. Work out how long it will take to travel to Mars and then back to Earth. (Remember: speed = distance/time)

3.19 Satellites

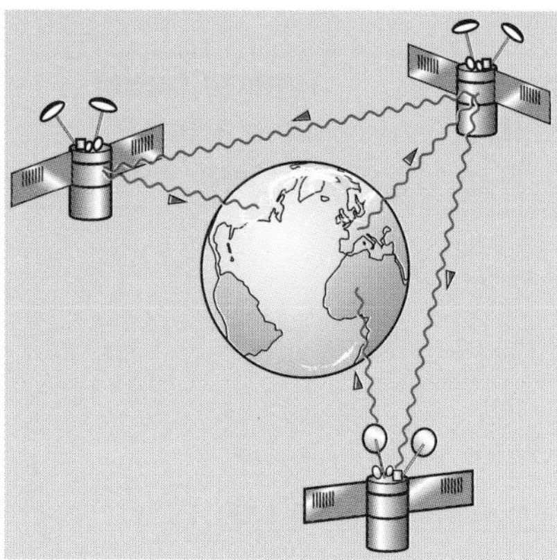

'Live' transmissions can be sent from one side of the Earth to the other via communications satellites, using microwaves

Satellite image of the 1987 hurricane over the UK

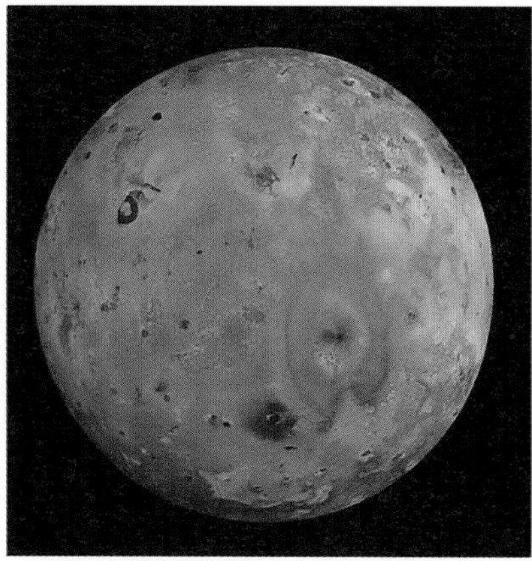

Io is the largest of Jupiter's moons. Its surface is covered with active volcanoes which release sulphur

Thousands of satellites are in orbit above the Earth. Some are communications satellites, used for radio, television and telephone transmissions. Other satellites monitor the weather, long-term climate changes, and can even detect which types of crops are being grown.

Geostationary satellites

'Geostationary' satellites are placed above the equator at a height at which their rate of rotation matches that of the Earth on its axis – i.e. one complete orbit every 24 hours. As the satellite orbits, it remains at the same point above the Earth. To anyone on Earth, the satellite appears stationary.

Communications satellites, such as the recently launched *Astra* satellites, are placed in a geostationary orbit high above the equator. We always know exactly where they are, and can beam signals directly to them, and receive signals directly from them, at any time.

Satellites which monitor environmental conditions are placed in low (i.e. fast) polar orbits – orbits which pass over the Poles of the Earth. They can then scan the whole Earth as it rotates beneath them.

The Hubble Telescope is in orbit well above the Earth's atmosphere. It provides much clearer pictures of the Universe than ground-based telescopes

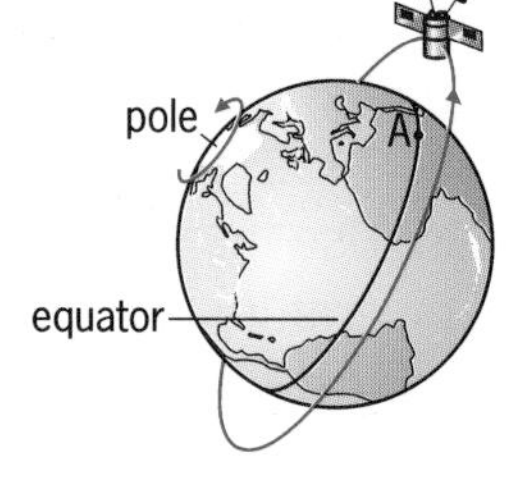

The geostationary satellite remains above point A on the Earth

Natural satellites

Our Moon is about 400 000 kilometres from Earth. It is a 'moon', *not* a planet, because it orbits the Earth – it is a natural satellite of the Earth. The Moon orbits the Earth in just over 27 days. Some of the other planets in the Solar System also have moons. Jupiter, for example, has 16 moons.

It is the gravitational force between a planet and its moon which keeps a moon in orbit.

Comets

Comets travel around the Sun in highly elliptical orbits. Most comets have a central core which is quite small – between 1 and 25 km in diameter – much of which consists of frozen gases and dust. As the comet approaches the Sun, the frozen gases begin to evaporate, releasing a plume of dust, ice and vapour such as water and ammonia vapour. This is the tail of the comet which can be thousands of kilometres long. Light from the Sun reflects from the comet and its tail – the comet does not give out light itself.

The best known comet is perhaps Halley's Comet, which becomes visible from Earth every 76 years. The movement of Halley's Comet is largely influenced by the Sun's gravity.

Halley's Comet was last seen in 1986

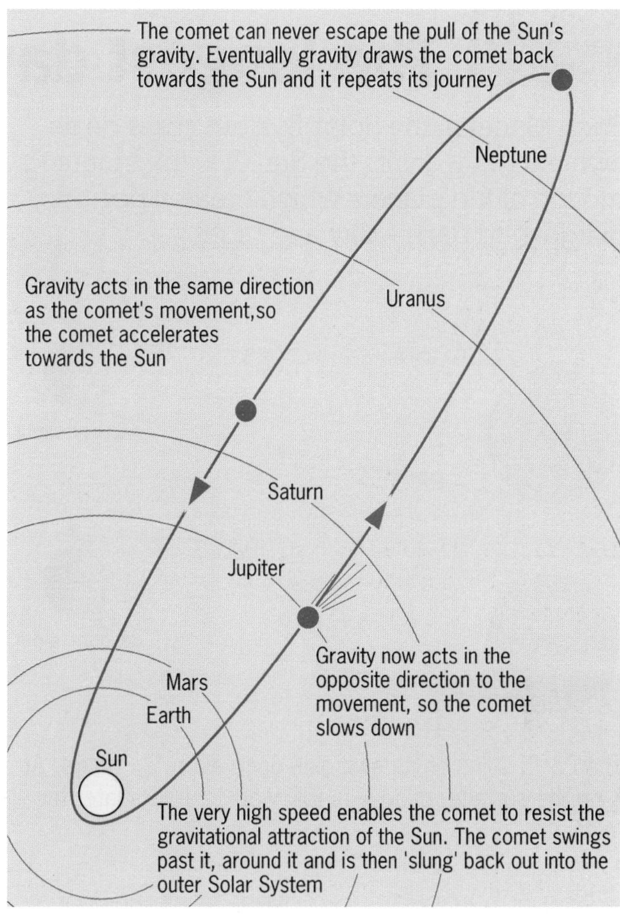
The comet can never escape the pull of the Sun's gravity. Eventually gravity draws the comet back towards the Sun and it repeats its journey
Neptune
Uranus
Gravity acts in the same direction as the comet's movement,so the comet accelerates towards the Sun
Saturn
Jupiter
Gravity now acts in the opposite direction to the movement, so the comet slows down
Mars
Earth
Sun
The very high speed enables the comet to resist the gravitational attraction of the Sun. The comet swings past it, around it and is then 'slung' back out into the outer Solar System

The path of Halley's comet

★ THINGS TO DO

1 Use your research skills to find as many uses as you can for satellites.

2 a) From this graph, calculate the speed which must be reached by a satellite if it is to remain in orbit 700 km above the surface of the Earth.

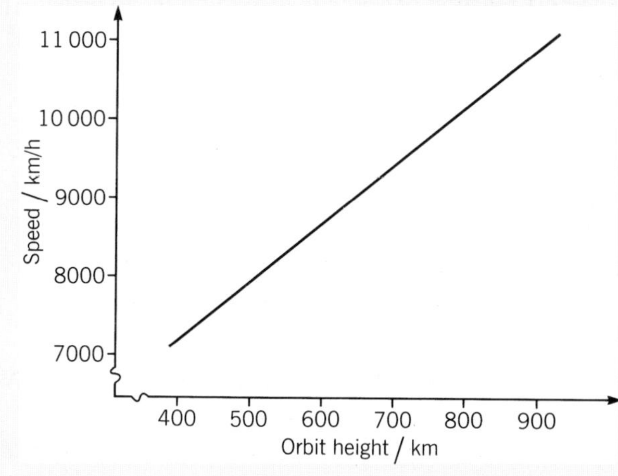
11 000
10 000
9000
8000
7000
Speed / km/h
400
500
600
700
800
900
Orbit height / km

b) Assuming the Earth's average diameter is 6400 km,

i) calculate the distance travelled by the satellite in one complete orbit (circumference of a circle = $2\pi r$),

ii) calculate the time for one orbit at a height of 700 km above the surface,

iii) calculate the height at which a satellite would go into geostationary orbit around the Earth.

3 Astronauts in orbit experience 'weightlessness'. This is a misleading term, because they do have weight in orbit – they just *seem* to be weightless. Write a short article for a science magazine explaining why astronauts seem to be weightless.

3.20 The longest day

Each planet in the Solar System spins on its own axis as it orbits the Sun. It is the spinning motion of the planets which creates periods of light and dark – day and night.

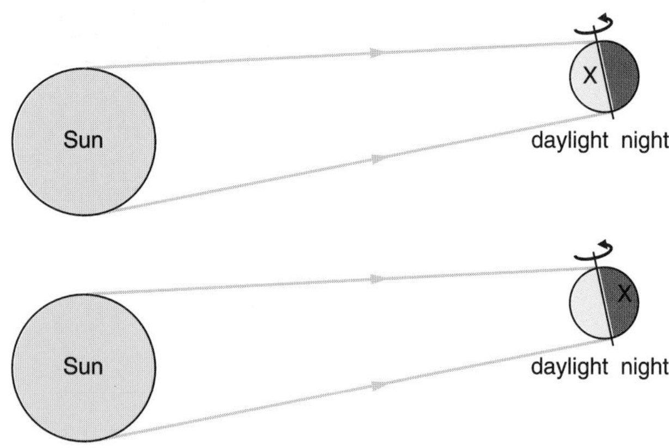

The Earth spins on its own axis once every 24 hours. At X on the surface, midday is followed 12 hours later by midnight

The Sun appears to move across the sky each day, but it is the Earth's spinning motion that creates this impression. The Sun does not move, but a point X on the Earth's surface moves around to face the Sun, then points away from it as day turns to night.

Each planet spins at a different speed, so the length of day and night varies from one planet to another. On Venus, for example, the daylight period would last the equivalent of 121 Earth days, followed by a period of darkness lasting the same time. One 'day' would be equal to about eight months of Earth time!

The planets do not give out their own light – they reflect light falling on them from the Sun. Sometimes they are so close to the Sun that we cannot see them against the bright background of the Sun itself.

Stars

Each star is a sun, just like our own. Each one is a huge source of nuclear energy, releasing its own light. Apart from our own Sun, the next nearest star to us is Alpha Centauri, which is just over 40 million million kilometres away. Light from Alpha Centauri, travelling at 300 000 kilometres per second, takes over four years to reach us!

We see some of the stars clearly at night. They are also there during the day, but you rarely see them because the sky is so bright. Some groups of stars (constellations) have been given names, such as Orion (the Hunter), Gemini (the Twins) and Perseus (the Winged Horseman). The stars stay in these fixed patterns because they do not move relative to one another.

The constellation of Perseus is marked by an arrow. The Pleiades group is also clearly visible, in the lower right of the photograph

Looking from the Earth, the constellations appear to move around us once every 24 hours. They are not really moving in this way but because the Earth is spinning we see different constellations come into view throughout the night.

At different times during the year, because of the Earth's orbital motion and the tilt of its axis relative to its orbit, different constellations come into view.

Planets among the stars

Some planets, although they do not give out their own light, can be seen clearly in the sky during late evening, night or early morning. Different planets are seen in different positions during the year. As the planets orbit the Sun, they appear to move through the constellations. They are, however, much closer to the Earth than any of the stars and are moving well in front of them. Where we see the planets depends on where they, and the Earth, are, in their orbits around the Sun.

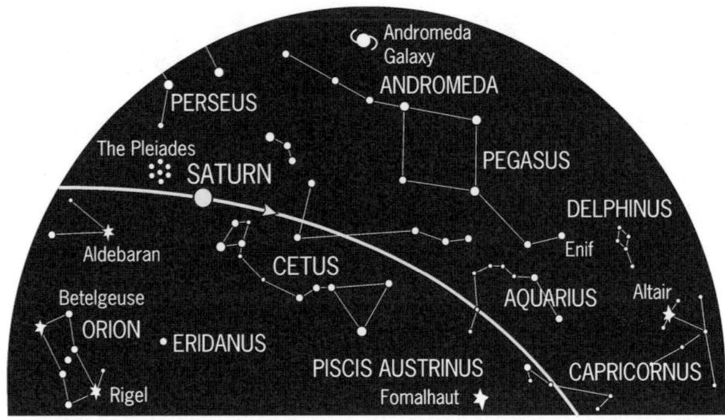

The path of Saturn through the constellations in November 1995 (looking South)

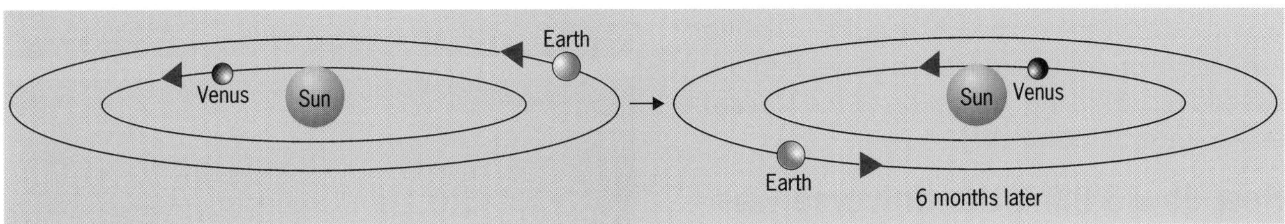

The orbital times of the planets differ, so their relative positions are always changing

★ THINGS TO DO

One constellation which many people can recognise is Ursa Major (the Great Bear), sometimes called the Plough. It can be seen clearly from the UK.

Polaris, the Pole Star, is directly above the North Pole of the Earth. Its position never significantly changes and can be found by following the line of two of the stars in Ursa Major. All the other stars appear to revolve around the Pole Star.

The diagrams show Ursa Major at two different times on the same night.

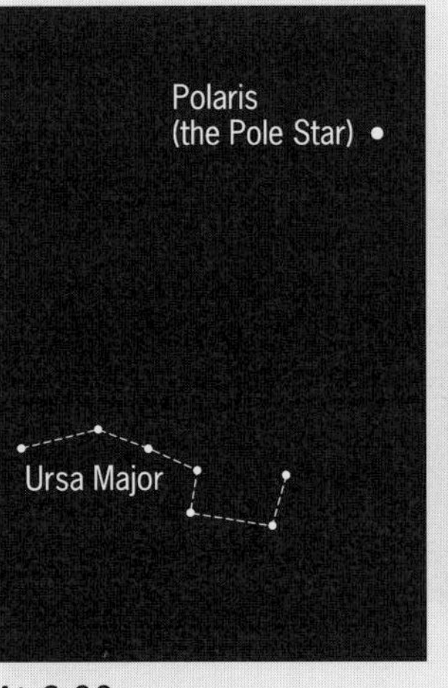

At 6.00 p.m.

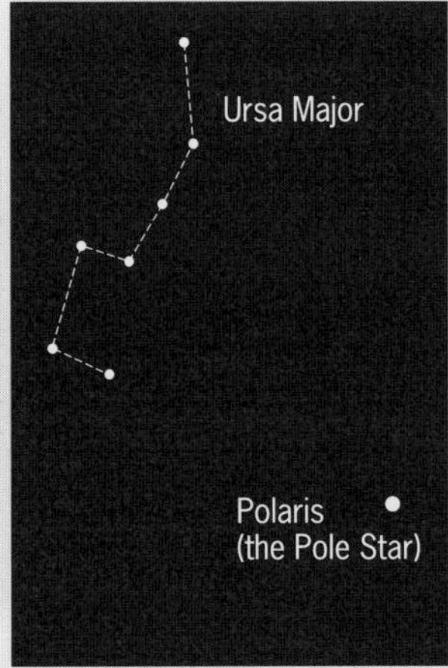

At 12.00 midnight

a) Talk with your friends about why Ursa Major seems to have turned. Discuss your ideas with others in your class. Make some notes about what this movement seems to suggest.

b) Draw another picture showing what Ursa Major would look like at 6.00 a.m. the next day.

c) Draw a series of pictures showing why the Pole Star appears in the same position whilst the other stars seem to revolve around it.

3.21 How it all began

Out there in space there are at least 10 000 million million million stars. Between the stars is mostly empty space, but there are small amounts of dust, ice and hydrogen gas. It is possible that some of the stars may have orbiting planets. The space that all of this takes up is called the Universe. No-one knows how big the Universe is. No-one knows whether the ideas shown in science-fiction films such as *Star Trek*, of other Universes beyond our own, are true. No-one is sure of how the Universe came into being. What we are fairly sure of is that forces played an essential part in the formation of the Universe as we know it today.

How do we think the Universe was made?

One modern idea is that everything started as an extremely dense, hot 'soup' of basic particles and electromagnetic radiation. At some time between 15 and 20 thousand million years ago it exploded. The 'big bang' was a far bigger explosion than anything we can imagine, releasing all the matter and energy that is in the Universe today.

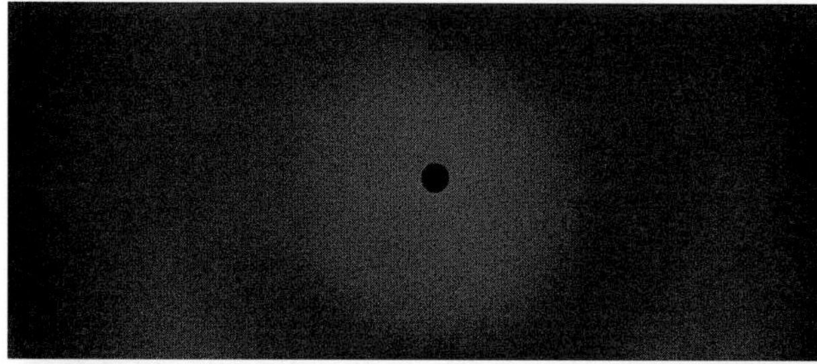

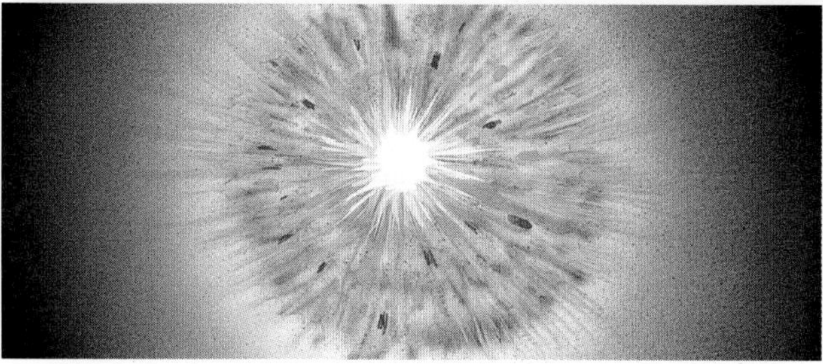

The newly formed Universe was like a huge fireball which expanded very quickly. Its temperature was probably over 100 thousand million degrees Celsius. For millions of years the debris from the 'big bang' continued to spread out. As it expanded it also cooled. Molecules of hydrogen formed.

Massive clouds of hydrogen gas formed in some places. Gravity began to draw the molecules closer together, and the clouds of hydrogen gas got smaller, denser and hotter. The hydrogen began to change into helium, releasing huge amounts of energy. These concentrations of matter were the early stars.

Gravitational forces drew stars towards one another, so there were places where there were more stars than others. Huge **galaxies** (areas where millions of stars gathered together) were formed. There may now be as many as 100 000 million galaxies in the Universe, each containing as many as 100 000 million stars. Within each galaxy the stars are millions of times further apart than the planets in our own Solar System.

The Universe today

Inside stars, nuclear reactions fuse light elements such as hydrogen together, forming heavier elements. These processes release huge amounts of energy, some of it as electromagnetic radiation including light.

As the original hydrogen in a star begins to run out, the star expands and may explode. These explosions (called **supernovae**) may occasionally be seen from the Earth, although they take place many millions of kilometres away. As a result of these explosions, atoms, including those of the heaviest elements, are scattered millions of kilometres into space. Some of them form new stars as they are drawn together by their own gravity. The rest drift between the galaxies as dust and ice. The fact that the inner planets of the Solar System contain atoms of these heavy elements, and that the Sun contains nuclei from the same elements, suggests that the Solar System may have formed from the debris of one of these explosions long ago.

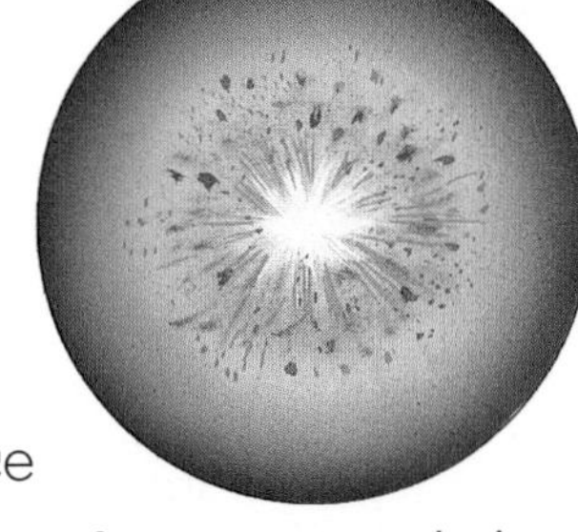

A supernova explosion

The Earth lies in a galaxy called the Milky Way. If you drove a car at 100 kilometres per hour it would take about one million million years to go from one side of the Milky Way to the other! If you could see the Milky Way from 'outside' it would look like a big spiral made up of millions of stars. Most of the stars, including our Sun, are in the arms of the spiral.

A spiral galaxy

Huge distances, millions of times greater than the distances between the stars within galaxies, separate one galaxy from another. The nearest galaxy to our own is the Andromeda galaxy, over 2 million million million kilometres away. It is a spiral galaxy similar to our own Milky Way.

Light (travelling at 300 000 kilometres per second) takes over 2 million years to reach us from the Andromeda galaxy. This means that we can only see it as it was 2 million years ago! Because of the huge distances in the Universe, we can never see it as it is 'today'. However, observations indicate that the Universe is still expanding – all galaxies are moving away from one another.

★ THINGS TO DO

1 What is the Universe? Make lists of similarities and differences between the Universe now and the Universe as it was millions of years ago.

2 What is a galaxy?

3 Place these in order of size: Solar System, planet, Universe, galaxy.

4 What would you say to someone who asked you how big the Universe is? Why will the Universe be bigger tomorrow?

3.22 The life and death of a star

When we look into the sky at night we see millions of stars. Each night any particular star looks the same. Over billions of years, however, all stars alter – sometimes spectacularly – as they follow a sequence of changes which takes them through strange-sounding stages such as 'red giant', 'white dwarf' and 'black hole'.

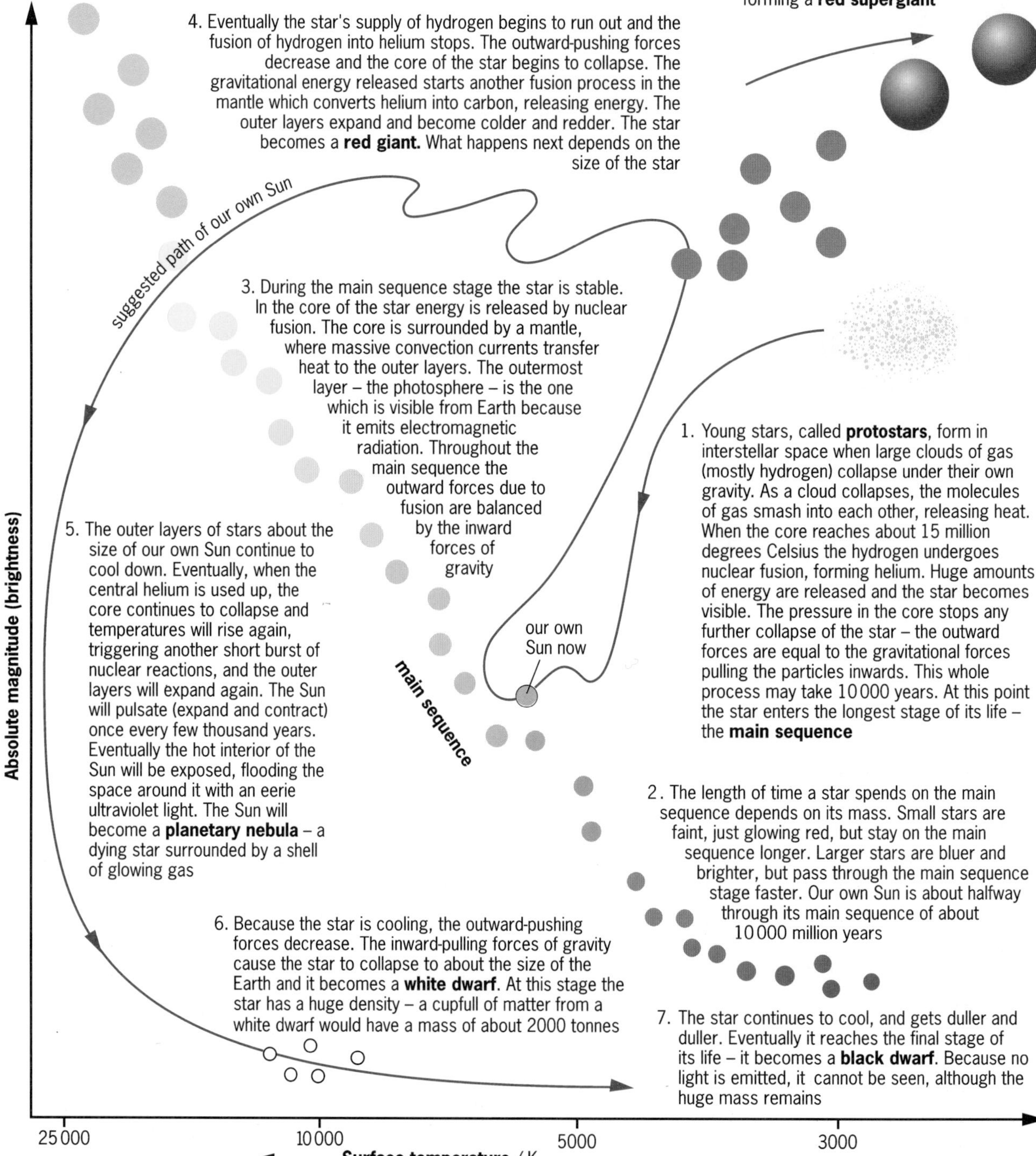

8. When a star at least four times as massive as our Sun leaves the main sequence, its core continues to contract as all the available helium is used up. The energy released is enough to fuse carbon atoms, and the outer layers expand enormously, often to 500 times the diameter of our Sun, forming a **red supergiant**
4. Eventually the star's supply of hydrogen begins to run out and the fusion of hydrogen into helium stops. The outward-pushing forces decrease and the core of the star begins to collapse. The gravitational energy released starts another fusion process in the mantle which converts helium into carbon, releasing energy. The outer layers expand and become colder and redder. The star becomes a **red giant.** What happens next depends on the size of the star
suggested path of our own Sun
3. During the main sequence stage the star is stable. In the core of the star energy is released by nuclear fusion. The core is surrounded by a mantle, where massive convection currents transfer heat to the outer layers. The outermost layer – the photosphere – is the one which is visible from Earth because it emits electromagnetic radiation. Throughout the main sequence the outward forces due to fusion are balanced by the inward forces of gravity
1. Young stars, called **protostars**, form in interstellar space when large clouds of gas (mostly hydrogen) collapse under their own gravity. As a cloud collapses, the molecules of gas smash into each other, releasing heat. When the core reaches about 15 million degrees Celsius the hydrogen undergoes nuclear fusion, forming helium. Huge amounts of energy are released and the star becomes visible. The pressure in the core stops any further collapse of the star – the outward forces are equal to the gravitational forces pulling the particles inwards. This whole process may take 10 000 years. At this point the star enters the longest stage of its life – the **main sequence**
5. The outer layers of stars about the size of our own Sun continue to cool down. Eventually, when the central helium is used up, the core continues to collapse and temperatures will rise again, triggering another short burst of nuclear reactions, and the outer layers will expand again. The Sun will pulsate (expand and contract) once every few thousand years. Eventually the hot interior of the Sun will be exposed, flooding the space around it with an eerie ultraviolet light. The Sun will become a **planetary nebula** – a dying star surrounded by a shell of glowing gas
our own Sun now
main sequence
Absolute magnitude (brightness)
2. The length of time a star spends on the main sequence depends on its mass. Small stars are faint, just glowing red, but stay on the main sequence longer. Larger stars are bluer and brighter, but pass through the main sequence stage faster. Our own Sun is about halfway through its main sequence of about 10 000 million years
6. Because the star is cooling, the outward-pushing forces decrease. The inward-pulling forces of gravity cause the star to collapse to about the size of the Earth and it becomes a **white dwarf**. At this stage the star has a huge density – a cupfull of matter from a white dwarf would have a mass of about 2000 tonnes
7. The star continues to cool, and gets duller and duller. Eventually it reaches the final stage of its life – it becomes a **black dwarf**. Because no light is emitted, it cannot be seen, although the huge mass remains
25 000
10 000
5000
3000
Surface temperature / K

10. Stars which were between four and ten times more massive than our own Sun during their main sequence stage leave behind an extremely dense mass composed only of neutrons, called a **neutron star.** Most neutron stars are only a few miles across. A cupful of matter from a neutron star would have a mass of about 20 000 million tonnes! They do not emit light but are 'seen' by pulses of radio emissions

9. Eventually the supergiant reaches a stage when fusion cannot take place, and it rapidly contracts as the gravitational forces draw matter inwards. The energy released causes the star to heat up again to temperatures at which fusion reactions begin again and the star explodes in a huge brilliant flash of light – a **supernova**

11. The biggest stars – those with masses greater than ten times the mass of our Sun, leave behind a supernova 'core' that collapses to form a **black hole**. A black hole is not, as some people might think, a hole in space. Rather it is a point where huge amounts of matter are compressed. The gravity force of a black hole is so large that it has an immense effect on its surroundings. Nothing can escape from it, not even light

★ THINGS TO DO

1 Draw flow charts showing the stages in the life and death of:

a) a star similar in size to our own Sun, and

b) a star much more massive than our own Sun.

The first stage for each one should be 'protostar'.

2 The illustration shows how the brightness of a star changes at different stages of its life cycle.

a) At which stage in its life is the surface temperature of a star highest?

b) Our own Sun is about halfway through its main sequence lifetime. It is expected to stay in the main sequence for a further 5000 million years. What will happen to the Sun after that?

c) In the main sequence the inward and outward forces on a star are equal – it neither contracts nor expands significantly. How do these forces influence the formation of (i) a red giant, (ii) a white dwarf?

d) Sirius is a 'blue giant' star. What is likely to be the surface temperature of Sirius?

The expanding Universe

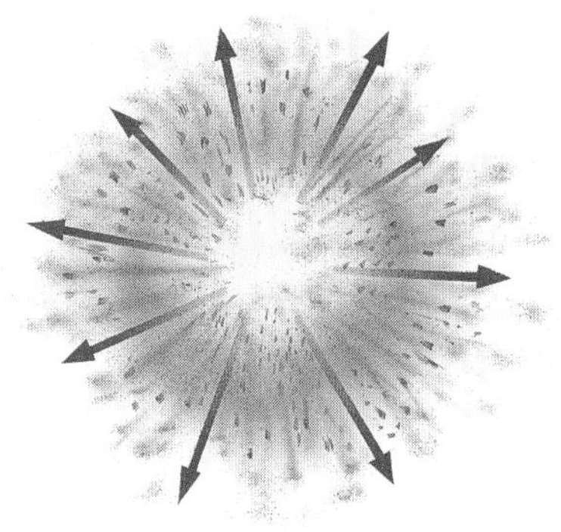

If the Universe was formed by a gigantic explosion – the big bang – then there must be evidence somewhere to support this view. Imagine what happens during an explosion.

In an explosion particles are scattered outwards in all directions by the force of the explosion. At any instant in time, it would be reasonable to expect to find some particles further away than others, and that the particles would be scattered fairly evenly throughout the space surrounding the explosion.

At some later instant in time, the particles would be further from the site of the explosion, and further apart than they were earlier.

It is also reasonable to suggest that the furthest particles must be moving apart faster, because the further they are from the centre of the explosion, the more spread out they become.

Radio waves provide vital information about the Universe but signals cannot be distinguished by ordinary telescopes. Radio telescopes with huge dish aerials are needed, or large arrays of aerials whose combined signal is deciphered by computer

Looking for evidence

Much of the information we can gather about the Universe is obtained from the electromagnetic radiation – from very short X-rays to long radio waves – that is emitted by stars. Highly sophisticated telescopes and specialised photographic techniques can record radiation which is invisible to the eye.

In one method of analysing the information from telescopes, the radiation is split up into a 'spectrum' – the different wavelengths of the radiation are separated. Dark lines on the spectrum provide clues about what elements are contained in the star being studied.

Evidence begins to gather

Edwin Hubble was an American astronomer who, in the 1920s, found direct evidence that:

- the Universe is expanding in all directions, and
- the galaxies furthest away are moving fastest – at speeds of up to 90 000 km per second!

Looking at the Universe as a whole it seemed as if a gigantic explosion had taken place millions of years ago.

The evidence for these observations came from a study of the spectra of distant galaxies. Hubble noticed that particular lines in the spectra were not where they should be in relation to those in our own Sun's spectrum, but were 'shifted' towards the red (longer-wavelength) end of the spectrum.

This shows the spectrum of visible light from the Sun. The dark vertical lines indicate which elements are present in the Sun's outer layers

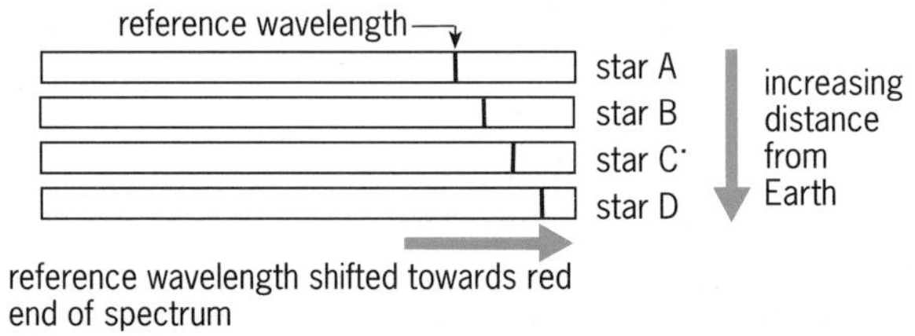

Spectra from distant stars show a 'red shift'

Hubble also noted that galaxies further from the Earth showed a bigger red shift. The red shift is due to the movement of the galaxy in relation to the Earth.

The faster a galaxy is moving away from the Earth, the greater is the increase in the wavelength of the radiation, i.e. the greater the red shift.

So what Hubble really found out was that galaxies are getting further apart and those that are furthest away are moving apart faster. This supports the view that the Universe is expanding and has been for millions of years, and is one piece of evidence which tends to support the theory of the big bang.

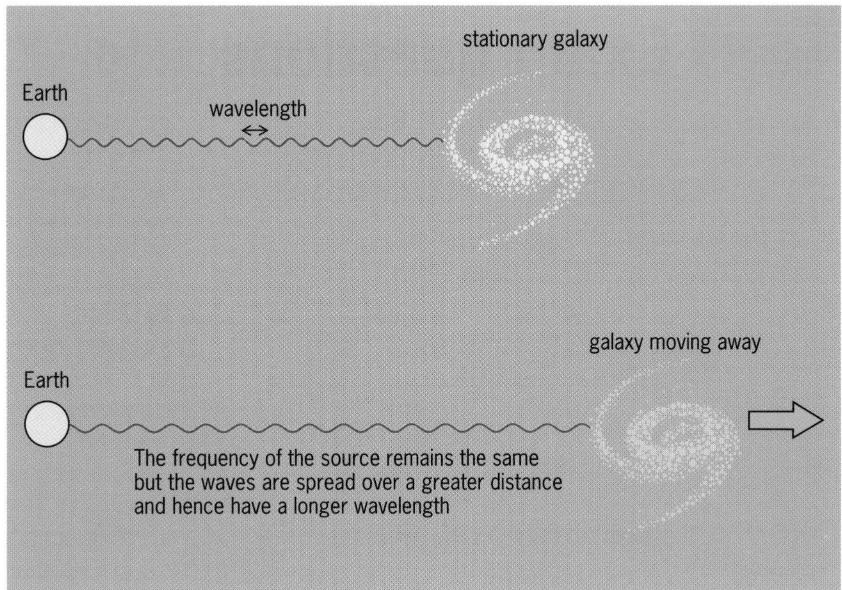

Radiation from a source moving away at high speed has its wavelength 'stretched' or red-shifted

The future of the Universe

From our current knowledge of the Universe as it is today – its structure, the positions of known galaxies and their relative velocity, it is possible to estimate that if the Universe was created by a big bang it must have taken place about 20 000 million years ago.

What will happen to the Universe in the future? No-one can really be certain what the future holds, but we do know that gravity will finally decide what will happen. Gravity holds everything in the Universe together. The size of the gravity forces depends on the mass of the matter in the Universe. The amount of matter will determine whether the Universe will:

- continue to expand, or
- eventually settle at some size, neither expanding nor contracting, or
- contract again, causing the galaxies to collapse in on themselves, possibly leading to another big bang.

★ THINGS TO DO

1 **a)** Summarise the evidence which supports the big bang theory of an expanding Universe.
b) Observations indicate that the rate at which the Universe is expanding is beginning to slow down. What could be causing this?

2 Light travels at a speed of 300 000 km/s through space. Light from the nearest star (other than the Sun) takes 4.2 years to reach the Earth. Light from some distant galaxies takes 40 million years to reach us. Why can it be said that 'when you look into the night sky you are looking into the past'?

3 Betelgeuse is a red supergiant that can be clearly seen in the constellation of Orion. It is 4.9×10^{15} (4900 million million) kilometres from Earth.
a) If light travels at a speed of 300 000 km/s, how long does it take the light from Betelgeuse to reach Earth?
b) What will be next stage in the life of Betelgeuse?

Exam questions

1 a) The diagram shows the forces **A**, **B** and **C** acting on an oil tanker moving forward through the sea. The length of each arrow indicates the size of each force.

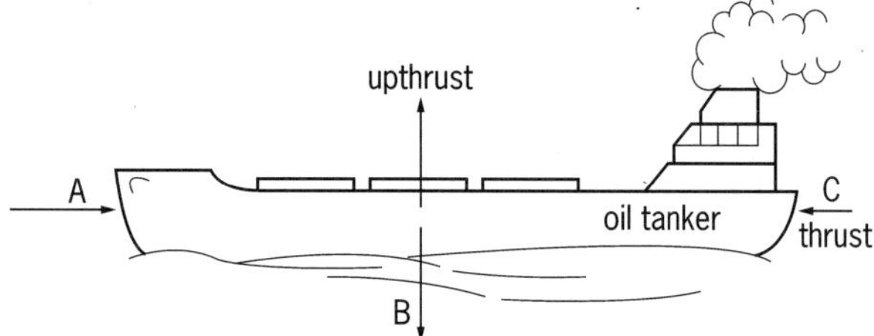

i) Choose the **best** words from the list to finish the sentences.

drag **mass** **lift** **weight**

Force **A** is the . . . . (2)
Force **B** is the . . . . (2)
ii) Explain how you can tell from the arrows on the diagram that
1 the ship is not sinking; (2)
2 the ship is slowing down. (2)
iii) Which force will **not** change if the ship takes on a heavy cargo? (1)
b) Trains rely on the friction force between the wheels and the track for their grip.

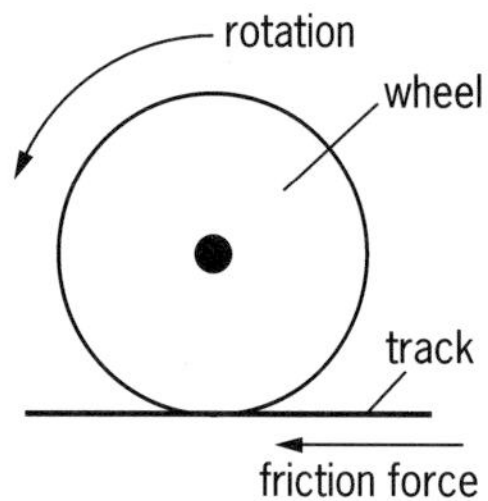

i) Explain why wet leaves on the track can cause problems for rail travel (2)
ii) One way of reducing the problem is to apply a mixture of sand and clay to the rails.
Suggest how the sand and clay mixture helps. (1)
(MEG, 1995 (part))

2 a) *zero resultant force*
resultant accelerating force
resultant decelerating force

[Copy and] complete **each** of the sentences below by using **one** of the above statements. Each statement may be used once, more than once or not at all.
i) A car moving along a straight track, at constant speed, experiences a . . . . (1)
ii) A free-fall parachutist, at the beginning of her fall, experiences a . . . . (1)
iii) A raindrop falling to Earth at its terminal velocity experiences a . . . . (1)
iv) A motorcyclist making an emergency stop experiences a . . . . (1)
b) A ship of mass 15 000 000 kg, with its engines stopped, decelerates at $0.02\ m/s^2$.
i) Calculate the size of the decelerating force. Write down the formula that you use and show your working. (3)
ii) Explain how the decelerating force was produced. (1)
iii) Explain how the ship could increase the size of the decelerating force. (1)
(WJEC, 1995)

3 A child stands a wooden brick on its end as shown in the diagram.
The child then pushes the brick to make it tilt.
How far must the brick be tilted to make it fall over?
Explain your answer.
(You may draw a labelled diagram if you wish.) (2)
(NEAB, 1995)

4 Some students have made a machine which will lift a 100 N weight using a smaller force.

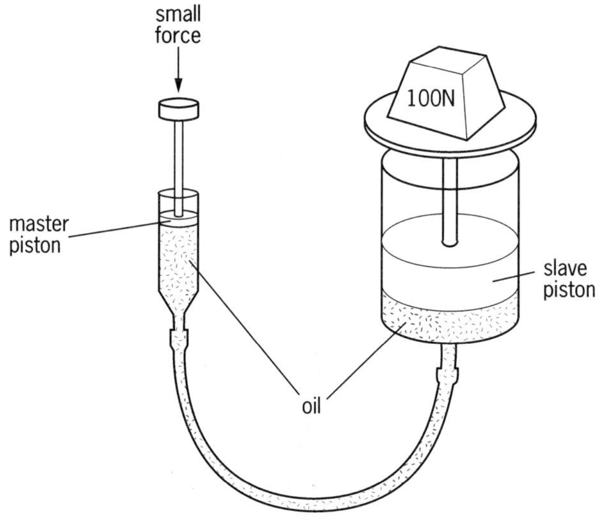

The oil is pressing up against an area of 20 cm^2 on the slave piston.

Calculate the oil pressure which is needed to lift the 100 N weight. (Show your working.) (3)

(NEAB Specimen Paper, 1998)

5 The graph shows distance plotted against time for a short car journey.

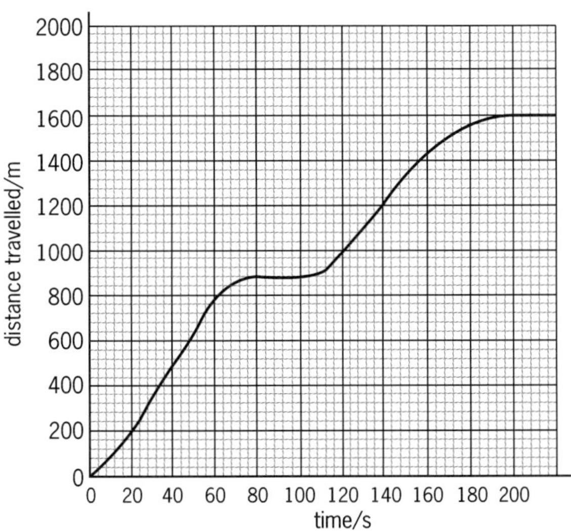

a) Use information from the graph to answer the questions.

i) What does the graph tell us about the speed of the car between 20 and 60 seconds after starting the journey? (1)

ii) How far did the car travel between 20 and 60 seconds? (2)

iii) Calculate the speed of the car between 20 and 60 seconds. Show your working (3)

b) What happened to the car between 80 and 100 seconds after starting the journey? (1)

(NEAB Specimen Paper, 1998)

6 The diagram shows a pulley system being used to lift a heavy load.

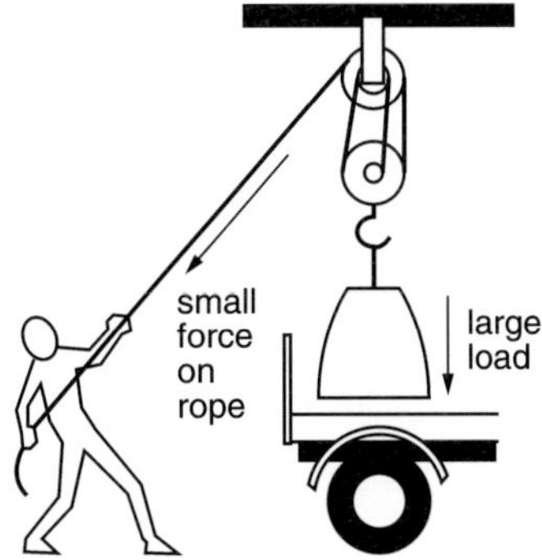

a) [Copy] the sentences below and choose words from this list to complete them.

divider easier harder
longer multiplier shorter

The pulley system makes it . . . . to lift a load. This is because the pulley system is a force . . . . . . To lift the load a certain distance, the rope must be pulled a . . . . distance. (3)

b) To lift the load, energy is transferred.

[Copy] the sentence below and choose a unit from this list to complete it.

J m N N/m^2

Energy is measured in . . . . (1)

(NEAB, 1995)

7 Curling is a game played by sliding heavy stones across ice.

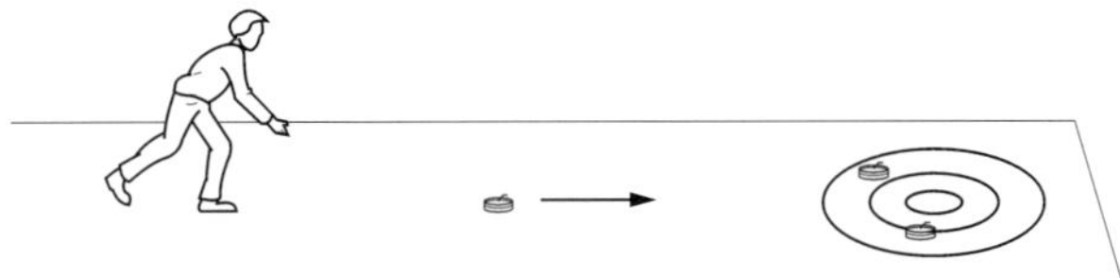

a) As the stones slide across the ice, they slow down and eventually stop.

Explain, as fully as you can, why this happens. (2)

b) Write down **two** effects the sliding stones will have on the ice. (2)

(NEAB Specimen Paper, 1998)

8 A crane is used to lift a steel girder to the top of a high building.

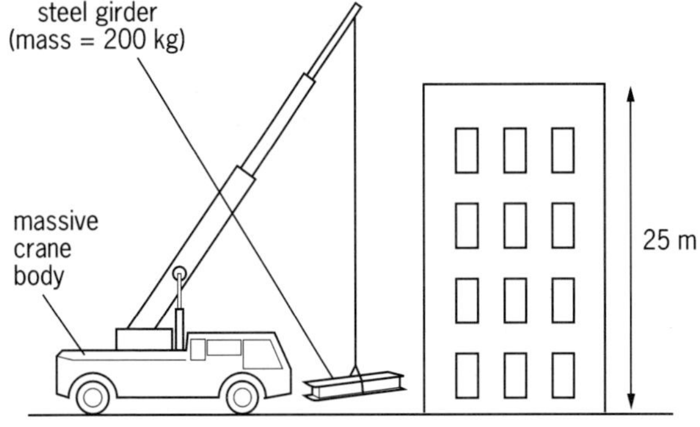

When it is lifted by the crane:

- the girder accelerates from rest to a speed of 0.6 m/s in the first 3 seconds;
- it then rises at a steady speed.

a) Calculate the **acceleration** of the girder. *(Show your working.)* (3)

b) i) What is the **weight** of the steel girder? (1)
ii) Calculate the **power** of the crane motor as it lifts the girder at a steady speed of 0.6 m/s.
(*Show your working. You can ignore the weight of the cable and hook which are small compared to the weight of the girder.*) (2)
c) A motor is fitted to the crane. This motor accelerates the girder at $0.3\,m/s^2$.
Calculate the **force** which the crane applies to the girder to produce this acceleration.
(*Show your working.*) (3)
(ULEAC, 1995)

9 A ball of mass 0.1 kg is thrown vertically upwards by a child and rises to a height of 5.0 m.

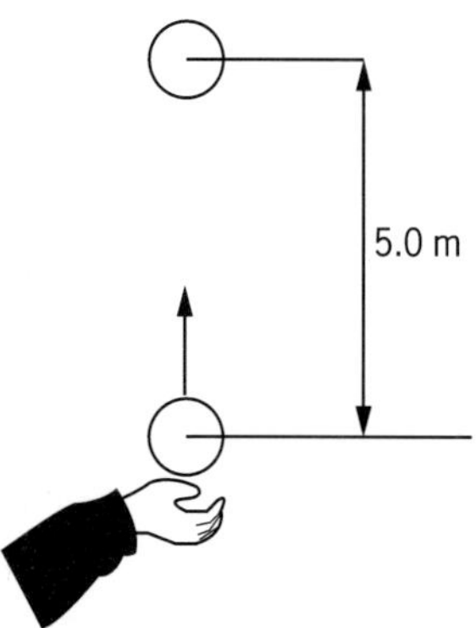

a) Calculate
i) the weight of the ball, (1)
ii) the potential energy gained by the ball when it reaches its maximum height. Write down the formula that you use and show your working. (2)
b) Ignoring air resistance, how much kinetic energy did the ball have when it left the child's hand? (1)
c) Calculate the speed with which the ball left the child's hand. Write down the formula that you use and show your working. (3)
(WJEC, 1995)

10 a) The following diagram shows a likely path for a comet orbiting the Sun. Explain why a comet does not travel at constant speed as it orbits the Sun. (3)

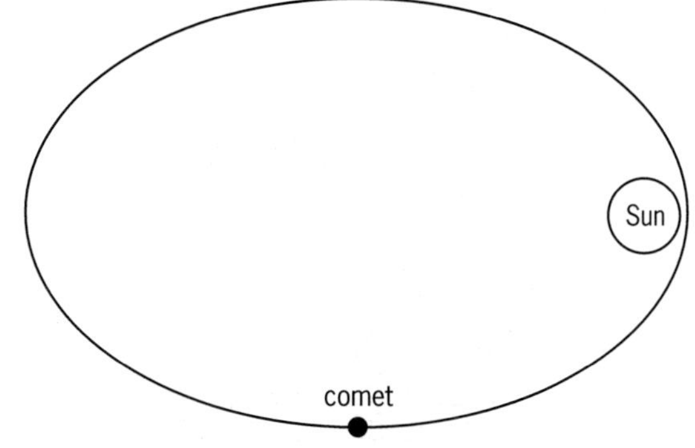

b) The diagram shows how stars may be placed into groups on the basis of their brightness and temperature.

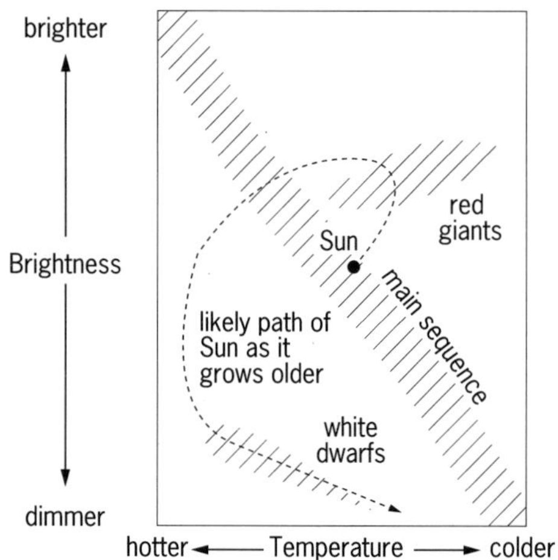

The Sun in now in the main sequence.
i) What major forces may be considered to be in equilibrium in the Sun at present? (2)
ii) Explain what will happen to the Sun as it passes into the red giant stage. (2)
iii) How does this differ from the white dwarf stage which follows? (2)
c) i) Name the process by which energy is produced by the Sun and give a brief account of this process. (4)
ii) The Sun loses approximately 4×10^6 tonnes of mass each second (1 tonne = 1000 kg). Use the equation:

energy given out (J) = change in mass (kg) × [speed of light (m/s)]^2

to calculate the amount of energy, in joules, released by the Sun each second. (Speed of light = 3×10^8 m/s.) (2)
d) Explain what is meant by the 'red shift' and discuss possible implications this has for the nature of the Universe. (6)
(ULEAC, 1994)

4

RADIATION AND WAVES

4.1 How are sounds made?

One of the loudest sounds ever produced was made when a volcano called Krakatoa in Java erupted. The sound of the eruption was heard over 3000 miles away

It is likely that the first sounds you ever heard were those of human voices. Since you were born you will have experienced millions of different sounds. Some are naturally occurring, such as the crash of waves onto the beach, or thunder, or the sounds produced by animals. Others are produced by machines.

This busker produces sound in five different ways. With the exception of the cymbals, the source of each sound is a regular vibration – something moving to-and-fro periodically. Regular vibrations such as this produce musical notes.

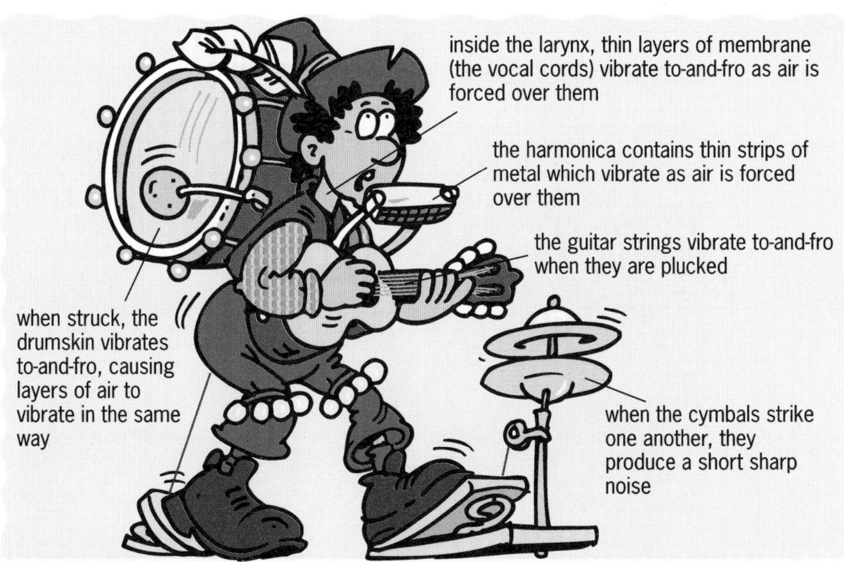
inside the larynx, thin layers of membrane (the vocal cords) vibrate to-and-fro as air is forced over them
the harmonica contains thin strips of metal which vibrate as air is forced over them
the guitar strings vibrate to-and-fro when they are plucked
when struck, the drumskin vibrates to-and-fro, causing layers of air to vibrate in the same way
when the cymbals strike one another, they produce a short sharp noise

The cymbals produce a different sound – a sudden 'clash'. Sounds such as this which produce irregular vibrations can be referred to as 'noise'.

We will only be considering sounds produced by regular vibrations.

Seeing the vibrations

When the prongs of a tuning fork are made to vibrate, a quiet but 'pure' sound is produced. It is difficult to see the vibration of the prongs, but if they are lowered into a beaker of water the movement is very apparent.

If small polystyrene balls or peas are placed on a vibrating drumskin, the pattern of vibrations can be seen more easily.

Vibration of tuning fork prongs

Vibration of a drumskin

In this Karaoke system the microphone converts the vibrations from the voice into an alternating voltage (see page 88). The voltage is then amplified before passing to the loudspeaker. The alternating voltage across the coil in the speaker makes the cone vibrate (see page 88) at the same frequency as the voice

The large cone in this loudspeaker reproduces low notes. High notes are reproduced by the 'tweeter' at the top

Karaoke

We hear sound when vibrations from the source reach our ears. The vibrations are carried by the air particles. Inside the ear, the vibrations are changed into electrical signals which then pass to the brain.

Imagine what happens when a continuous note is sounded by a loudspeaker.

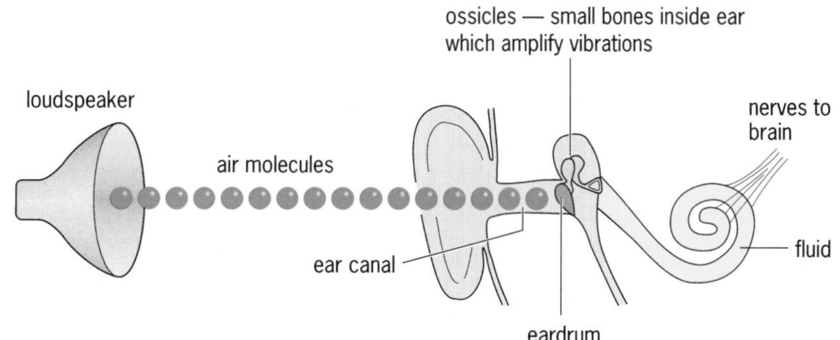

The vibrations of the loudspeaker cone are transferred to your ear by the air molecules

As the speaker cone moves to the right it pushes the air molecules in front of it. They push on neighbouring molecules and they, in turn, push on their neighbours. Eventually the moving air molecules push on your eardrum and you hear the sound. This takes only a fraction of a second if the loudspeaker is nearby.

After being pushed to the right, the air molecules close to the cone 'bounce' back after hitting other molecules. They return to the cone where they are pushed once more, and begin the process of transferring the next vibration.

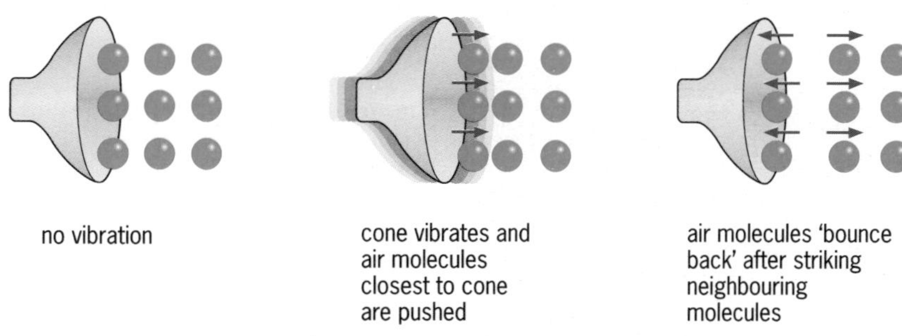

The vibration progresses through the layers of air molecules

At any time some air molecules will be travelling towards the left of the illustration while others are travelling towards the right. This pattern of movements through the air is the **sound wave**. If we could see the molecules at any time we would notice that some were 'bunched together' whereas others were more spread out.

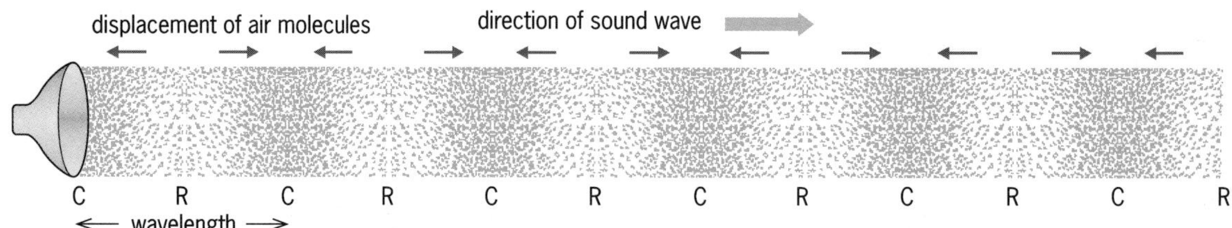

A sound wave

The regular pattern of 'compressions' (C) and 'rarefactions' (R) produced by the vibrations of the loudspeaker cone form a continuous wave. The distance from the centre of one compression to the centre of the next compression is the **wavelength** of the sound which is being transferred.

The **frequency** – the number of complete to-and-fro vibrations each second – at which the air molecules vibrate (and the frequency at which your eardrum vibrates) is the same as the frequency of the loudspeaker cone. The sound you hear is a copy of that produced by the loudspeaker.

It's quiet on the Moon

Particles are needed to transfer sound vibrations from place to place. There is no atmosphere around the Moon, so there is nothing to carry sound. Sound cannot pass through a vacuum.

Simulating sound waves

We cannot see the movement of the air particles as a sound wave passes, but we can simulate their behaviour using a long spring (called a 'slinky' spring).

When one end of the spring is quickly pushed in and out, a 'pulse' travels through the spring. Each coil moves to-and-fro as the vibration passes along, eventually reaching the other end of the spring.

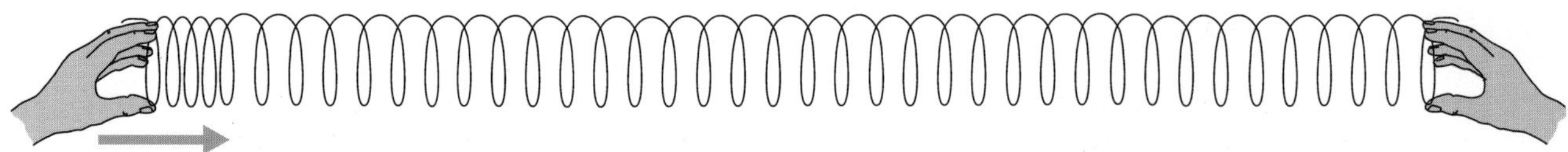

The spring is pushed inwards at one end, transferring energy to the spring

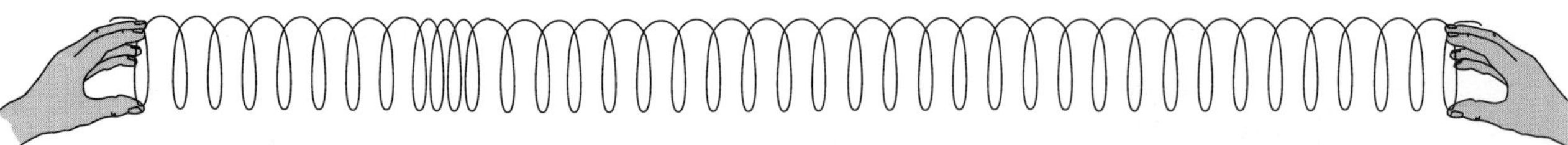

A fraction of a second later the vibration has passed further along the spring

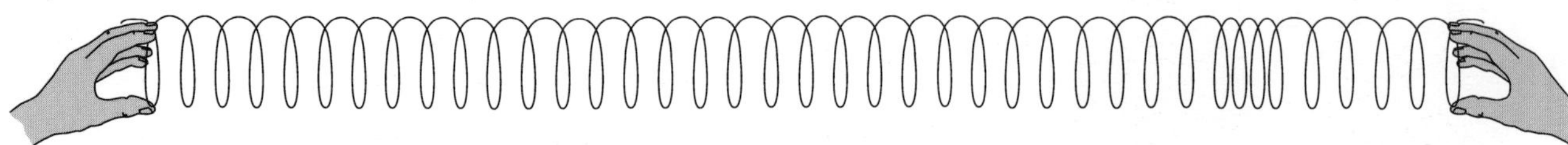

The vibration has now passed through the spring and will reach the opposite end

If the end of the spring is pushed in and out regularly, a regular pattern of compressions and rarefactions – a continuous wave – can be seen to travel through the spring.

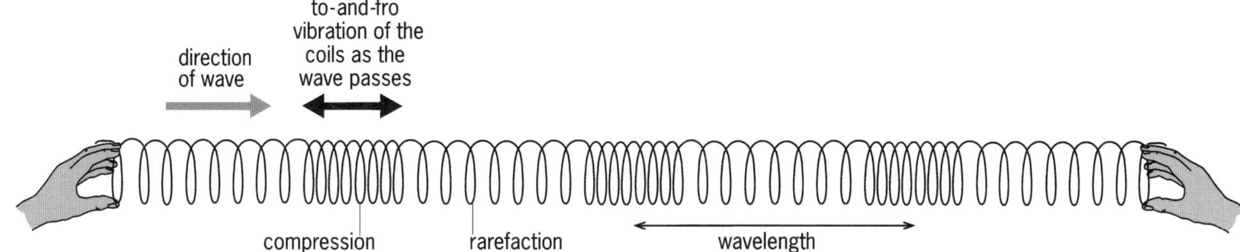

A sound wave simulated by a slinky spring

There are a number of important features to note about the vibrations of each coil of the spring.

1 The coils vibrate to-and-fro *parallel* to the direction in which the wave is travelling.
2 Energy is transferred from one point to another as the wave passes along the spring.
3 Each coil vibrates at the same rate as the source of the vibrations – if the spring is pushed in and out four times each second, each coil will vibrate four times each second.
4 The vibrations get smaller as the wave moves along the spring. This is because some energy is 'wasted' as the wave progresses through the spring.
5 The vibration may be reflected from the opposite end of the spring (rather like the echo of a sound wave).

This type of wave is called a **longitudinal wave**. All sound waves are longitudinal waves, regardless of the material through which they are travelling.

★ THINGS TO DO

1 Use a guitar or a violin to investigate how the pitch of a note (how 'high' or 'low' it sounds) depends on:
   a) the thickness of the string,
   b) the length of the string which is vibrating,
   c) the tightness (tension) of the string.

Make your own notes describing what you find out. Include illustrations if they are appropriate.

2 Design and carry out an experiment to find out who in your group has the best hearing. Make sure you think about how to design a 'fair test' before you start. Write an account of your investigation, including any measurements you make, and say what you found out.

3 Do you get excited by the sound of your favourite music? Talk with others in your group about how you could find out how your heart-beat is affected by different kinds of music.
   Do your own tests and make a note of what you find out. (Use personal stereos to keep the noise down in the classroom.)

4 Look inside a piano with your teacher. Make a list of similarities and differences between the way in which sounds are produced by a piano and by a guitar.

4.2 Sounds different

Sounds are produced in many different ways. The sound produced by bagpipes, for example, is quite different from that produced by a guitar. By looking at the pattern of vibrations in a sound wave we can begin to understand why the sounds are so different.

One way of 'looking' at a sound wave is to change the vibrations of the air into an electrical signal, using a microphone. If the microphone is connected to an oscilloscope, the pattern of the sound wave appears on the screen as a 'trace'.

The trace really shows us the changes in the pressure of the air as it strikes the microphone. The crests (the top parts) of the wave represent compressions, or regions of high pressure, whilst the troughs (the bottom parts) of the wave represent the rarefactions, or regions of low pressure.

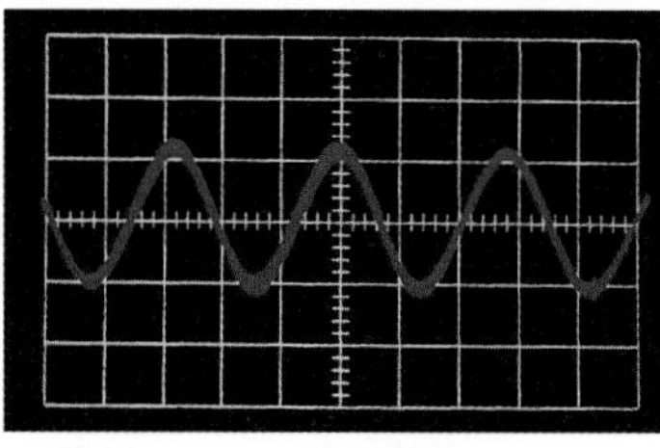

Frequency

How 'high' or 'low' a note sounds is its **pitch**. The pitch depends on the frequency of the sound wave – the number of vibrations which occur each second. The higher the frequency, the higher the pitch of the note produced.

The unit of frequency is the **hertz** (Hz). Something vibrating with a frequency of 250 hertz (250 Hz) produces 250 vibrations each second. Larger units, used for higher frequency sounds, are the kilohertz (1 kHz = 1000 Hz) and the megahertz (1 MHz = 1 000 000 Hz). Most people can hear sounds over the frequency range 20 Hz – 20 kHz.

The thicker strings on a guitar vibrate with a lower frequency than the thinner strings (assuming the same length is used each time) so they produce lower-pitched notes.

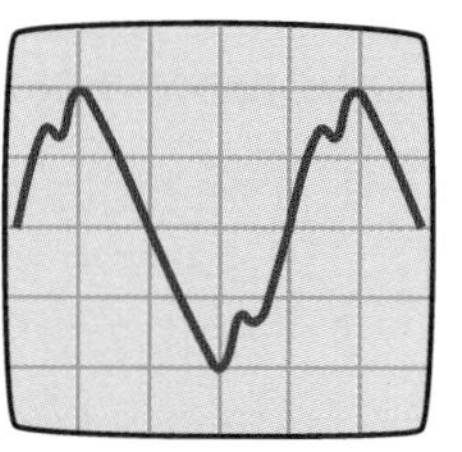

The thicker strings produce lower frequency sounds. There is a longer time between one vibration and the next, so the compressions are further apart

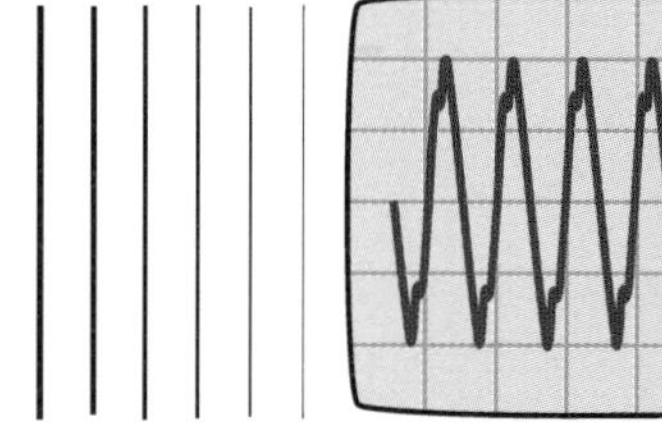

The thinner strings produce higher frequency sounds. Because there is a shorter time between one complete vibration and the next, the compressions are closer together

By changing the length of the vibrating strings (moving the fingers along the frets) the guitarist can produce many different notes, each with a different frequency (and hence pitch). Tightening the strings also affects the sound produced.

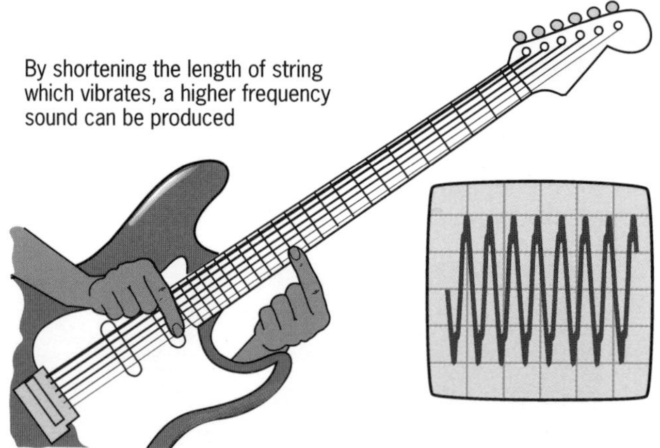

By shortening the length of string which vibrates, a higher frequency sound can be produced

Notice that the shape of the wave produced by the guitar is different from that of a 'pure' note. These variations in shape – each type of musical instrument produces a different shape – affect the 'quality' of the sound we hear, although the frequency may be the same.

Wavelength

The wavelength of a sound wave is the distance between two successive compressions or two successive rarefactions. On an oscilloscope trace, the wavelength is the distance between any two corresponding points (points which are in the same position in their to-and-fro motion), such as the distance between two consecutive crests, or two consecutive troughs. Because the wavelength is the *distance* occupied by one complete vibration, it has the same units as length – centimetres, metres or kilometres.

The wavelength depends on the frequency of the vibrating source. The higher the frequency of the source, the shorter the wavelength (because the speed of the wave is the same, so there is less time between one vibration and the next).

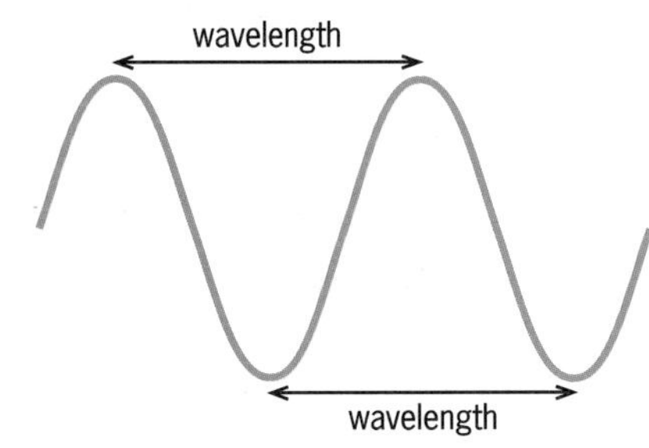

50Hz note

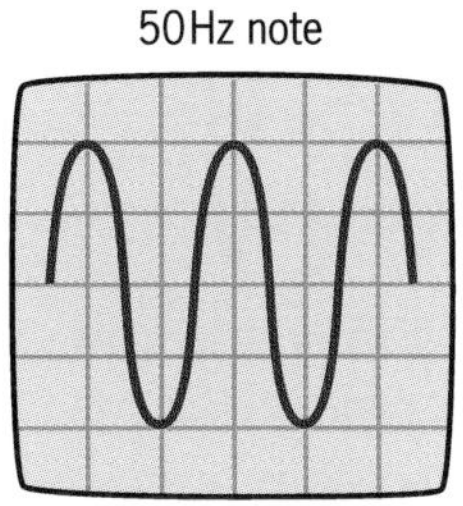

100Hz note

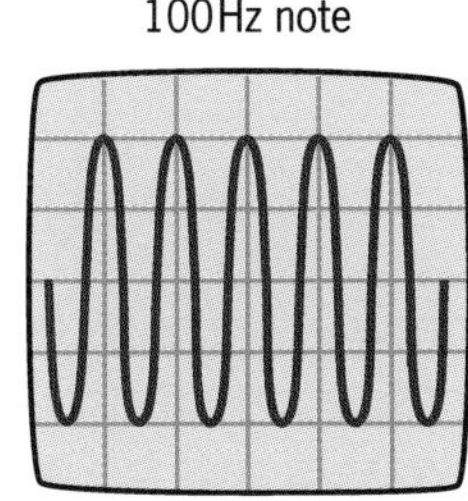

If the frequency is doubled, the wavelength is halved

Amplitude

A drumskin vibrates when it is struck, causing the air around it to vibrate at the same frequency. If the drum is struck harder, more energy is transferred to the drumskin. It vibrates at the same frequency but the to-and-fro movement is much bigger – it vibrates with a larger **amplitude.** This causes the air molecules to vibrate with a larger amplitude. The resulting sound wave transfers more energy to the eardrum each second and we hear a louder sound.

This note has a small amplitude. The sound will be quiet

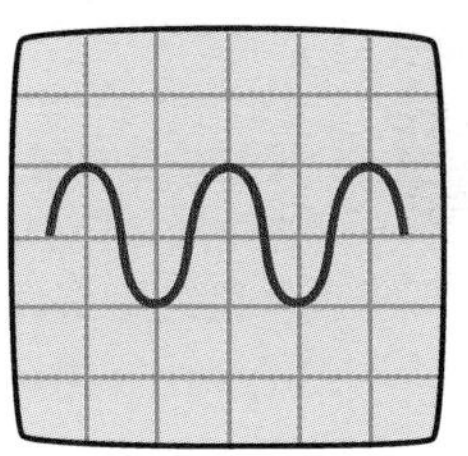

This note has the same frequency but a greater amplitude. The pitch will be the same but the sound will be louder

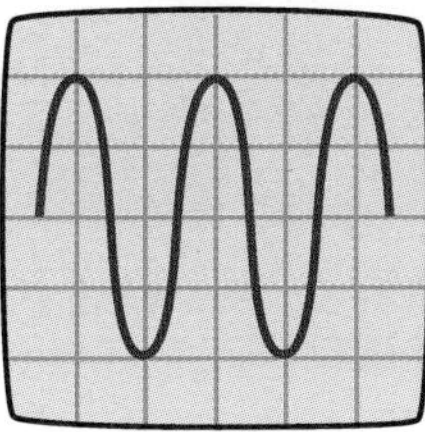

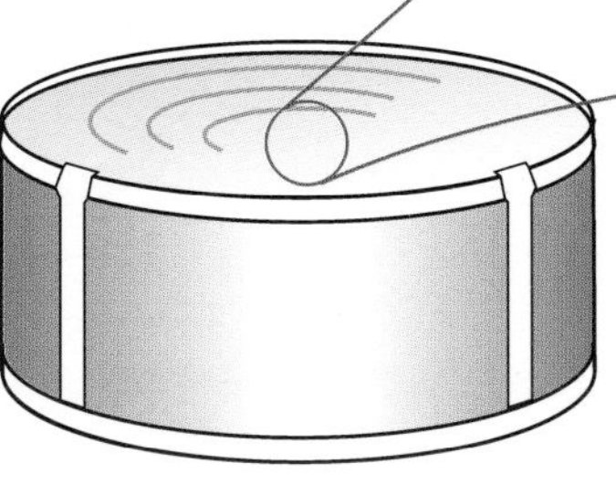

The amplitude of a vibrating object is the maximum distance reached from its rest position (when it is not vibrating). The loudness of the sound produced depends on the amplitude of the vibration

Energy and sound

The early flights of Concorde caused problems for many families living near the flight path as this huge aircraft accelerated to beyond the speed of sound. As it 'broke the sound barrier' the shock wave it created was carried through the air and shattered the windows of homes on the ground. Instructions were issued restricting Concorde to subsonic speeds (slower than the speed of sound) until it was far enough from property to minimise damage.

The amount of energy transferred by a wave in any given time depends on (a) its frequency, and (b) its amplitude.

Consider, for example, two waves which have the same amplitude but different frequencies.

A single vibration of each wave transfers the same amount of energy. The frequency of the second wave is twice that of the first, so twice as many waves will be transferred in any given time and so they will transfer twice the amount of energy.

Regular or prolonged exposure to loud sounds can damage our hearing, particularly our ability to hear sounds with high frequencies.

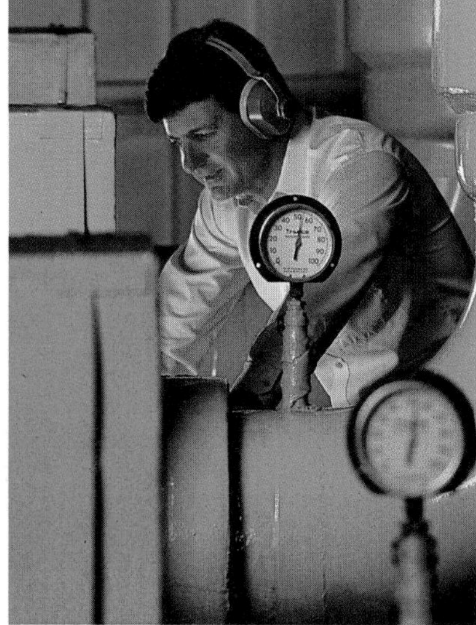

Many workers now wear ear protection to minimise the risk to their ears

Energy 'losses'

The loudness of any sound decreases as you move away from the source. This is because the energy becomes increasingly 'spread out' as it passes through the air. You can see in this series of illustrations that as the distance from the source increases, the frequency of the sound remains unchanged but the amplitude decreases.

Each time the distance between the source of sound and the microphone doubles, the amplitude drops to one-quarter

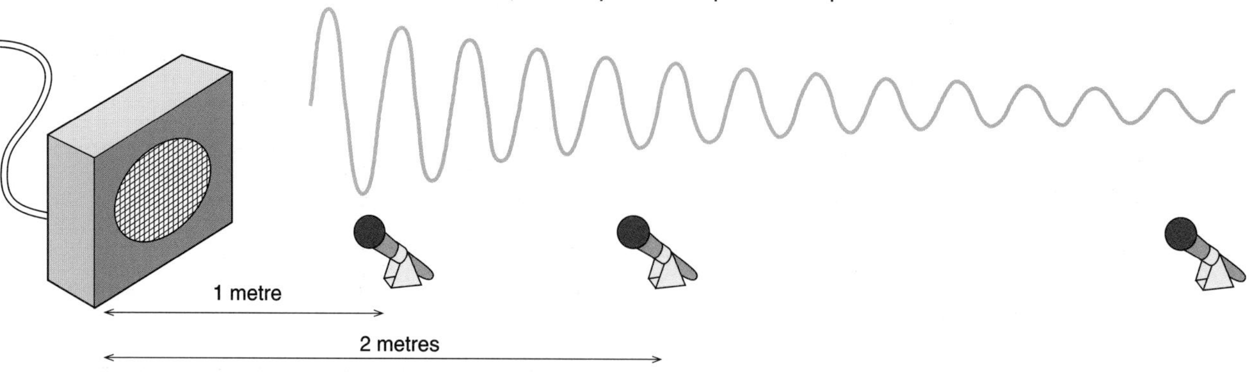

The speed of sound

Sound travels at about 330 metres per second in still air at 20 °C (that's about one-quarter of a mile each second). Light travels much faster – at about 300 000 000 metres per second (186 000 miles each second). That is why, when you are watching a fireworks display, you see a rocket burst high in the sky and then hear the 'crack' of the explosion a fraction of a second later – the light reaches you before the sound.

The speed of sound depends on the material through which it is travelling. In general, sound travels faster through solids than through liquids, and faster through liquids than through gases.

Speed of sound in:	
Air	330 m/s
Water	1400 m/s
Wood	4000 m/s

The equation *speed* = *distance*/*time* can be used to calculate the speed of sound.

★ THINGS TO DO

1 The diagrams show three sound waveforms on an oscilloscope screen.

i

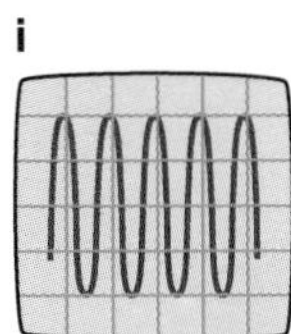

ii

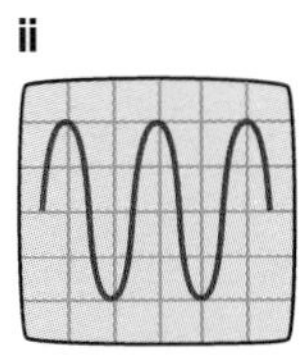

iii

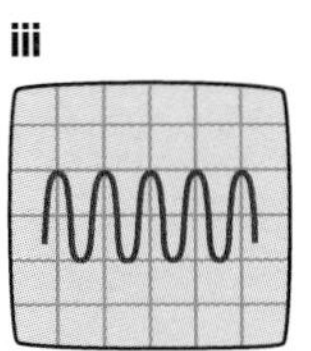

a) Which note has the lowest frequency?
b) Which note has the longest wavelength?
c) Which two notes have the same amplitude?
d) Which two notes have the same frequency but different amplitudes?

2 This note was produced by a guitar string. Trace it into your notebook.

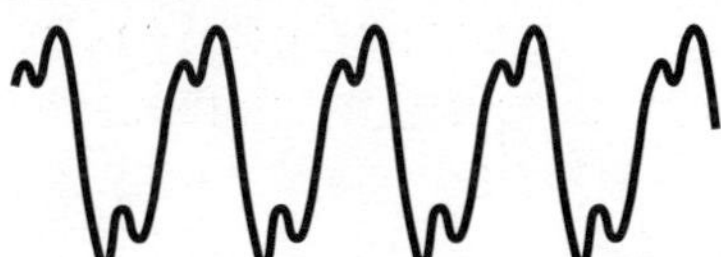

a) Draw the waveform which you would see if a thicker string had been used.
b) Draw the waveform which you would have seen if the string had been shortened by moving a finger down the frets.
c) Draw the waveform which you would have seen if the string had been tightened.

3 Sounds which are too loud can damage your hearing. In some cases the damage can be permanent. Read the article on the right and then answer the following.

a) Why are personal stereos potentially dangerous?
b) How could you tell whether someone is playing their personal stereo at a dangerous level?
c) The article says that 'the sound may have the same effect on the ear as a nearby pneumatic drill'. How can that be true?
d) Why are children more likely to suffer damage than adults?
e) What are the warning signs that your hearing is being damaged?
f) What is meant by 'a cumulative and damaging effect'?

Personal stereos can damage your health

A recent study suggests that personal stereos may be affecting the hearing of thousands of young people. Regular exposure to loud sounds in excess of 80 decibels is known to have a cumulative and damaging effect on our hearing. Most workers who are regularly exposed to sounds of this loudness, such as those operating heavy machinery, are advised to wear ear protection.

Personal headphones are worn close to the ears and cause large pressure changes on the eardrum. The sound may have the same effect on the ear as a nearby pneumatic drill. Experts advise that if the sound from personal headphones can be heard by others nearby, then it may cause damage to the wearer. Young people whose hearing is not fully developed are particularly susceptible to damage.

Because damage takes place over a long period of time, it may not at first be noticed. The first signs most people notice are when they begin to misunderstand words, or have difficulty following normal conversation when in a group of people.

4.3 Echoes

Sound can be reflected. The reflected sound is called an echo. Sometimes, particularly in the mountains, several echoes can be heard – each one has reflected from a different hill somewhere around you – even behind you!

Just a whisper

In the whispering gallery in St Paul's Cathedral your whispers can be heard by someone over 25 metres away. The wall of the gallery is curved. When you whisper, the sound of your voice is repeatedly reflected from the wall. Each time the sound is reflected from the wall at the same angle as it strikes the wall.

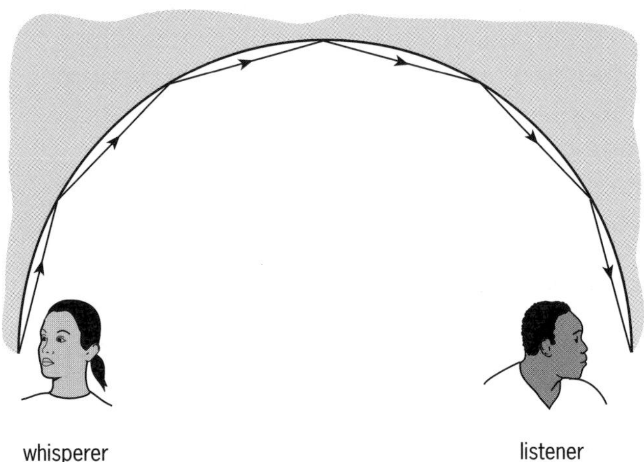

The acoustics are superb

Sound from a radio in your bedroom is reflected from the walls, ceiling and furniture. You hear the original sound and several echoes very quickly afterwards. You cannot distinguish the echoes clearly because there is such a short time between them.

In a fairly open space outdoors, little sound is reflected from the surroundings. The radio sounds quite different because the only sound you hear reaches you directly from the radio.

Concert halls are designed to make the best use of the way in which sound is reflected from the walls and the ceiling.

If a hall is poorly designed, then the reflections from around the hall can spoil the quality of the sound, especially if the hall is fairly empty. It may take several seconds for the echoes to die away. This effect is called 'reverberation'. Sounds may appear muffled and words may sound 'slurred' as one echo mixes with another.

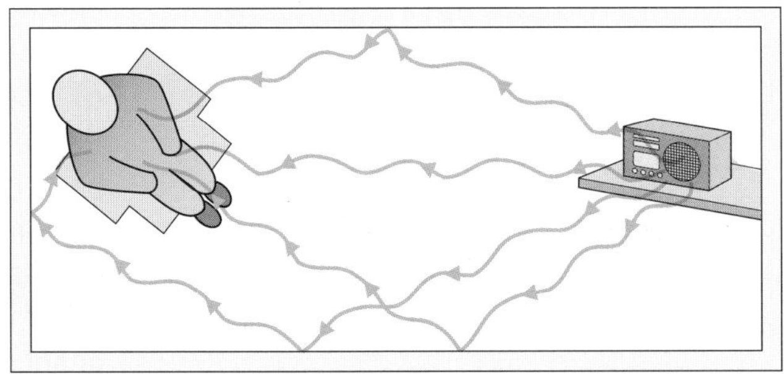

Inside a room you hear reflected sound as well as direct sound

The shape of the hall and the reflectors on the ceiling work together to provide high quality sound

Absorbing sound

In a professional recording studio any reflected sounds would spoil the quality of the recording. Steps are taken to reduce echoes so that the only sound which is recorded is that of the person or instrument which is performing. The walls and ceiling are often irregular and covered with soft materials which absorb sound.

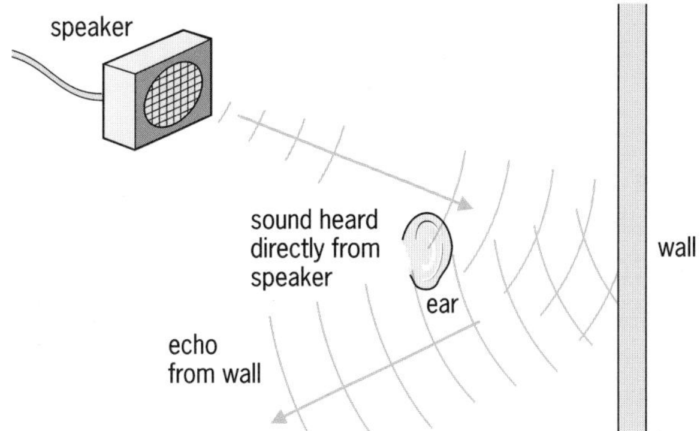

Most of the sound is reflected from hard, smooth surfaces

The cushioned ceiling of this recording studio reduces reflection of the sound

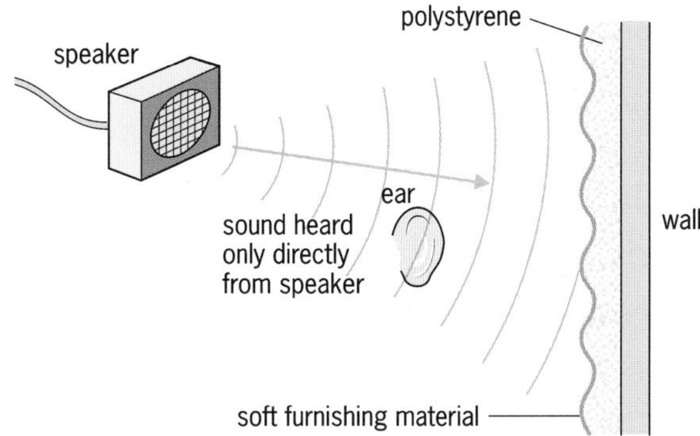

Soft materials absorb most of the energy of the sound. The rest is reflected in many different directions because of the irregularity of the surface – the energy becomes spread out. The amount reflected in any one direction is minimal

★ THINGS TO DO

1 The speed of sound can be found by standing well in front of a high wall and measuring the time taken for a sound to travel to, and reflect from, the wall.

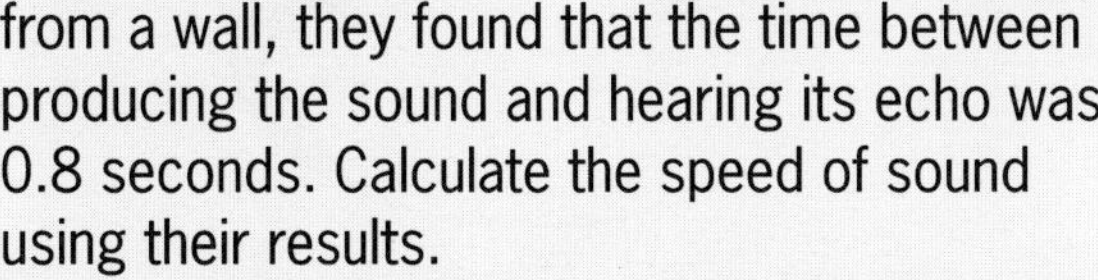

a) When this experiment was carried out by two pupils standing 100 metres from a wall, they found that the time between producing the sound and hearing its echo was 0.8 seconds. Calculate the speed of sound using their results.

b) Someone in the class suggested that their results would be affected by the wind direction. The pupils said that the effects of the wind would be cancelled out. What was their reasoning? Were they right?

2 The crew of a small fishing boat were unsure about their exact distance from a rocky coast. They saw the flash of light from a lighthouse, and heard the sound of the foghorn 5 seconds later. They heard a second sound 2 seconds later.

a) Assuming the speed of sound was 330 m/s, calculate the distance of the boat from the lighthouse.

b) When the crew looked at their chart they saw that the lighthouse was some way from the shore and stood in front of tall cliffs.

i) How does that explain why they heard two sounds from the foghorn?

ii) How far from the shore was the lighthouse?

4.4 Ultrasound

When we walk we can see things that are in front of us, and take steps to avoid them. Bats, flying at night, cannot do so because they are effectively 'blind'. Instead of relying on sight, they rely on their own form of radar to detect objects which lie in their path.

Ultrasound waves have a frequency between 20 kHz and 10 MHz – above the limit of human hearing, but within the range which can be heard by some animals.

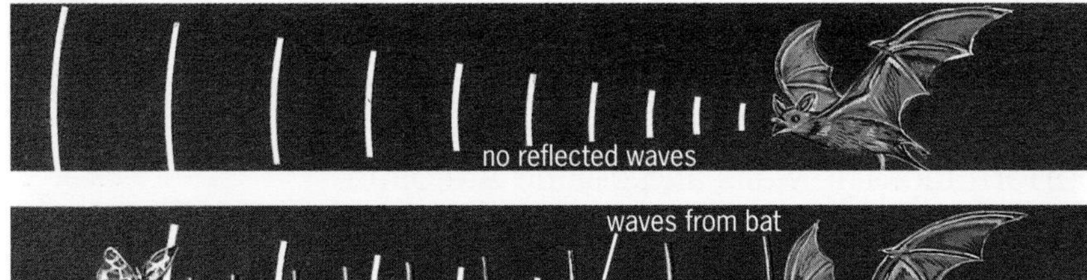

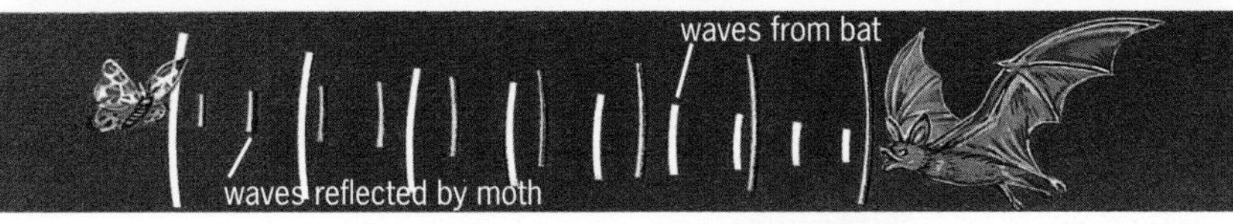

The bat sends out a sound wave which has a frequency beyond the hearing of humans. It is an ultrasound (or ultrasonic) wave. When the wave strikes something it is reflected. The bat's ears are especially adapted to receive any reflected waves. When the bat receives the 'echo' its brain immediately works out the location of the reflecting object. The bat knows exactly where things are!

Checking the baby

Doctors like to check on the development of unborn babies. X-rays cannot be used as they might harm the baby. Ultrasound is used instead, as it is safe and painless. The results of an ultrasound scan can tell doctors about the position of the baby in the mother's womb, how well it is growing, and can identify certain problems long before the baby is due to be born.

An ultrasound scan in progress

The big advantage of ultrasound over normal sound waves is that an ultrasound source and a detector can be tuned to exactly the same frequency. The detector will then pick up reflected waves which have come only from that particular source. Other frequencies will not be detected.

The probe sends out pulses of ultrasound with a frequency of about 3.5 MHz. A sensor in the probe detects the reflected pulses a few thousandths of a second later. At the boundary between two different types of tissue (such as muscle and bone) the pulses are reflected strongly. At the boundary between similar types of tissue (such as fat and muscle) the reflected signals are much weaker.

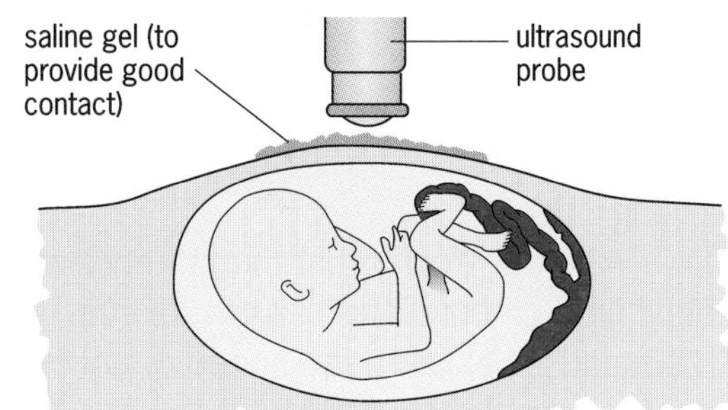

The reflected signals are processed by a computer, which turns them into a 'picture' of the baby inside the womb.

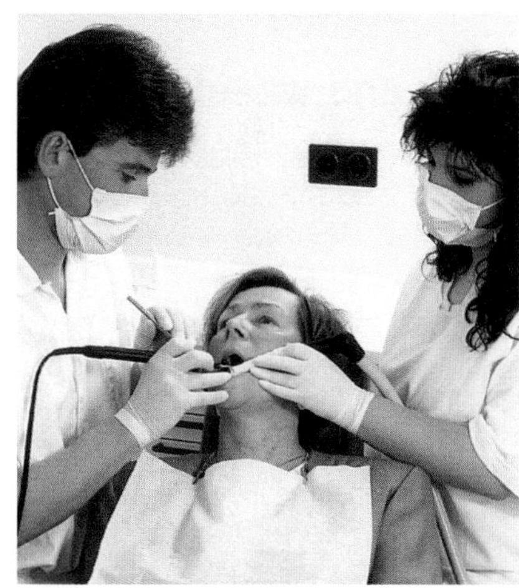

The hard coating of tartar is 'shaken' from the teeth by the ultrasonic vibrations

Other uses of ultrasound

Ultrasound can be used for cleaning clothes and other materials. The very high frequency of the ultrasonic vibrations shakes the dirt from the clothing. Dentists may use ultrasound to clean the coating of tartar from your teeth, helping to prevent gum disease.

Ultrasound is also used to detect cracks in the metal of aircraft bodies and wings, where continuous flexing may have caused 'stress fractures'.

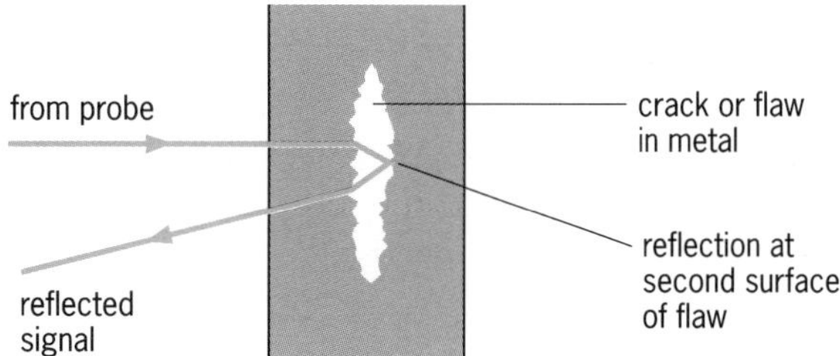

Any fracture in the metal will reflect the ultrasound waves. By analysing the echoed signal, a trained engineer can spot any dangers immediately

★ THINGS TO DO

1 The speed of sound in human tissue is about 100 m/s. If a baby is 10 centimetres below an ultrasound probe, how long will it take the pulse of ultrasound to travel from the probe, to the baby, then back to the probe?

2 Ultrasound can be used in the search for underground oil and gas reserves. An ultrasonic signal is sent down into the ground at different places. The time taken between the pulses being transmitted and received is measured.

The results shown below were taken over a long section of land in the Middle East.

a) Calculate the depth from which the first returned pulses were reflected. (The speed of sound through the rock is 4 km/s.)

b) Calculate the depth from which the second pulses were reflected.

c) Draw a diagram showing what you think the ultrasound survey shows below the surface. Could it be an oil or gas pocket? Explain your answer.

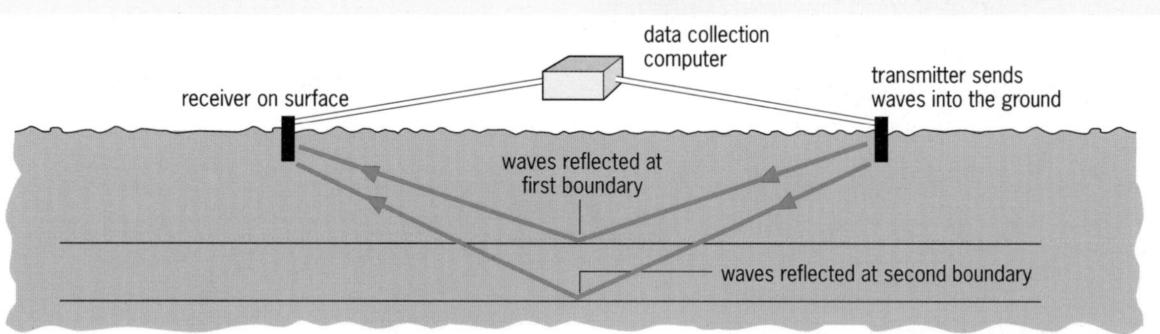

Position	A	B	C	D	E	F	G	H
Time to first echo/s	2.0	1.8	1.7	1.5	1.2	1.4	1.6	1.9
Time to second echo/s	2.0	1.9	2.0	1.8	2.1	2.0	1.9	1.9

4.5 Transverse waves

Water waves are an example of another type of wave called a **transverse wave**. As waves pass through water, the particles of water move up and down. It is this vertical oscillation of the water which is used to generate electricity using wave generators (see page 39).

Transverse waves can be demonstrated using a long length of rubber tubing laid across the floor. By flicking one end regularly, a wave can be seen passing through the tubing. The movement of the tubing transfers energy from one end to the other.

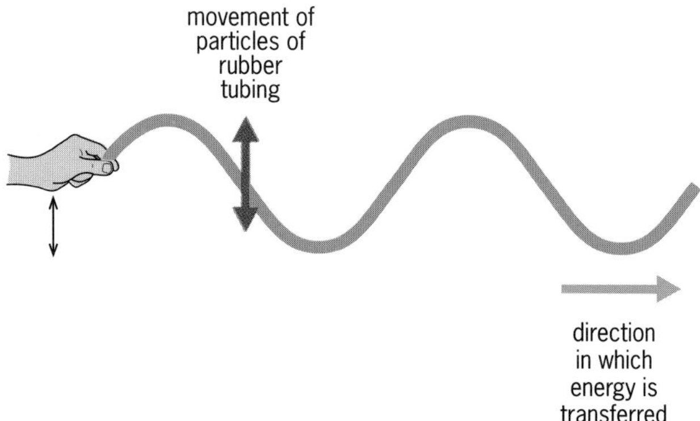
movement of particles of rubber tubing
direction in which energy is transferred

Notice that each particle of the tubing moves at right angles to the direction in which the wave is transferring energy. (Remember that in a longitudinal wave the particles move parallel to the direction in which the wave is travelling.)

By flicking the tube faster (increasing the frequency of the 'source') the wavelength of the waves decreases.

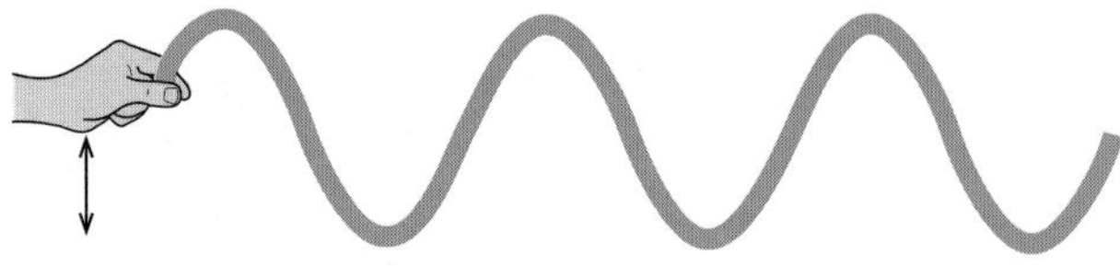

You may recognise the similarities between these waves and longitudinal waves as represented on an oscilloscope.

Speed, frequency and wavelength

All waves are characterised by their wavelength, frequency and speed.

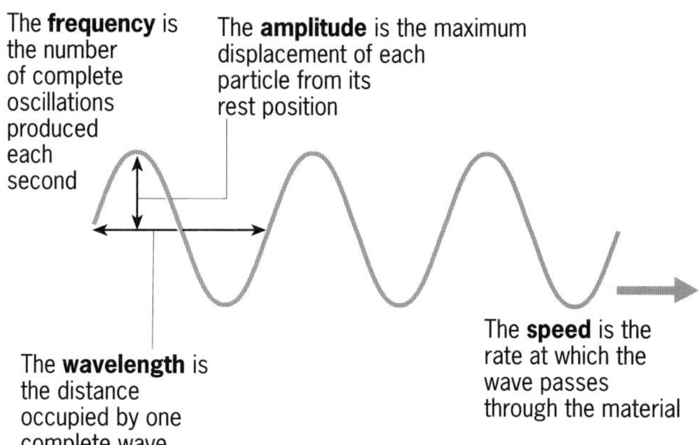
The **frequency** is the number of complete oscillations produced each second
The **amplitude** is the maximum displacement of each particle from its rest position
The **wavelength** is the distance occupied by one complete wave
The **speed** is the rate at which the wave passes through the material

Wave characteristics for a transverse wave

The wavelength depends on the frequency of the wave. Imagine that this transverse wave has a frequency of 5 Hz (5 complete

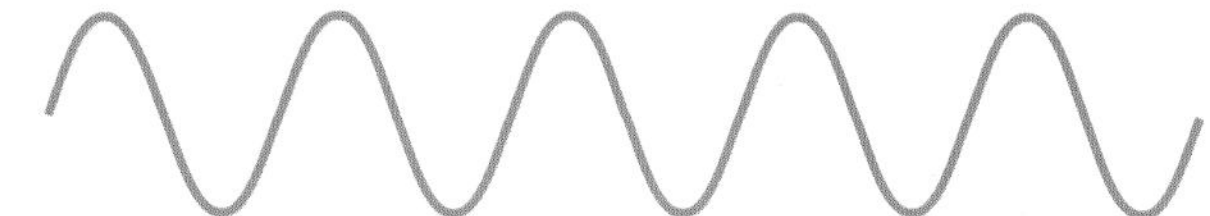

oscillations or vibrations take place each second). One complete oscillation is produced every one-fifth of a second. The distance occupied by each wave (the wavelength) is therefore equal to the distance travelled by the wave in one-fifth of a second (distance = speed × time).

If the frequency is doubled to 10 Hz, then one complete wave is produced every one-tenth of a second. The distance occupied by

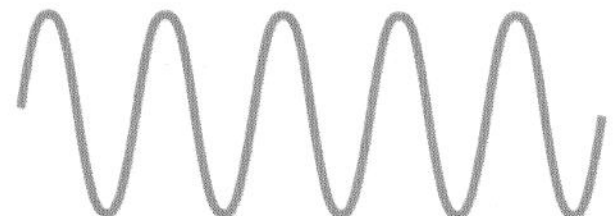

one wave (the wavelength) will be the distance travelled in one-tenth of a second. Assuming the speed is constant this will be half of the original value, so the wavelength will be half of the original value. As the frequency has doubled, the wavelength is halved.

Electromagnetic waves

Most of the waves we will study in this part of the book belong to a family called **electromagnetic waves** – so called because they consist of electrical and magnetic oscillations. Radio waves, TV waves, microwaves and light all belong to this family. All electromagnetic waves are transverse waves which can pass through a vacuum, and they have a common speed – 300 000 000 m/s (or 300 x 10^6 m/s) in a vacuum.

The wave equation

We have seen that the wavelength of a longitudinal or a transverse wave depends on its frequency and its speed. It therefore seems reasonable to assume that there is a general relationship which applies to both types of wave. The relationship is the **wave equation**:

$$\text{speed (m/s)} = \text{frequency (Hz)} \times \text{wavelength (m)}$$

Knowing, for example, that the wavelength of Radio 1 is 275 m (see your newspaper), we can then calculate the frequency of the waves which carry the signal to us.
The frequency of Radio 1 is therefore:

$$\text{frequency} = \frac{\text{speed}}{\text{wavelength}}$$
$$= \frac{300\,000\,000\ \text{m/s}}{275\ \text{m}}$$
$$= 1\,090\,000\ \text{Hz or } 1090\ \text{kHz}$$

★ THINGS TO DO

1 Copy and complete this table.

Wave type	**Speed**/m/s	**Frequency**/Hz	**Wavelength**/m
sound wave	300	50	
wave on rubber tubing	3		1
water wave		0.5	4

2 The photograph shows a water droplet falling into a pond. Why does the amplitude of the ripples get smaller as they move further away from the point where the water droplet hits the water?

3 When a swimming-pool wave machine was turned on, a young boy floating on an inflatable ring was seen to bob up and down 12 times per minute. It took each wave 5 seconds to travel through the 25 metre pool.
a) What was the frequency of the waves in the pool? Explain your answer.
b) Calculate the speed of the waves through the water.
c) Calculate the wavelength of the waves produced.

4 A microwave oven produces waves which have a frequency of 2.5 × 10^9 Hz (or 2500 000 000 Hz). Assuming the speed of electromagnetic waves is 300 000 000 m/s, calculate the wavelength of the waves in the microwave oven.

4.6 Visible light

Light is an important member of the family of electromagnetic waves because it is visible. Because we can see light, we can study how it behaves under different conditions. That provides us with clues about the nature of waves in general, and how other electromagnetic waves might behave under similar conditions.

Light is visible because the cells on the retina of the eye respond to its range of wavelengths (see *GCSE Science Double Award Biology*, topic 1.26). The same cells cannot respond to other wavelengths, such as those of X-rays, so these waves are invisible.

SONY

Light is reflected from smooth, shiny surfaces, allowing us to see things even when we may not be looking directly at them

Reflections

We see things when light from them enters our eyes. By arranging a mirror at just the right angle we can see things which would otherwise be outside our 'field of view'.

In all cases, the light is reflected at the same angle at which it strikes the mirror.

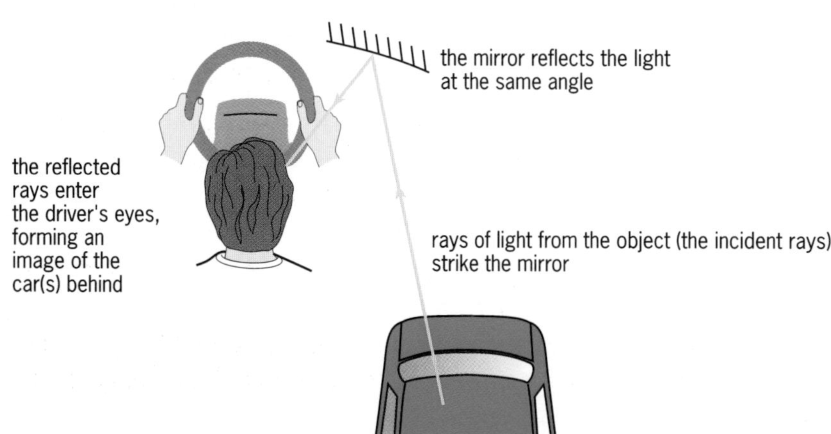

the mirror reflects the light at the same angle
the reflected rays enter the driver's eyes, forming an image of the car(s) behind
rays of light from the object (the incident rays) strike the mirror

Drivers need to know whether other cars are approaching them from behind

Shopkeepers need to see what is going on out of their sight

The angle of incidence and the angle of reflection

The rays of light which reach a mirror from an object are called the *incident rays*. After reflection, they are called the *reflected rays*. To help us draw accurate ray diagrams a line is drawn at 90° to the mirror at the point where a ray strikes it. The line is called a *normal*.

The angle between the incident ray and the normal is called the *angle of incidence*. The angle between the reflected ray and the normal is called the *angle of reflection*.

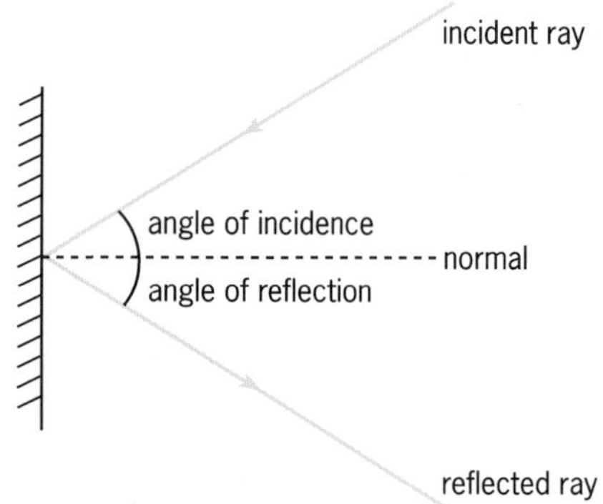

incident ray
angle of incidence
normal
angle of reflection
reflected ray

Whenever reflection occurs, from any polished surface such as a mirror, *the angle of incidence is equal to the angle of reflection.*

Reflected twice

The direction of light can be changed several times by using more than one mirror. A simple periscope, for example, changes the direction of light twice using two mirrors.

The light emerges from a periscope at a different level to that at which it entered. The driver of this bus can see what is happening on the upper deck without leaving her seat!

★ THINGS TO DO

1 This plan shows the exit from a park. The exit road meets the main road on a bend. Drivers leaving the park cannot tell whether there is anything approaching them from the right.

Draw the plan in your notebook and show where you would place a mirror so that drivers leaving the park could see around the bend. Add any notes about the angle at which the mirror must be placed.

2 Why is the writing on the bonnet of this ambulance 'back-to-front'? Test your idea using a plane mirror. How would you write your own name so that it looked the 'right way round' when reflected?

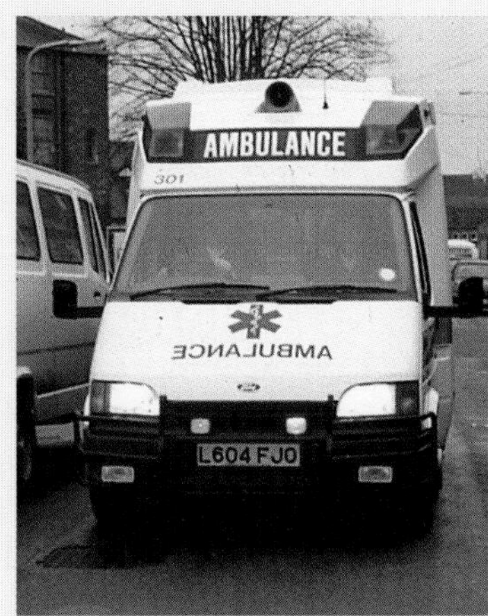

3 Design and carry out an experiment using a plane (flat) mirror to show someone that the angle of incidence is always equal to the angle of reflection.

Write a full account of your experiment, including any measurements which you make. Don't forget to say what you found out.

4 This diagram shows what happens when light strikes a mirror and then enters your eye.

a) Trace the rays which enter the eye backwards to find out where they appear to be coming from (i.e. where the eye sees the image of the object).

b) What is the connection between the position of the object and the position of the image seen by the eye?

c) How could this deceive drivers using their mirrors to judge distances?

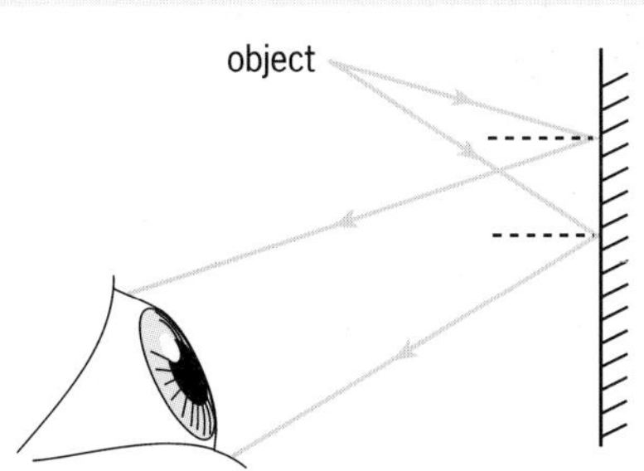

4.7 Refracting light

There are situations when we need to change the direction of light but cannot use mirrors. The lenses in spectacles, for example, must allow the light to pass through them but must also change the direction of the light by the right amount to correct any defects in the vision of the wearer.

The person will then be able to see objects clearly. The light has been 'refracted' – its direction is changed as it passes through the lens.

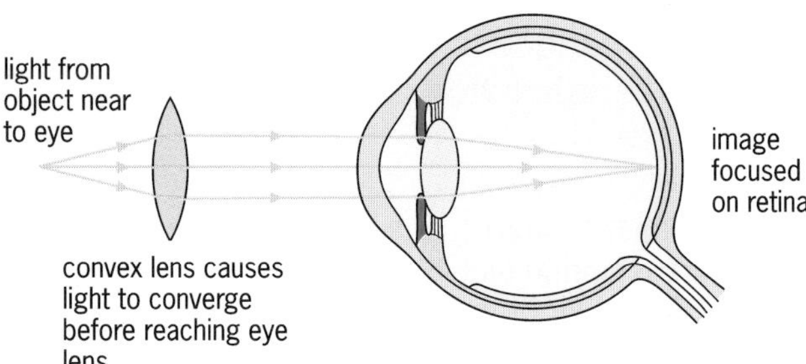

A spectacle lens (or contact lens) changes the direction of the light so that it is focused at the retina

Refraction occurs whenever light (and other waves) passes from one substance into another.

Light passes easily through gases such as the air. It travels more slowly through other substances, such as glass, water or perspex, which are optically 'denser'. As a result, when light passes from one substance into another its speed changes. There is also a change in wavelength.

The change in speed can cause a change in direction. The diagrams show what happens as light passes through a block of glass.

If the light meets the block at 90° it passes straight through with no change in direction. The light slows down as it passes into the glass and speeds up again as it passes from the glass back into the air

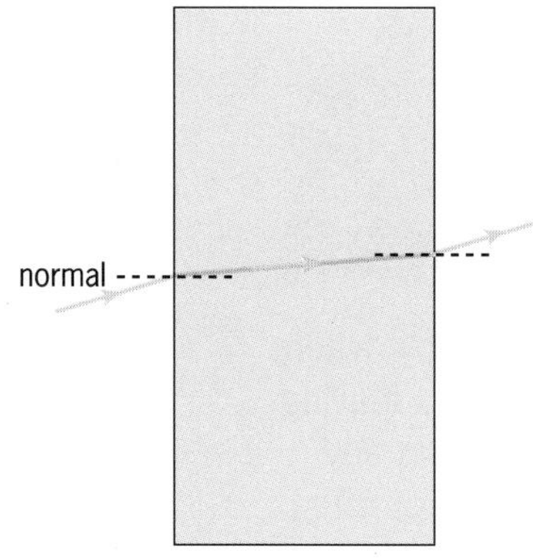

When the light meets the block at any angle other than 90°, its direction changes at the boundary between the two substances. Because it is passing into a 'denser' material, the ray is refracted towards the normal (a line drawn at 90° to the surface at the point where light strikes it).

As the light passes from the block back into the air – a less dense substance – it is refracted away from the normal. Notice that the ray leaving the block is parallel to the incident ray, but slightly displaced to one side

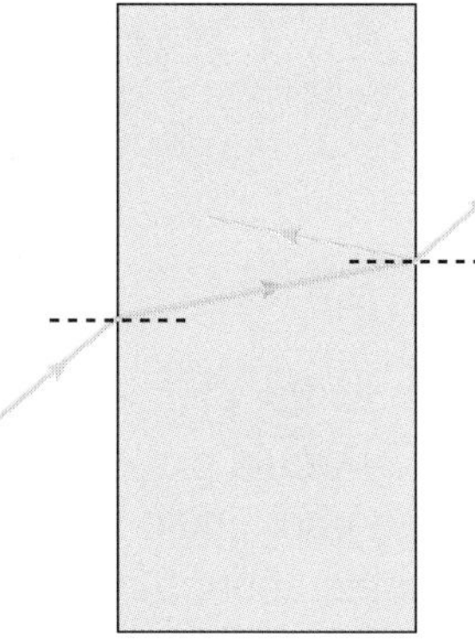

Larger angles of incidence produce a greater degree of refraction at both surfaces, and the ray which emerges from the block is displaced more to one side.

Notice that at the boundary where the light passes from the denser material (glass) into the less dense material (air), some light is reflected. The amount which is reflected depends on the angle of incidence of the light on the boundary – the larger the angle of incidence, the brighter the reflected part

Seeing is not believing

Refraction explains some strange effects which you may have already noticed. The bottom of a swimming pool, for example, always looks closer to the surface than it really is. Similarly, a fish near the bottom of a river or a pond is always deeper than it seems.

Light reflected from the fish travels through the water towards you. As it passes from the water into the air, it refracts away from the normal because it has travelled from a denser substance (water) into a less dense substance (air).

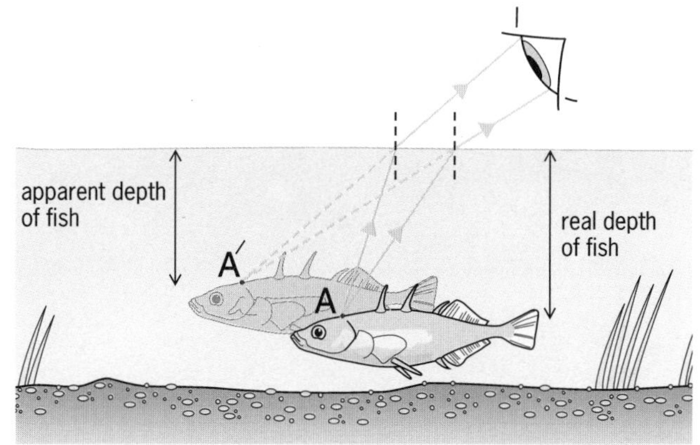

Refraction makes the fish appear nearer the surface

The light entering your eye from point A on the fish appears to come from point A′. Your eye 'sees' the fish higher up than it really is. The 'apparent depth' is less than the real depth.

★ THINGS TO DO

1 Glass is (optically) denser than water. Water is denser than air. Copy and complete the following diagrams showing what happens to a ray of light as it crosses the boundary between two of these substances.

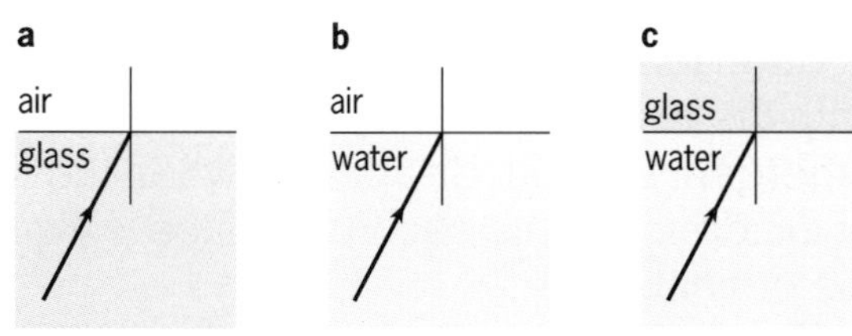

2 The illustrations below show two perspex blocks, each with one curved surface. Perspex is denser than air.

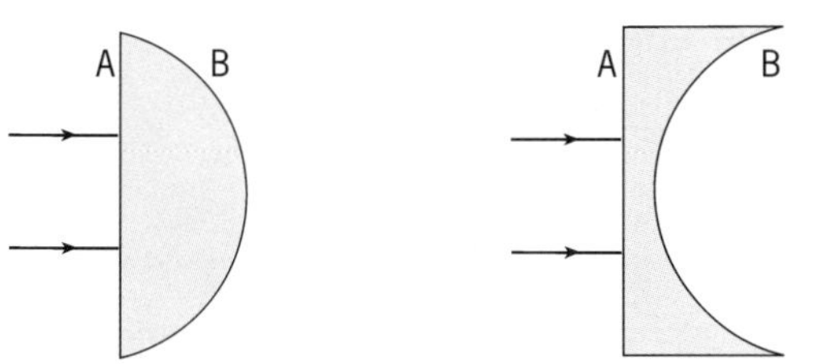

a) Copy the diagram and draw the path of the two rays as they pass through both blocks into the air on side B.

b) How does your diagram compare with what happens as light passes through a convex lens?

3 a) The illustration below shows rays of light striking two glass lenses. Trace them into your notebook. Use the information on the opposite page to predict the path of the rays as they pass through each lens. Test your ideas using a ray box and lenses.

b) What do your diagrams suggest about the relationship between the thickness of a convex lens and the distance between the lens and the point at which the rays will converge (the focal length)?

Plan how you could test your ideas. If possible, carry out your tests and prepare a report describing what you find out.

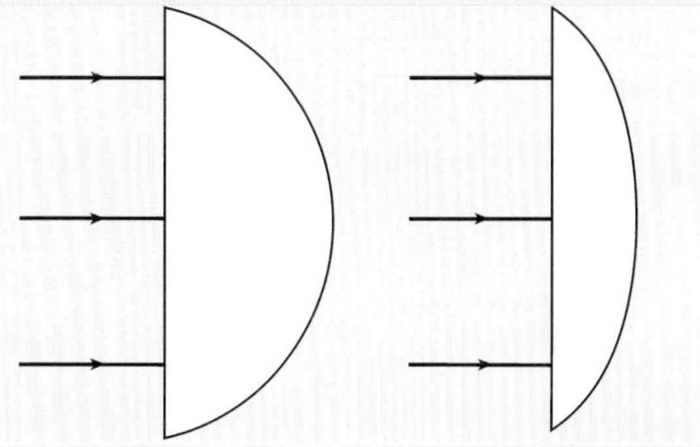

Internal reflection

'Cats' eyes' are specially shaped blocks of glass or plastic which *reflect* light from car headlights back towards the driver. This type of reflection, which takes place inside a transparent substance, is called *internal reflection*.

Total internal reflection

In the previous topic you saw that when light is refracted at a boundary, some light may also be reflected. *Internal reflection only happens as light passes from a dense substance into a less dense substance.* The amount of light which is reflected depends on the angle at which the incident ray strikes the boundary.

At small angles of incidence – **a**, the refracted ray (leaving the block) is strong but the reflected ray is weak. The angle at which the ray is reflected from the boundary is the same as the angle of incidence. As the angle of incidence increases – **b**, the reflected ray becomes stronger

At a certain angle of incidence, called the **critical angle**, the emergent ray is refracted at 90° to the boundary – **c**. If the angle of incidence is increased again, making it bigger than the critical angle, then all of the light is reflected – **d** — this is **total internal reflection**

Measuring the critical angle

The critical angle for glass or perspex can be measured using the apparatus shown here.

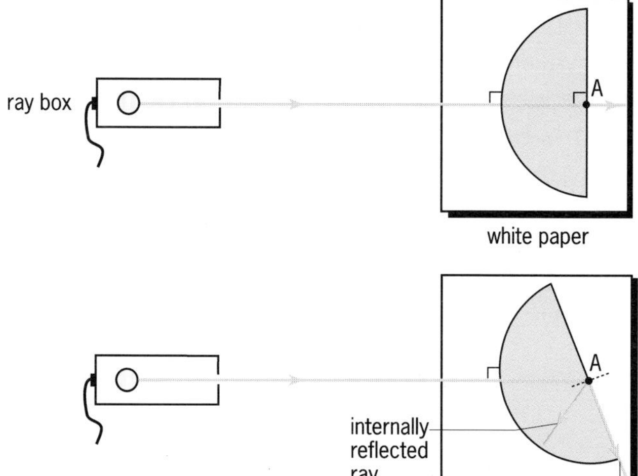

The ray is directed towards a point (A) marked on paper below the 'centre' of the semicircular glass block. Because the light strikes the first surface at 90° it will pass directly to the second surface with no change in direction. If the block is then slowly turned with the ray still incident on point A, the emergent ray will 'disappear' when the angle of incidence at the second surface is equal to the critical angle.

The outline of the block can be drawn on the paper, the positions of the incident ray and the refracted ray can be marked, and a normal can be constructed at point A.

The critical angle can then be measured from the lines on the paper.

a

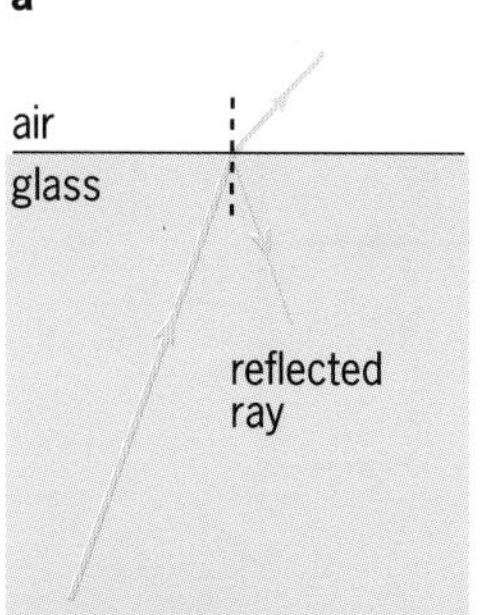

b

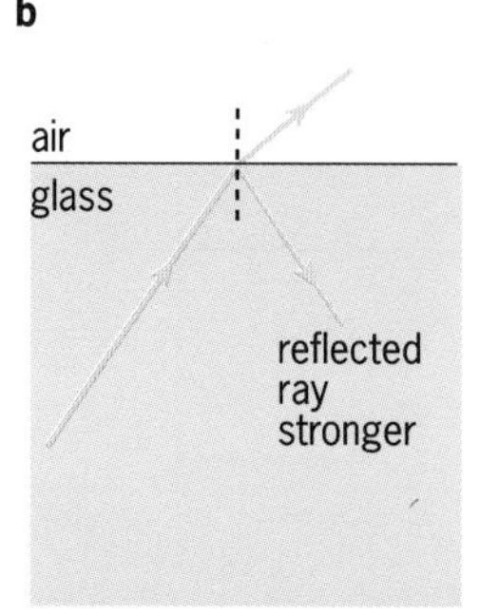

c **d**

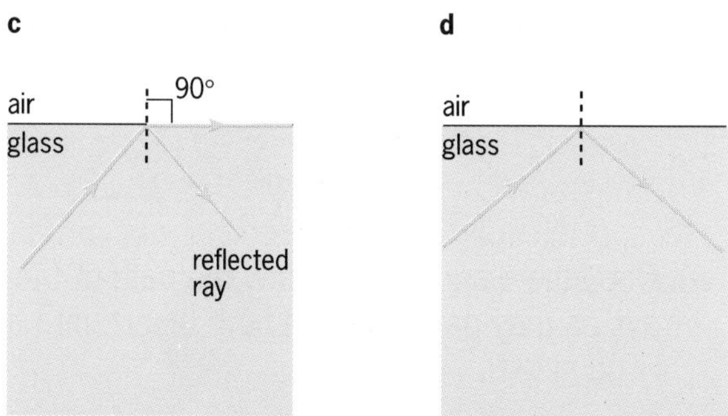

Prism binoculars

Binoculars can produce large magnifications and yet be conveniently short because they use right-angled prisms. The prisms are arranged in such a way that the light strikes the boundary between the glass and the air at an angle which is greater than the critical angle. The light is then totally internally reflected to the second prism where the same thing happens. After being reflected the light emerges from the eye lens, producing an upright, highly magnified image.

There are two major advantages of using prisms to reflect the light, rather than mirrors:

- the surfaces of prisms do not deteriorate in the same way as the silvered surface of a mirror,
- the image is brighter – when total internal reflection occurs, more of the light is reflected than would be the case from the surface of a mirror.

To get a really big magnification, binoculars using just lenses (like a telescope) would be so long that you wouldn't be able to hold them steady – and you would see everything upside down!

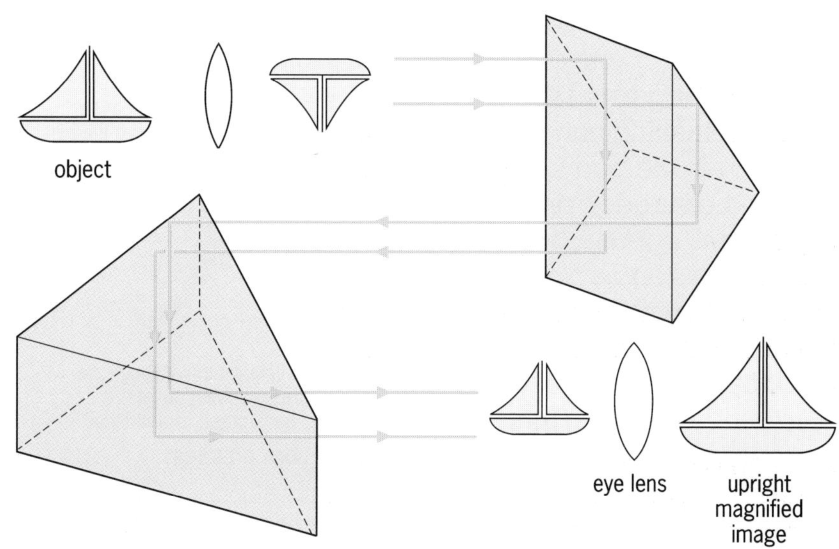

Prisms reflect light through binoculars

★ THINGS TO DO

1. Carry out the experiment described opposite to find the critical angle for glass or perspex.
2. Draw some sketches showing how you would design 'cats' eyes' using blocks of plastic. You should show the shape of the plastic block, and how it will reflect the light from headlights back towards the driver.
3. The diagrams show two ways in which prisms can be arranged so that light is internally reflected. Copy each of the diagrams and complete the rays showing how they will pass through each arrangement.

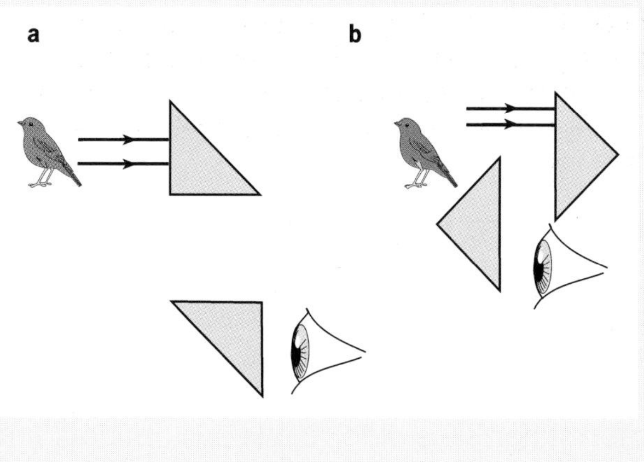

4.9 Through the keyhole

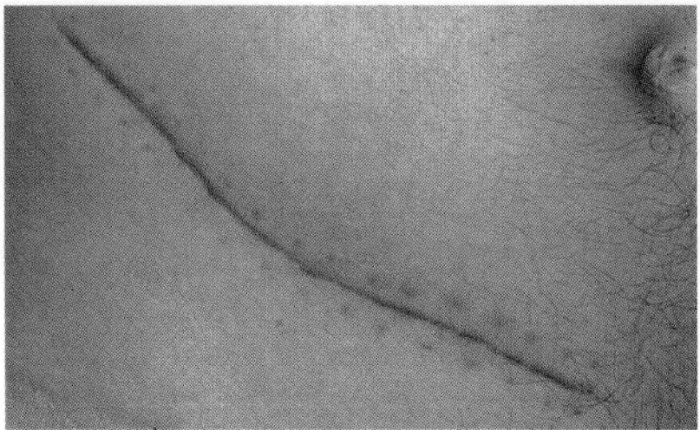

In the past people took several weeks to recover from the effects of a major hospital operation. Much of the recovery time was spent waiting for muscle and other tissue to heal after being cut open

The use of optical fibres allows the surgeon to see inside the body – the part which is being operated on is viewed on the screen of the monitor

Surgeons can now carry out some major operations using ‘keyhole surgery’. This involves making only a small opening in the body, through which the surgeon passes very small operating instruments and a bundle of **optical fibres**. The patient suffers much less discomfort and there is less damage to surrounding tissues than with ‘open surgery’.

Light passes through the inner bundle of fibres, illuminating the inside of the body

Reflected light returns through the outer fibres, carrying an image which is transmitted to a monitor

Optical fibre bundles

Optical fibres are long, fine, flexible fibres of a material through which light can pass. They are used in bundles. There may be two bundles – one inside the other.

The light passes through optical fibres because it enters at a large angle – greater than the critical angle of the material of the fibre. The ray is totally internally reflected inside the fibre, passing through with successive reflections from the sides. Eventually it emerges from the opposite end of the fibre, with very little light loss.

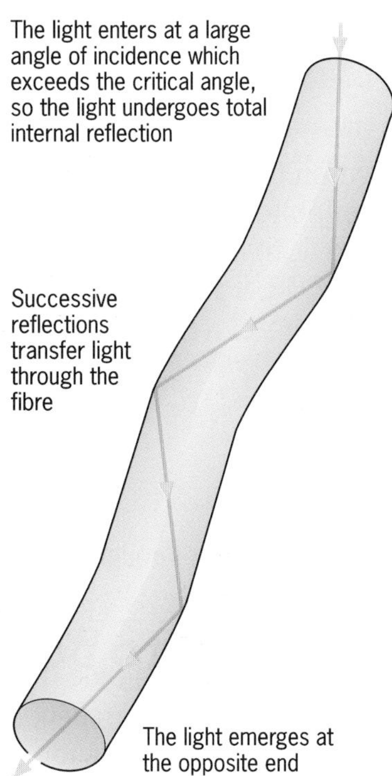

The light enters at a large angle of incidence which exceeds the critical angle, so the light undergoes total internal reflection
Successive reflections transfer light through the fibre
The light emerges at the opposite end

Light transmission through an optical fibre

The future of communications

Cables of optical fibres are now replacing the copper cables which have been used to transfer information through our telecommunications system. Optical fibre cables are lighter and cheaper than copper cables and can transmit much more information. The older cable system could transmit up to 1000 telephone conversations simultaneously. Optical cables can transmit as many as 11 000 conversations through *each pair* of fibres!

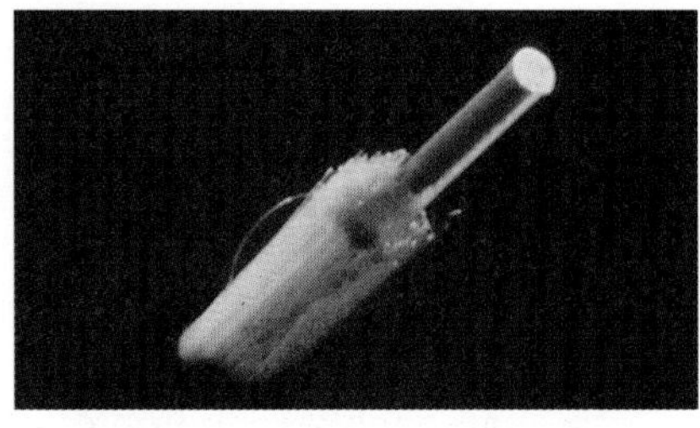

Optical fibres and strength member in an optical cable

The principles are similar to those described opposite – coded 'light messages' pass through the optical fibre undergoing successive total internal reflections. A form of infra-red 'light' is used because it is purer and passes through glass better than visible light.

Before information is transmitted through the fibres, *analogue* information (such as the alternating voltage from a telephone mouthpiece) is converted into a *digital* signal. Digital signals are effectively coded 'pulses', each pulse representing a *bit* of information.

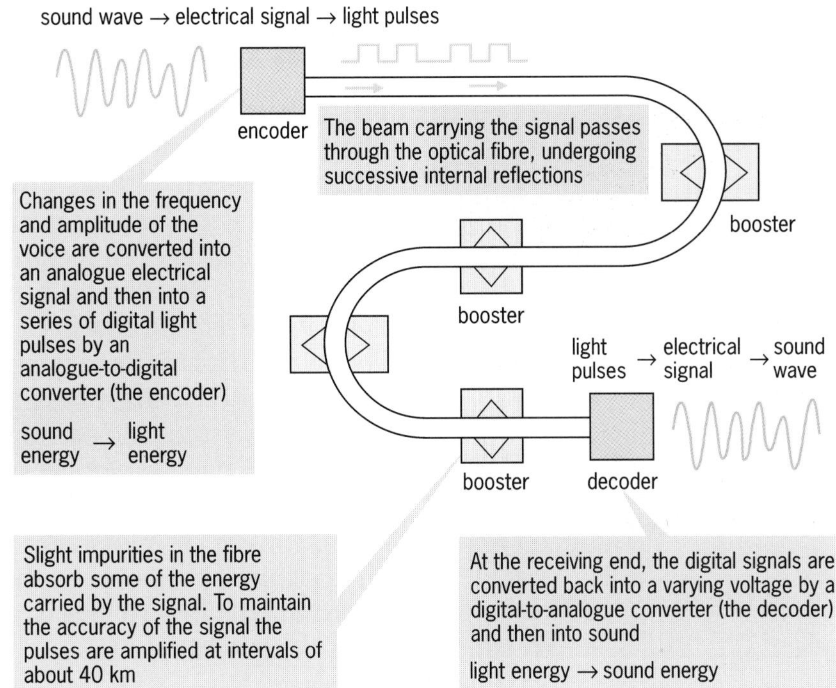

sound wave → electrical signal → light pulses
encoder
The beam carrying the signal passes through the optical fibre, undergoing successive internal reflections
booster
Changes in the frequency and amplitude of the voice are converted into an analogue electrical signal and then into a series of digital light pulses by an analogue-to-digital converter (the encoder)
sound energy → light energy
booster
light pulses → electrical signal → sound wave
booster
decoder
Slight impurities in the fibre absorb some of the energy carried by the signal. To maintain the accuracy of the signal the pulses are amplified at intervals of about 40 km
At the receiving end, the digital signals are converted back into a varying voltage by a digital-to-analogue converter (the decoder) and then into sound
light energy → sound energy

Further advantages of optical cables over copper cables are that less energy is lost in transmission (so fewer boosters are needed) and there is no interference ('noise' or 'cross-talk') as there is with electrical signals.

In the future, if you want to watch a video, you may just have to make a phone call ordering the video of your choice and stating the time at which you want to watch it. The video will be transmitted through optical cable direct to your home.

★ THINGS TO DO

1 This illustration shows a reflector on the rear mudguard of a bicycle. Copy the diagram and complete the rays showing what happens to the light after striking the reflector.

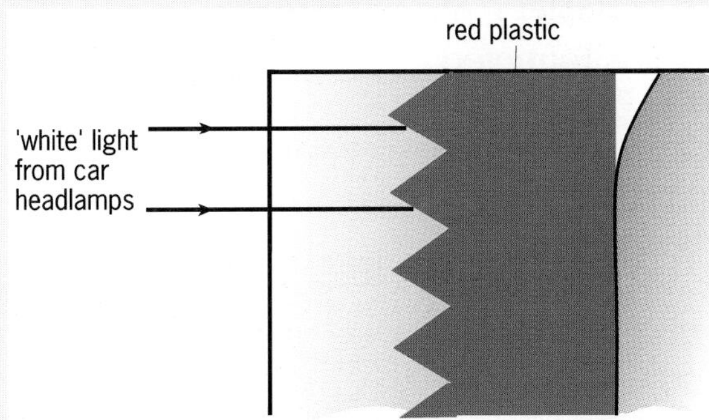

2 Draw the diagram on the right of an optical fibre.

a) Sketch the path of the single incident ray through the fibre.

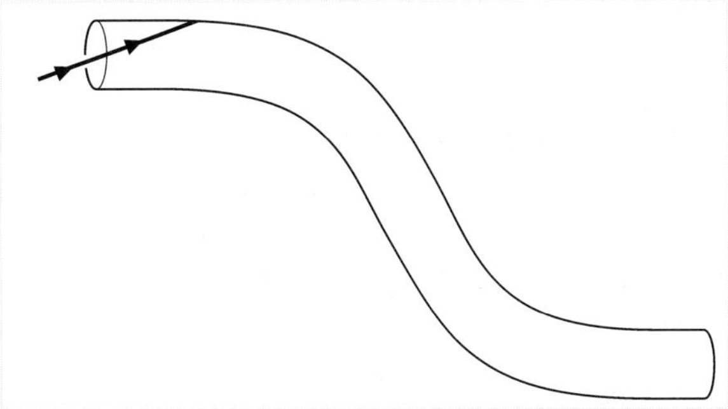

b) Mark two angles on your sketch which should have the same value.

c) The critical angle for the fibre is 43°. How will this affect the transmission of light through the fibre?

3 Make a list of the advantages of using optical fibres rather than metal cables for communication.

4.10 All the colours of the rainbow

The colours of the rainbow are not only formed in the sky. They can be formed in the spray from a hosepipe, in water drops, in pieces of glass or in diamonds, or even in icicles. The colours are formed because white light (sunlight) 'splits up' as it is refracted through these materials.

Light from the sun and from very hot lamps is often referred to as 'white' light because it has no discernible colour to it. The 'white' light is, in fact, seven colours which cannot be distinguished by the eye when they are mixed. When the light is refracted the seven colours sometimes become separated so that they can be clearly seen. (In the case of a rainbow the colours are formed when the light passes from dry air into a layer of water droplets which hang in the air after a shower.) The colours are known as the **spectrum** of white light. The effect of 'splitting up' the white light into these colours is called **dispersion**.

wavelength=0.0007 mm

wavelength=0.0004 mm

Red light has a longer wavelength than blue light

Colour and wavelength

All of the colours seen when white light is dispersed are electromagnetic waves with slightly different wavelengths. As we move through the spectrum from red to violet the wavelength decreases.

The wavelength of visible light is extremely small. Red light, for example, has a wavelength of 0.0007 mm. (That means that just over 1400 red light oscillations would fit into one millimetre.) Blue light has a wavelength of 0.0004 mm. Although the differences between these waves are very slight, they cause a different effect on the eye. It is our eyes and our brain, working together, which interpret these effects in terms of colour.

Dispersion through a prism

When a beam of light enters a glass prism at a non-zero angle of incidence, it is refracted. It passes through the glass and is refracted again as it leaves the glass and passes into the air.

Notice the direction in which the light is refracted at each surface and the angle through which the light is deviated. The larger the angle of incidence, the larger the angle of deviation.

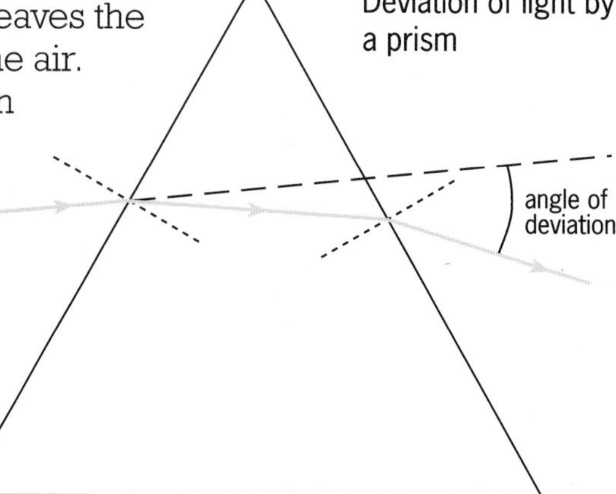

Deviation of light by a prism

At a certain angle of incidence, the colours of an incident beam of white light separate to form broad bands, each merging into the next. The spectrum can be seen on paper placed either below the prism, or held vertically behind it. Red light is deviated through the smallest angle and violet light is deviated through the greatest angle. This is because the shorter the wavelength, the greater the refraction at a boundary.

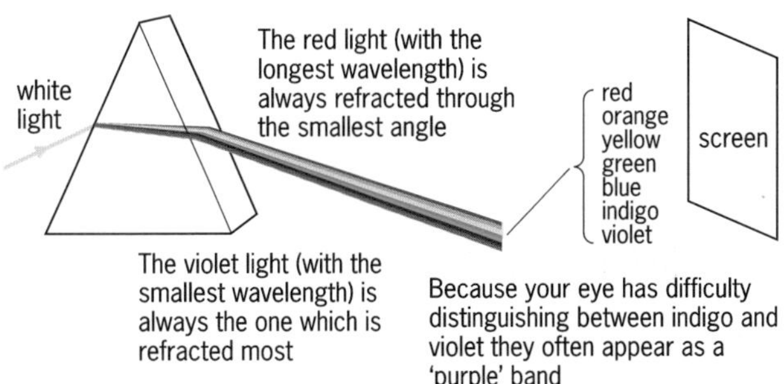
white light
The red light (with the longest wavelength) is always refracted through the smallest angle
red
orange
yellow
green
blue
indigo
violet
screen
The violet light (with the smallest wavelength) is always the one which is refracted most
Because your eye has difficulty distinguishing between indigo and violet they often appear as a 'purple' band

Forming a spectrum with a prism

Mixing the colours again

The colours of the spectrum can be re-mixed if a convex lens is placed in the path of the emerging beams. As they overlap, the colours form a white band again.

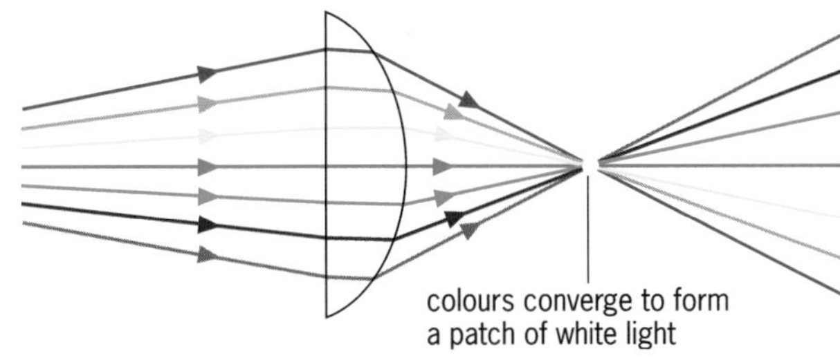
colours converge to form a patch of white light

Re-combining colours with a lens

Another way to show what happens when the colours are mixed is to use a disc on which the seven spectral colours are painted. When the disc is still, the colours are easily seen by reflected light: red paint reflects red light, etc. When, however, the disc is spun at high speed, the colours merge to form white again. (In this case they merge on the retina because your eye 'holds' an image of each colour for a short time.)

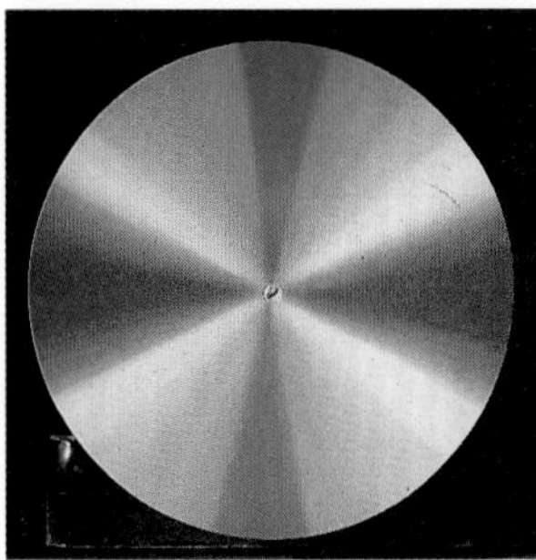

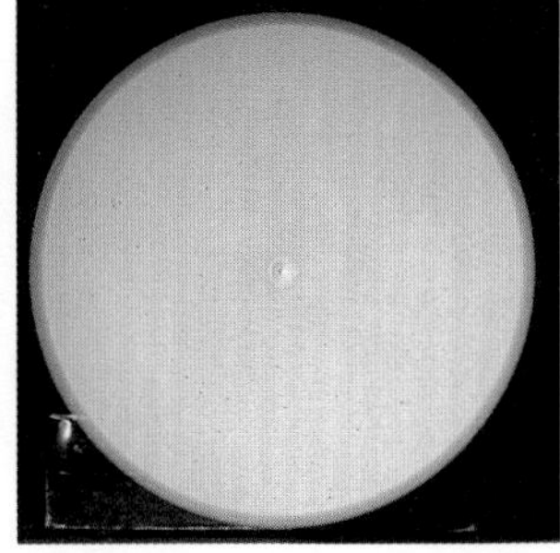

Re-combining colours with a colour disc

A world of colour

How many different colours do you think you see every day? 20? 100? 1000? Why does the grass look green? What causes the reds, oranges, yellows and browns of autumn trees? How many different coloured flowers are there? Imagine what the world would be like if we could not see colour.

Coloured materials contain chemicals called pigments. Different pigments reflect different colours. A material which contains a red pigment will reflect red light. It absorbs other colours, so they are not reflected into our eyes. Other pigments reflect green light, so the material appears green.

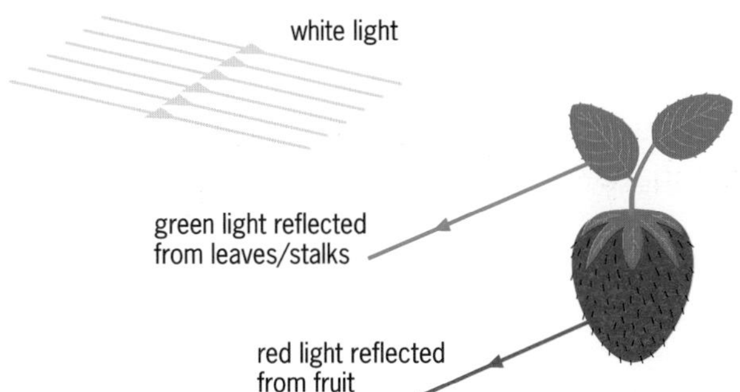
white light
green light reflected from leaves/stalks
red light reflected from fruit

When white light strikes a ripe strawberry containing a red pigment, only the red part of the light is reflected. All other colours in the white light are absorbed. Because only red light is reflected we see a red strawberry.The leaves and stalk contain a green pigment, so only the green part of the light is reflected. We see a green stalk and green leaves

Most dyes and pigments are not 'pure'. Each reflects a range of colours, producing the great variety of colours we see.

Black and white

Some materials reflect all the colours of white light. The colours enter your eye and are re-mixed, forming a white light image. The material therefore looks white.

Other materials, on the other hand, absorb all the colours in white light. No light is reflected and the eye perceives the absence of light as black.

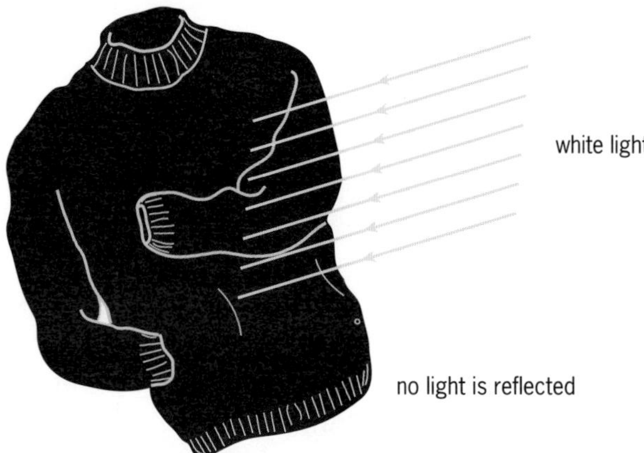

A black jumper absorbs all the incident white light

What colour are they really?

The colour of our food is important. Some food is even referred to by its colour – 'greens', for example, and of course the orange. We can sometimes tell that food has 'gone off' by its colour – greens become yellow, for example, and the white of a cut apple becomes brown. However, the instantly recognisable yellow of a banana, or the red of a tomato, is only true in white light. Seen in other coloured light these foods can look quite different.

The colour of an object depends on the colour of the light by which it is seen

Even what we think are natural food colours may not be what they seem. Salmon from fish farms, for example, do not naturally have pink flesh. Their flesh is 'artificially' coloured by pigments in the food provided for them.

INGREDIENTS: Sugar, Cornflour, Starch, Fumaric Acid, Salt, Acidity Regulator: Sodium Citrate; Lemon Oil, Corn Oil, Gelatine, Colour: Tumeric, Annatto.

Some foods have their colours enhanced using chemical or natural pigments

Coloured filters

When a coloured filter is placed in front of a white light source, only the light which has the same colour as the filter passes through. The other colours present in the white light are absorbed by the filter.

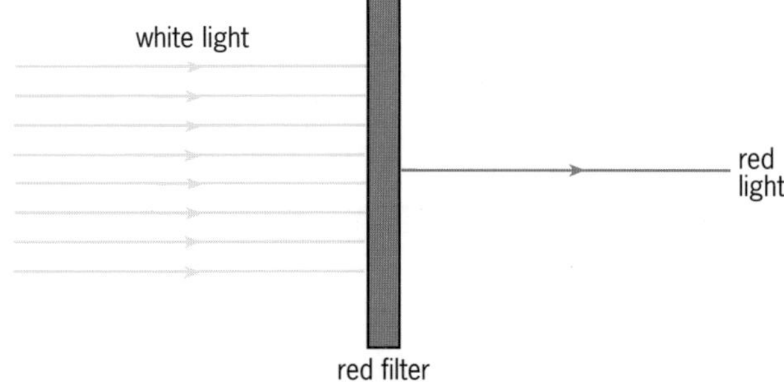

A red filter produces red light; a blue filter would produce blue light

Photographers often use filters to create special effects.

These pictures show how a photograph (*left*) can be altered with special filters and masks (*right*)

Primary and secondary colours

Red, blue and green are called **primary colours**. By mixing light of these colours in different ways you can make any other colour imaginable. On a television screen very small red, blue and green dots (arranged in triangles) are 'illuminated' by a stream of electrons. If the red and green dots are illuminated more than the blue, they produce yellow and that part of the screen appears yellow. Illuminating the dots in different ways produces other colours on the screen.

Yellow, magenta and cyan, each produced by equal mixing of two of the primary colours, are called **secondary colours**. If all three primary colours *or* all three secondary colours overlap they produce white light.

Each primary colour has a *complementary* secondary colour. The illustration on the right shows yellow is the secondary colour 'opposite' to blue. They are complementary colours. Similarly red and cyan, and green and magenta are complementary colours. When mixed they produce white light.

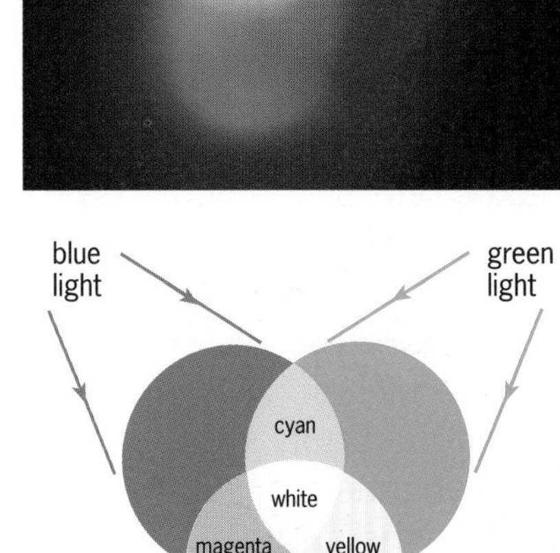

blue light
green light
cyan
white
magenta
yellow
red light

Mixing the primary colours to give the secondary colours

★ THINGS TO DO

1 Use a prism and a white light source to produce your own spectrum on some white paper or card.

Write your own notes, including a diagram, describing what you do and what you see.

2 Produce the spectrum of white light on a screen as you did in the previous activity. Now place a piece of red plastic (or gel) in the path of the light emerging from the prism. Make a note of what happens to the spectrum seen on the screen.

Do the same using blue and green gels and describe what happens. What happens if you use all three gels together?

Try to explain the effects you see using diagrams.

3 Some people say that insects are more attracted to green and yellow materials than to any other colour. Plan how you could test this idea. If possible, carry out your tests and report what you find out.

4 The flowers in this picture were photographed in white light. Complete the table describing how each flower would appear when seen in the other coloured lights.

Colour of light	Red rose would appear	White rose would appear
red		
blue		
green		

4.11 Is light really a wave?

So far we have seen that light can be reflected and refracted. We have also said that the colours of the spectrum of white light have different wavelengths. This makes one big assumption – that light really is a wave.

After all, a solid object such as a rubber ball will be reflected when it strikes a wall or the floor, and the angle of reflection will be equal to the angle of incidence. The same ball, rolled down a slope which suddenly gets steeper (causing a change of speed), may also change direction in a similar way to light when it is refracted. So why can light not be a stream of particles?

To find out more, we need to make more comparisons between the behaviour of water waves and light waves.

Reflection of water waves

By placing barriers, either straight or curved, in the path of water waves in a ripple tank, the behaviour of the waves when reflected can be seen. When this is compared with the reflection of light in similar conditions, it is clear that water waves and light waves behave in the same way.

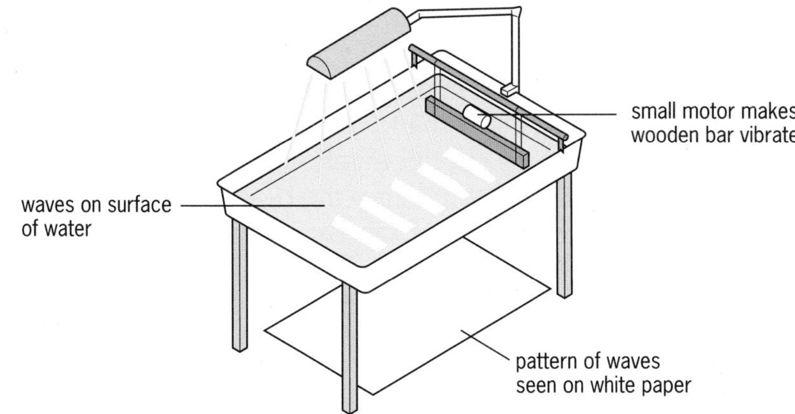

The way in which water waves behave can be studied using a ripple tank

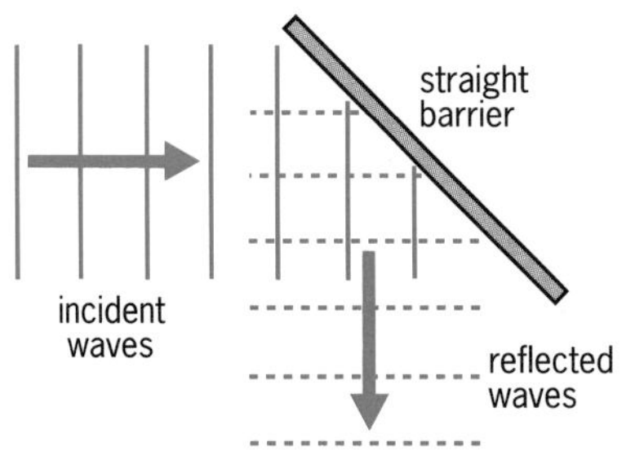

Water waves are reflected from the barrier at the same angle as they strike it

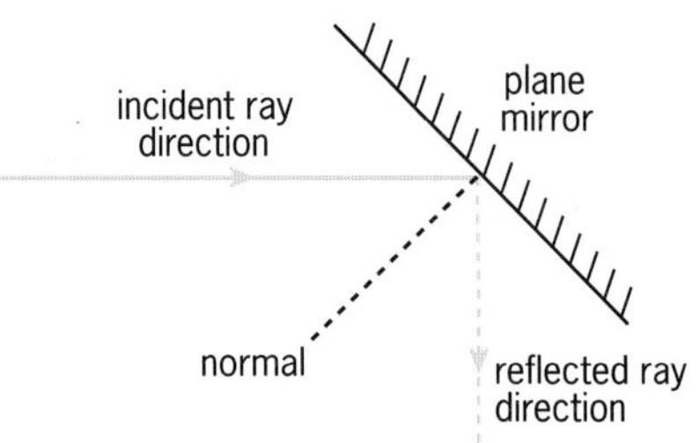

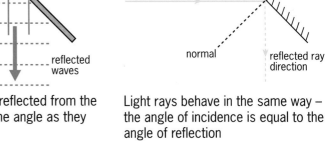

Light rays behave in the same way – the angle of incidence is equal to the angle of reflection

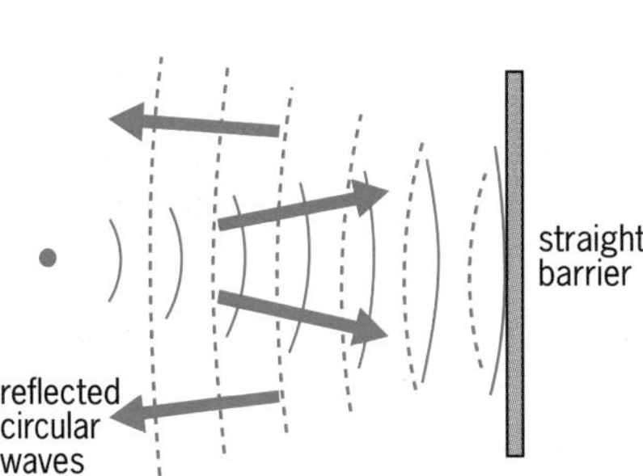

Diverging (circular) water waves diverge further after being reflected

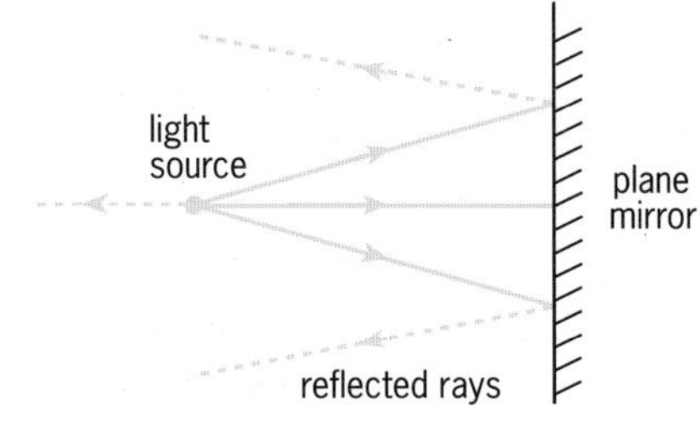

Diverging light rays behave in the same way

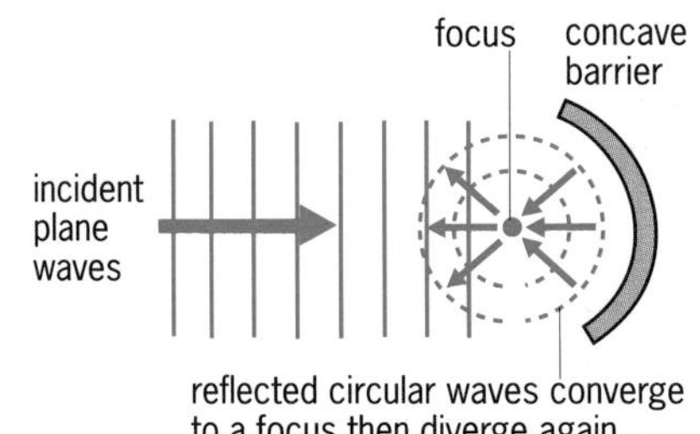

When parallel water waves strike a concave reflector they converge to a focus in front of the barrier and then diverge from it

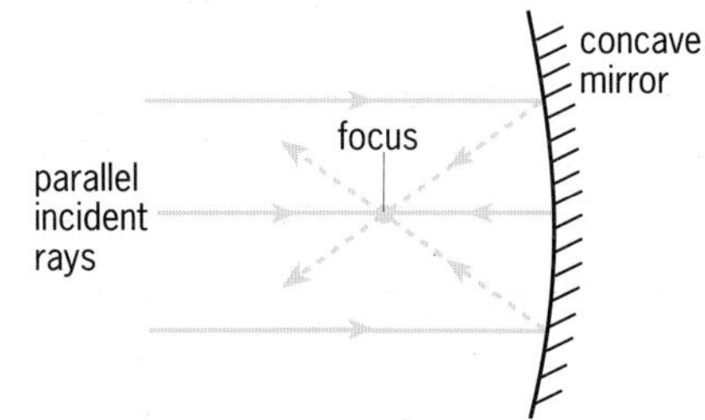

Similarly, when parallel light rays strike a concave mirror they reflect to a focus in front of the mirror and then diverge

Refraction of water waves

Water waves travel more slowly in shallow water than in deeper water. This can be shown by placing a flat perspex or glass plate in the bottom of the ripple tank to reduce the depth of the water in one section.

As the water waves pass into the shallow section at any angle other than 90° to the boundary, the direction of the waves changes and their wavelength decreases. (The frequency of the waves does not change.) These changes happen because the speed changes. As the waves slow down (entering the shallow water) they are 'bent' towards the normal. Their behaviour is exactly the same as that of light passing from one substance into an optically denser substance.

If the piece of perspex placed in the tank is convex, then the waves can be seen to behave in the same way as parallel rays of light striking a convex lens.

At a boundary where the speed of the water waves is reduced, the waves are refracted towards the normal

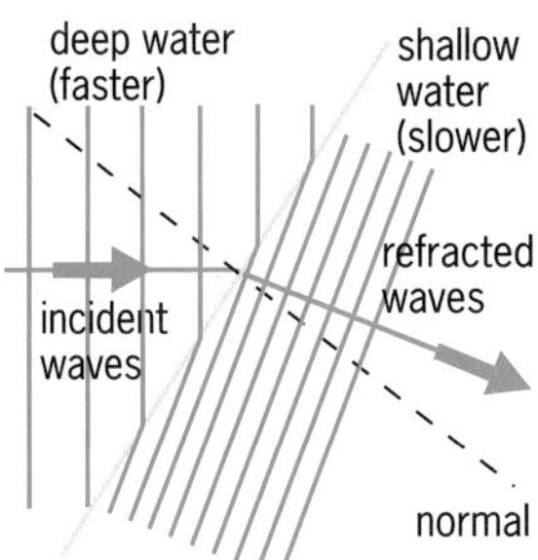

Light rays are refracted in the same way on entering a denser substance

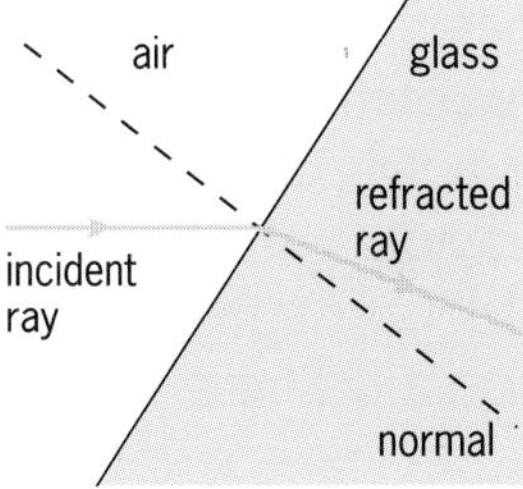

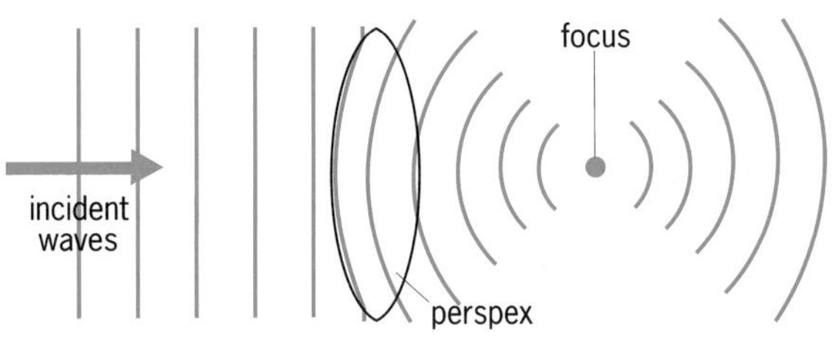

Parallel water waves converge to a focus after passing through a convex piece of perspex

convex lens

focus

incident rays

Parallel light behaves in a similar way on passing through a convex lens

It is observations like these, and others which we consider later, that lead us to believe that, because light behaves in the same way as transverse water waves, the light itself must be travelling as a transverse wave.

★ THINGS TO DO

1 Use a ripple tank and a ray box to carry out your own experiments comparing the behaviour of water waves and light rays.

2 At a shoreline the depth of the sea decreases as illustrated. Make a sketch of the illustration and show what will happen to the waves as they move closer to the shore. Add labels to your diagram to describe any changes which cannot be shown.

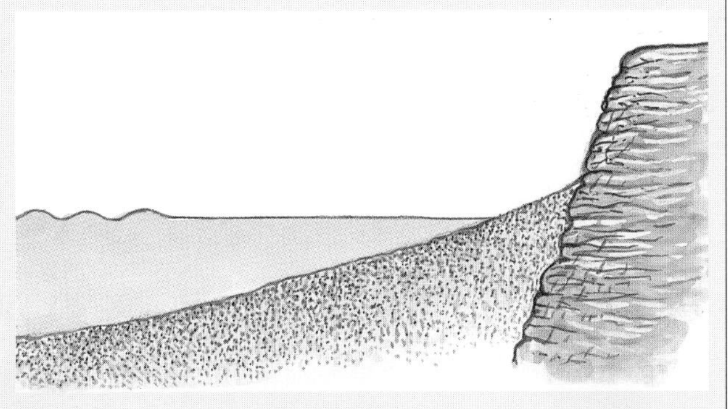

The electromagnetic spectrum

On page 180 we described how visible light consists of a group of waves which have slightly different wavelengths. The cells of the retina interpret these slight differences as different colours.

Visible light is one group of a much larger family of electromagnetic waves which together make up the **electromagnetic spectrum**. Each group of waves in the spectrum has a different range of wavelengths from each other group. Because electromagnetic waves obey the wave equation (see page 171) and all travel at the same speed, each group may also be characterised by its *frequency* range.

Electromagnetic waves have certain features which are common to them all. They:

- transfer energy from place to place,
- are transverse waves,
- travel at the same speed (the speed of light) – around 300 000 km/s in a vacuum,
- can be reflected and refracted,
- can spread out (*diffract*) around obstacles in their path (see topic 4.13),
- raise the temperature of anything which absorbs them.

Each group consists of waves with similar, but not identical, properties. The slight differences in their properties are due to differences in their wavelength and frequency. Long-wave infra-red radiation, for example, is absorbed by glass but short-wave infra-red can pass through it.

There are significant differences between the properties of one group compared with another, because of their different ranges of wavelength and frequencies. The properties determine how the waves are used.

Radio waves

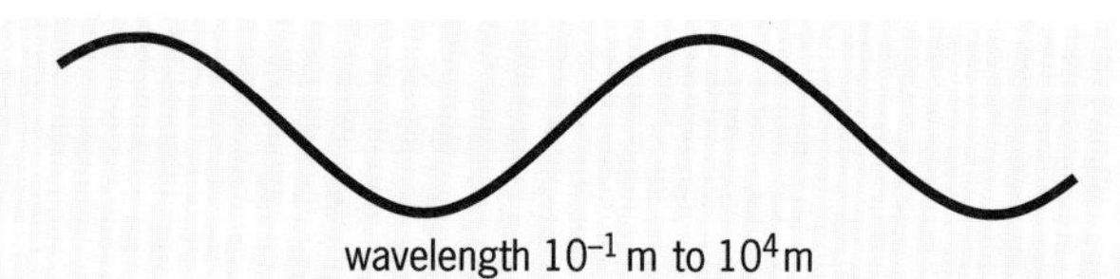

Radio (and TV) waves have the longest wavelengths in the electromagnetic spectrum. Radio waves are produced by oscillating (alternating) electric currents in a transmitting aerial. The frequency of the wave is the same as the frequency of the current. The waves pass through the air and are 'picked up' by a receiving aerial which converts them back into an alternating current with the same frequency as the wave. This is then converted into sound by a radio.

The waves which carry the signals from different radio stations have different wavelengths and frequencies.

Radio station	Wavelength	Frequency
Radio 1	285 m	1053 kHz
Radio Scotland	370 m	810 kHz

The electromagnetic spectrum

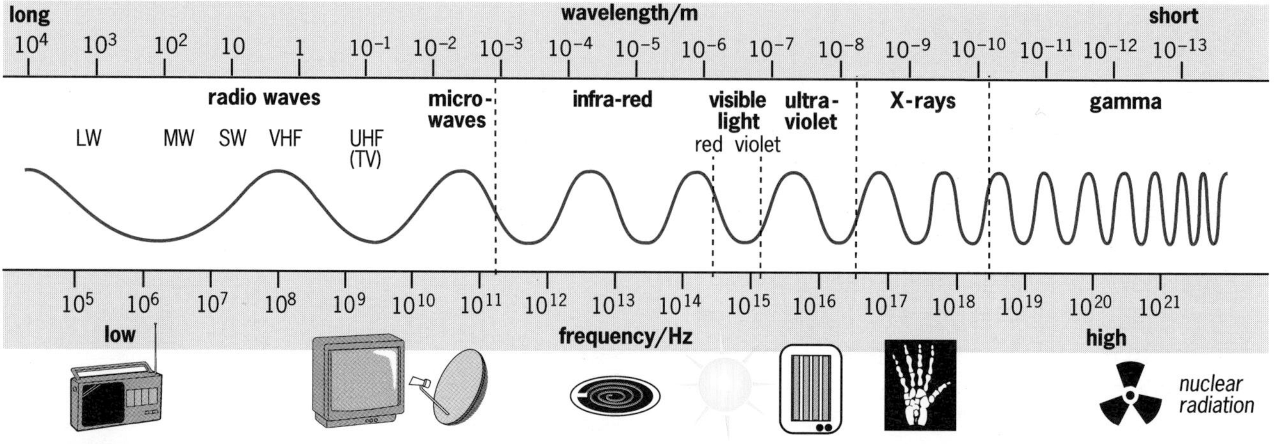

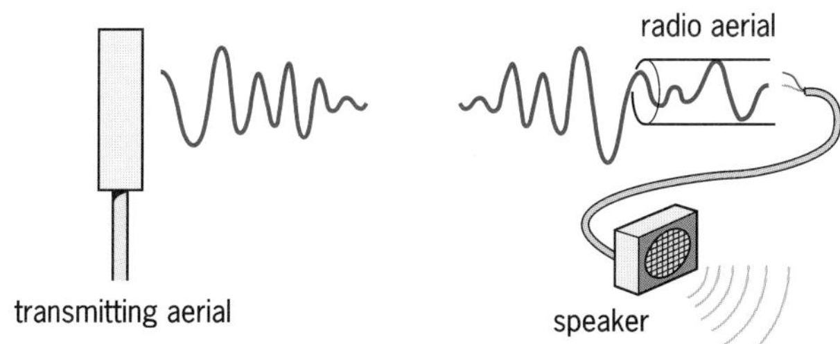

Radio waves carry energy from the transmitter to the aerial in your home or inside a radio. The radio converts the information carried by the waves back into sound

Long- and medium-wave radio transmissions can reflect from a layer of charged particles in the upper atmosphere (the ionosphere). This enables them to travel over long distances despite the curvature of the Earth's surface.

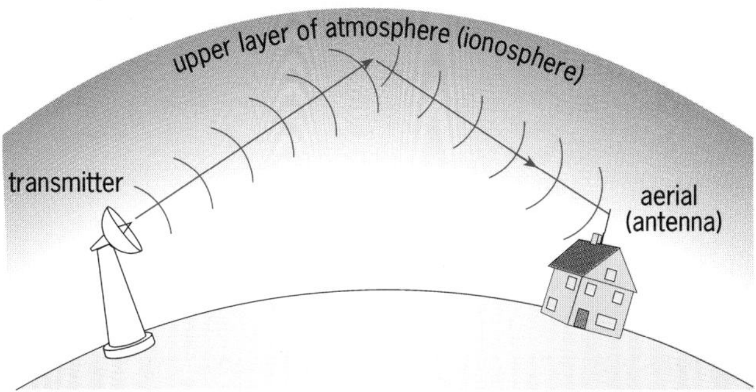

Long-distance radio transmission via the ionosphere

Microwaves

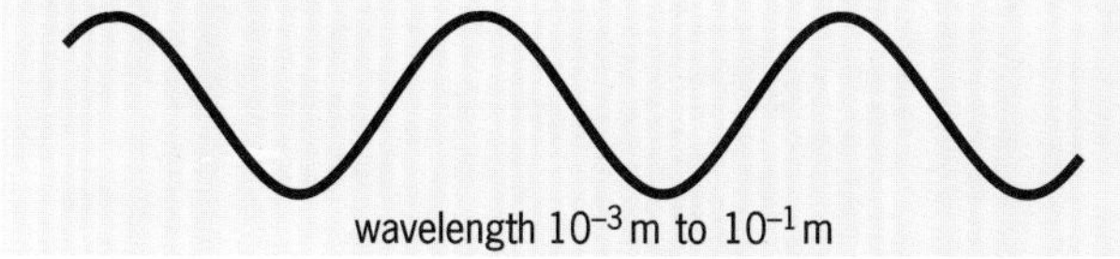

The waves produced by microwave ovens have frequencies which closely match the natural frequency of vibration of water molecules. They are therefore readily absorbed by the water molecules in food.

The advantage of cooking with microwaves is that they pass deep into the food, cooking it evenly throughout. (A conventional oven cooks food from the outside, so the outer layers can be properly cooked whilst the inner layers are still 'raw'.) Microwave cooking is also much quicker, and can be cleaner.

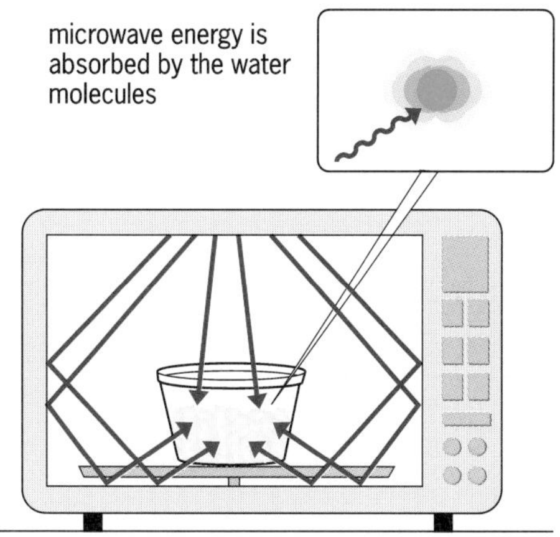

When microwaves pass into food, their energy is absorbed by the water molecules, raising the temperature and cooking the food

Microwaves striking living tissue can cause burns, damaging cells. The cells may even be killed by excess exposure. To prevent accidental exposure, microwave ovens cannot be operated unless the door is closed.

Microwaves which have wavelengths similar to short-wavelength radio waves (i.e. a few cm) can pass easily through the atmosphere and are used for satellite communications. The waves travel in a straight line, so they can be easily focused on the satellite by a concave dish transmitter. The satellite then re-routes the microwaves back to Earth to be received by now-familiar 'satellite dishes'. The receiving dish collects the waves over a large area, focusing them onto a 'transducer' which changes the electromagnetic waves into an electrical signal.

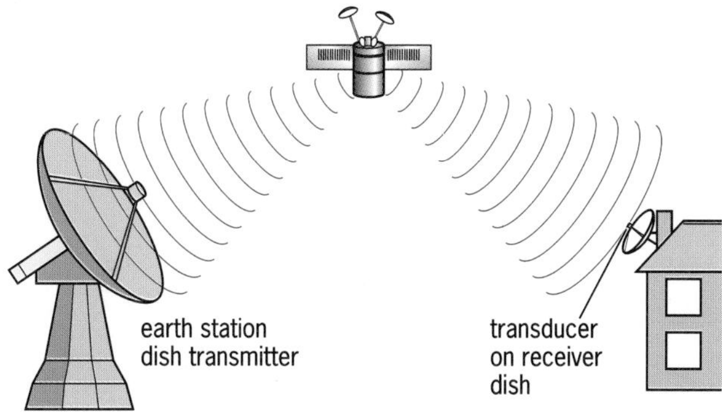

Transmission and reception of a microwave signal via a satellite

Infra-red radiation

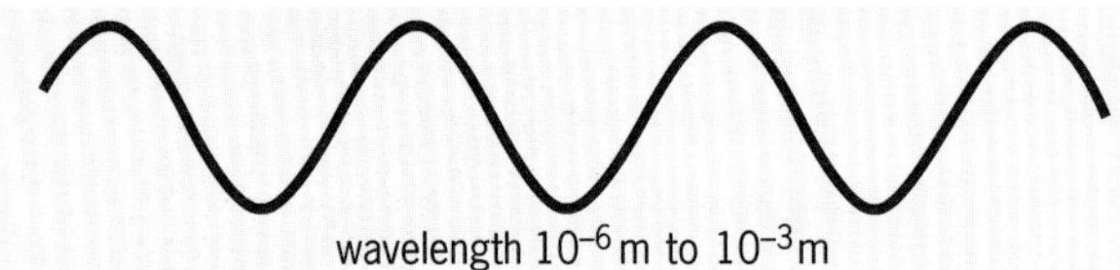

Everything emits infra-red radiation, even you (see topic 1.11). The radiation is produced by the vibration of atoms. The hotter an object is, the faster the atoms vibrate and the more radiation the object emits.

The different colours on this infra-red photograph represent different temperatures

Food can be cooked using infra-red grills but, unlike microwaves, infra-red waves do not penetrate food beyond a few millimetres below the surface. Toasters emit infra-red radiation, heating bread strongly on the outside.

Sunlight contains a wide range of electromagnetic waves, from infra-red to ultra-violet. Some of the infra-red radiation is absorbed by the skin, making you feel warm. Excessive exposure to infra-red can cause burns.

Ultra-violet

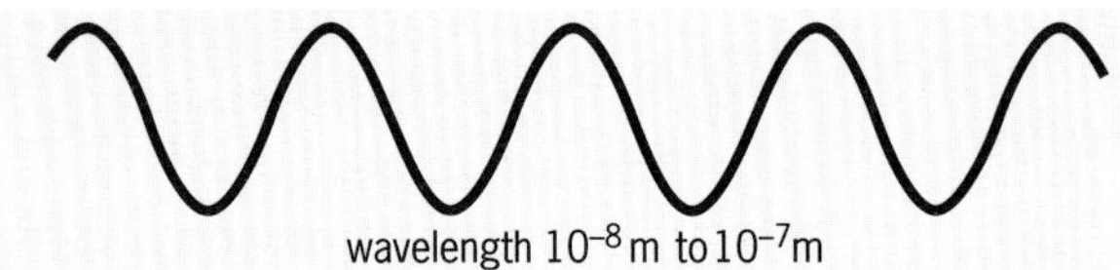

The wavelengths of ultra-violet radiation lie just beyond the blue region of the visible spectrum. It causes tanning and also stimulates the production of some vitamins in the body. Excessive ultra-violet radiation can, however, penetrate into the deeper tissues of skin, damaging the cells. Some of the damaged cells may turn to cancers. Dark skin absorbs ultra-violet better than light skin. As a result, less radiation reaches the deeper tissues so there is less risk of cancer.

'UV' lights are often seen above fresh food counters – the radiation kills any microbes and small insects which may be present

Some chemicals 'fluoresce' when ultra-violet radiation falls on them. They absorb the ultra-violet radiation and emit visible light. Security paints contain fluorescent chemicals which cannot normally be seen but can be seen clearly when illuminated by ultra-violet.

The use of fluorescent security marks enables the police to return stolen goods to the owners when they are recovered

'Strip' lights produce ultra-violet light which could be harmful. They are therefore coated with a fluorescent chemical which absorbs any ultra-violet radiation emitted by the gas in the tube. The chemical then emits safer white light as it fluoresces.

X-radiation (X-rays)

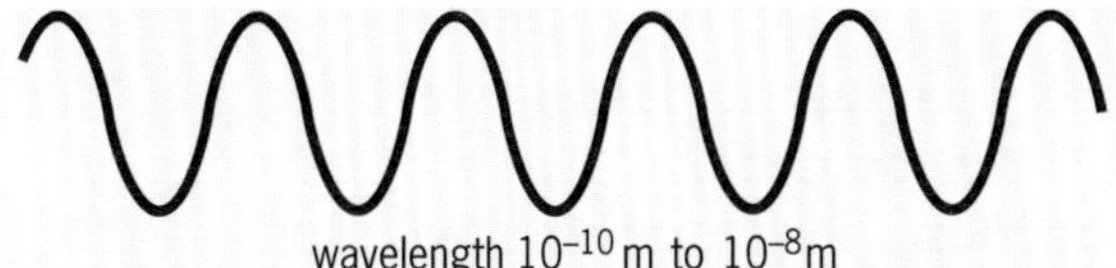

X-rays have very short wavelengths which are able to pass through most solid materials, including flesh, with very little of their energy being absorbed. When X-rays fall on photographic film the chemicals on the film change. When developed the film appears dark where the X-rays struck it. Photographic film is used to take X-ray pictures of the body.

When X-rays pass through a part of the body, more of their energy is absorbed by bone than by flesh, so bones appear lighter in the photograph than the tissues which surround them

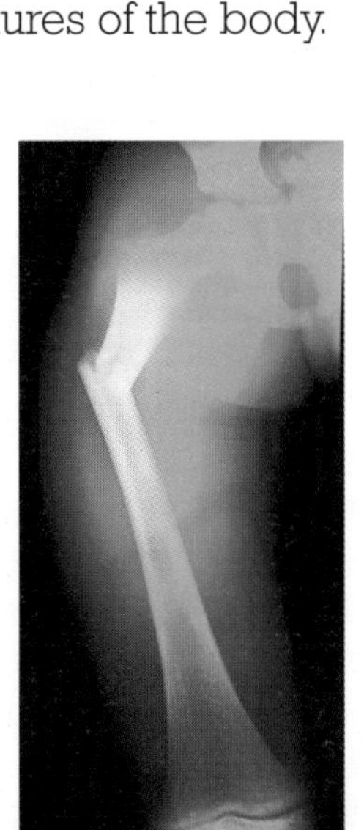

X-rays can be used in a similar way to test metal objects for fractures and other weaknesses.

X-radiation is an **ionising radiation** – it can cause changes in the atoms of materials through which it passes. Excessive exposure to X-radiation can kill human cells. Lower doses can cause cancers. Hospitals make sure that you are not exposed to excessive doses of X-radiation and also take steps to protect the staff who must work with X-rays regularly.

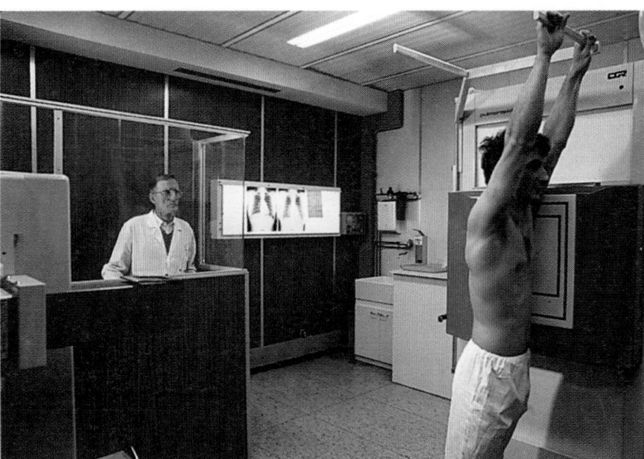

Radiographers stand behind a protective screen when they operate an X-ray camera

Gamma radiation

wavelength 10^{-13} m to 10^{-10} m

Gamma radiation has even shorter wavelengths than X-radiation. It can penetrate tissues easily and has a greater ionising power than X-radiation, so it is highly dangerous to all living things. Exposure to gamma radiation can cause cancers or kill cells entirely. Perhaps surprisingly, cancers can also be cured by killing the cancerous cells with the same gamma radiation, in limited doses. Medical treatment using radiation is known as 'radiotherapy' (see page 192).

Gamma radiation is used to sterilise medical instruments and dressings – it kills any bacteria present.

It can be used similarly to 'irradiate' food, thereby extending its shelf-life.

★ THINGS TO DO

1 Go back through this topic and then make a table listing the main groups of electromagnetic radiation and showing, for each group:
- **a)** the range of wavelengths,
- **b)** the uses,
- **c)** the dangers, if any.

Include visible light.

2 Some washing-powder manufacturers put small amounts of fluorescent chemicals into their powders. The chemicals become embedded in the material when the clothes are washed. When they are hung out to dry they look 'whiter than white'. Explain why they look like this.

4.13

Around the hills

Model harbour used to study wave behaviour

When water waves pass between two piers, they appear to 'spread out'. This is an example of **diffraction** – the 'spreading out' of waves after passing through or around some obstacle placed in their path.

The effect is most evident with waves which have long wavelengths compared with the size of the obstacle.

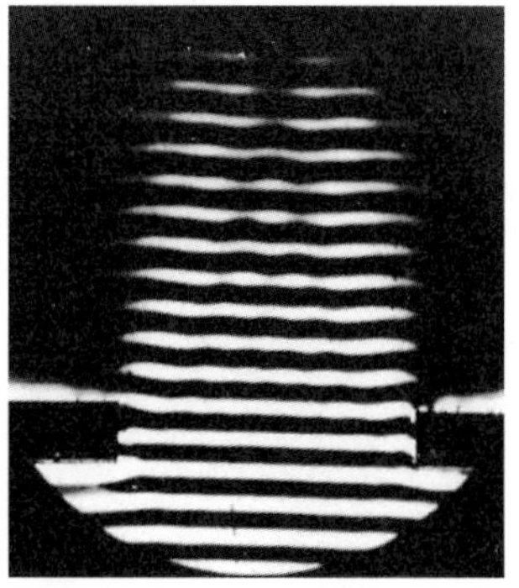

Waves spread out more when the obstacle is narrow

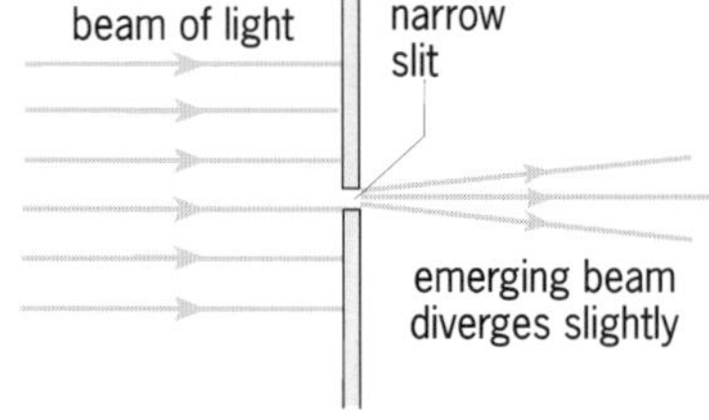

Diffraction of light at a narrow slit

For a given obstacle, the longer the wavelength of the waves, the greater the angle through which the waves are diffracted.

The effect can be seen when a beam of light strikes a very narrow slit. The emerging beam spreads out, or is diffracted, beyond the edges of the slit. Once again, longer wavelengths are diffracted through greater angles.

As a result of diffraction, the energy carried by the waves becomes increasingly spread out.

Diffraction of radio waves

In some places radio and TV reception is extremely poor due to the surrounding hills and mountains. Small 'relay transmitters' can be installed to receive the incoming signal from the distant transmitter, and relay it into the isolated spots.

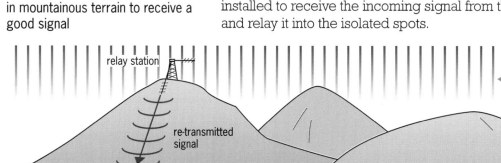

A relay station enables communities in mountainous terrain to receive a good signal

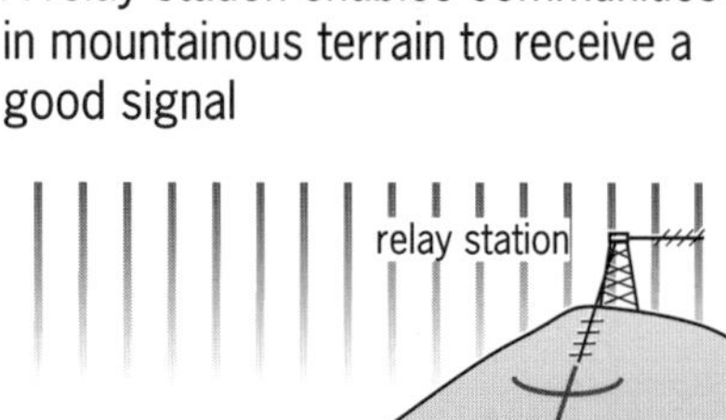

Some of these areas are able to pick up long- and medium-wave radio transmissions, however, without the use of relay stations because longer-wavelength radio waves are diffracted around mountains. The waves spread out and some of their energy is transferred into the valley below.

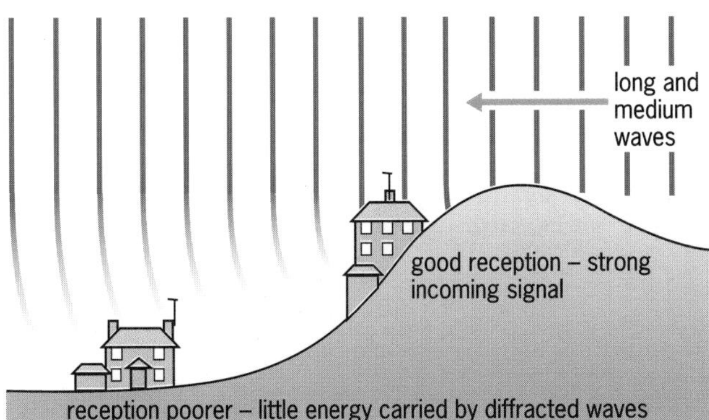

Longer-wavelength radio transmissions are diffracted around 'obstacles'

The energy becomes increasingly spread out, so the signal is stronger higher up the mountainside. Lower down, the signal may be so weak that reception is still poor. Aerials are often placed high up, where signals are stronger, and these then relay the signal through cables to the homes below.

Longer wavelengths diffract through a greater angle than shorter wavelengths, so it is often possible for remote villages to receive some radio stations but not others.

The fact that radio signals (and other types of electromagnetic radiation) behave in a similar way to the transverse water waves lends further support to the theory that they travel in the form of waves.

Diffraction of sound

It is extremely difficult to see diffraction effects with light, but with sound it is much more noticeable. Most sounds have fairly long wavelengths, ranging from a few centimetres to a few metres. These long wavelengths diffract around the edges of buildings and doorways.

We can hear around corners because sound waves are diffracted

★ THINGS TO DO

1 The list below shows the frequencies at which some radio stations transmit their signals.

Radio 1:	1053 kHz (1 053 000 Hz)
Radio 3:	1215 kHz (1 215 000 Hz)
Radio 5:	909 kHz (909 000 Hz)
Classic FM:	101.9 MHz (101 900 000 Hz)

a) Use the wave equation (page 171) to calculate the wavelengths of each radio wave. Remember, they have a common speed – 300 000 000 m/s.
b) Which of the radio stations are people in remote areas more likely to receive? Explain your answer using clear illustrations.

2 You are lost in a remote forest. You know people are looking for you. You can either shout or use a whistle to attract their attention. The whistle has a frequency of 15 000 Hz. Your voice has a frequency of 80 Hz. The speed of sound in air is 330 m/s.
a) Calculate the wavelength of the sound waves each would make.
b) Which is more likely to attract attention? Explain your answer.

Radioactivity

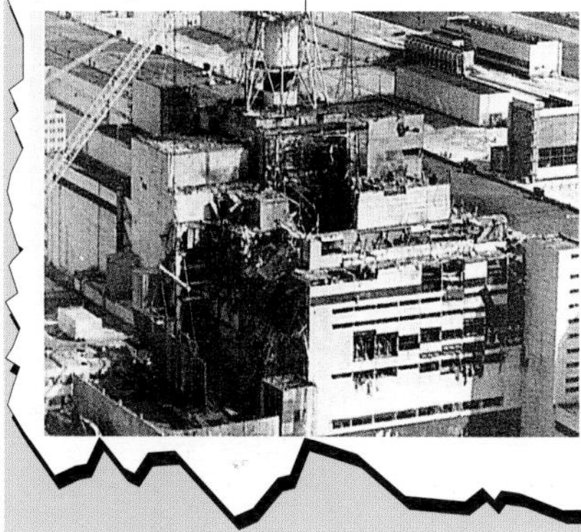

Explosion destroys nuclear power plant at Chernobyl

Scientists fear the worst after one of the world's worst nuclear accidents resulted in hundreds of tons of nuclear debris being thrown into the atmosphere. Whilst much of the dust settled within 10 miles of the site of the explosion, a significant amount is being carried over Eastern Europe by the prevailing winds.

People living in the vicinity of Chernobyl are hurriedly being evacuated from their homes to reduce the risks of contamination. It is estimated that over 2000 people may die from the effects of contamination by radioactive material.

We often hear about **radioactivity**, especially when there has been an accident involving radioactive substances, such as an explosion at a nuclear power station.

It's not all bad

The newspaper article highlights some of the dangers associated with radioactive materials. There are, however, ways in which radioactive substances are used to our advantage, such as in the treatment of cancer.

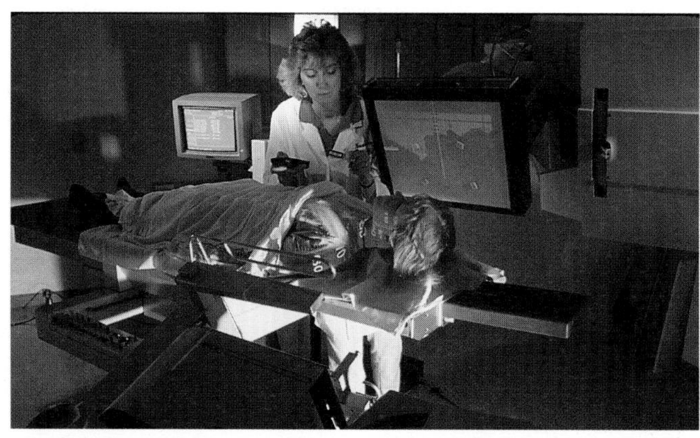

This patient is being prepared for radiotherapy. Gamma radiation from radioactive cobalt will be used to destroy cancer cells

When used in radiotherapy, the amount of radiation is carefully controlled to avoid damage to healthy cells.

Background radiation

What we do not perhaps realise is that we are exposed to nuclear radiation every day, although in extremely small amounts. Some rocks, such as granite, contain radioactive material. Naturally occurring radiation from such rocks is one of many sources of 'background radiation'.

The background radiation does not produce any noticeable effects on our health. That does not mean, however, that it does us no harm. Doctors and scientists believe that any exposure, no matter how small, poses some risk to our health.

Sources of background radiation

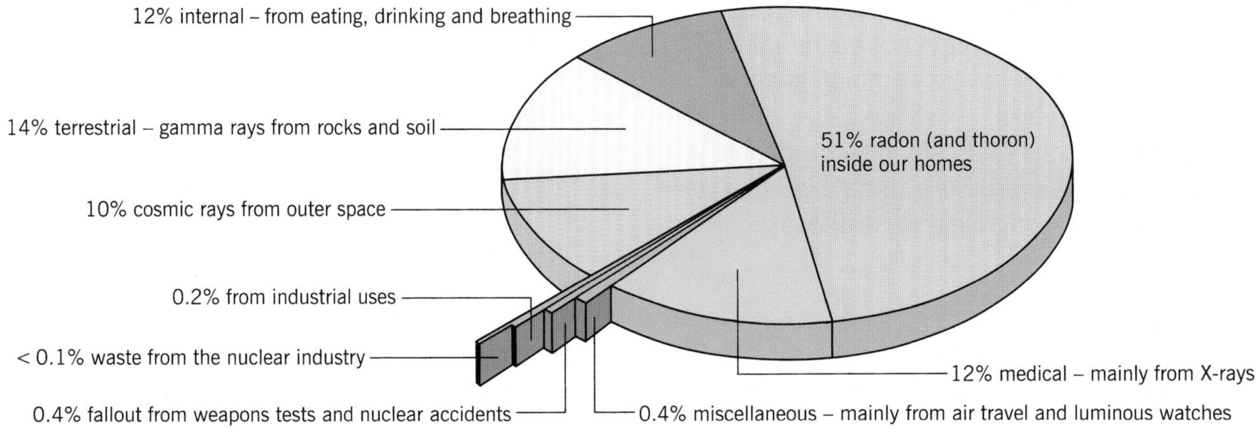

What is nuclear radiation?

There are three types of radiation produced by radioactive materials – alpha (α), beta (β) and gamma (γ) radiation. They are all produced as a result of changes which take place inside the nucleus of an atom. Each type has different properties.

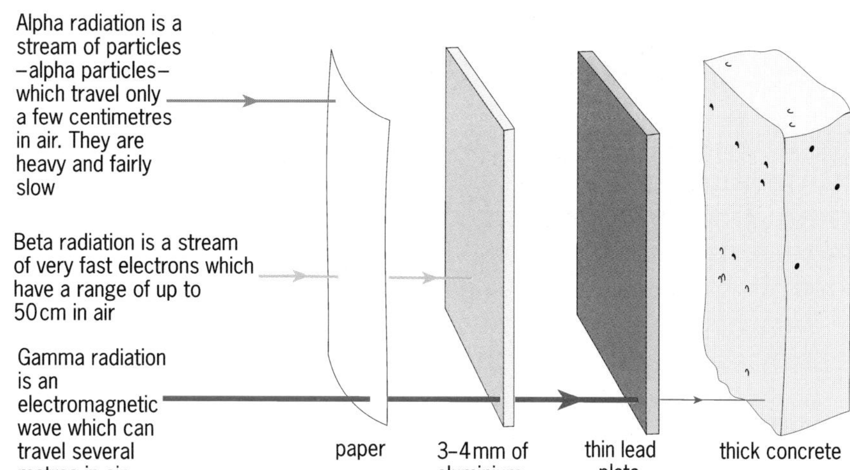
Alpha radiation is a stream of particles –alpha particles– which travel only a few centimetres in air. They are heavy and fairly slow
Beta radiation is a stream of very fast electrons which have a range of up to 50 cm in air
Gamma radiation is an electromagnetic wave which can travel several metres in air
paper
3–4 mm of aluminium
thin lead plate
thick concrete

The three types of nuclear radiation and their penetrating powers (a general guide based on laboratory sources)

Ionisation

When radiation from radioactive sources strikes neutral atoms or molecules, it can alter the structure of the atoms leaving them as charged particles or **ions**. This type of radiation is **ionising radiation** and is particularly dangerous to health. Alpha, beta, and gamma are all ionising radiations. In general alpha has the greatest ionising power and gamma the weakest.

As with some other forms of ionising radiation, such as ultra-violet or X-rays, the greater the exposure, the greater the risk to health. Ionising radiation can alter the structure of molecules inside all living organisms, causing cells to become cancerous. Excessive exposure to ionising radiation may kill the cells altogether.

Ionising radiation can be detected using a Geiger-Müller tube connected to a scaler or a ratemeter.

★ THINGS TO DO

1 Write a short article for a science magazine about background radiation and where it comes from.

2 a) Which type of nuclear radiation travels furthest in air?
b) Which type has the greatest penetrating power (ability to pass through materials)?
c) Which type would be stopped by the skin?
d) Which type is stopped by a thin piece of aluminium?
e) Radioactive sources for use in schools and colleges are stored in lead containers. Why is this the most appropriate material?

3 Radioactive materials are used in industry in automatic packaging systems. In the system illustrated, when the level of the powder reaches the level of the sensor, the beta radiation is blocked. The sensor detects that the packet is full and stops the flow of powder until the next packet moves into place.

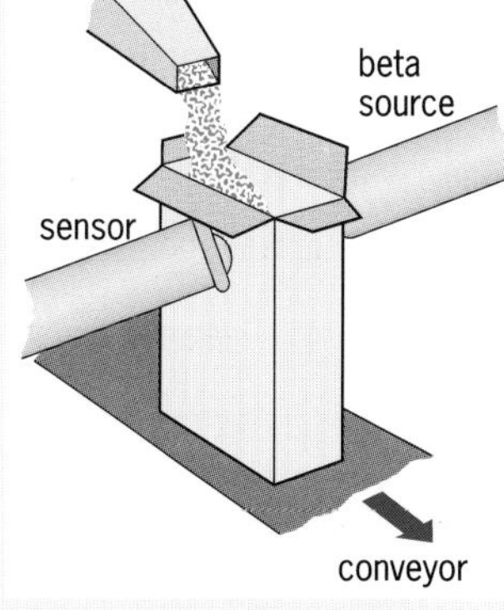
beta source
sensor
conveyor

a) Why is a beta source used? Explain your answer.
b) What would happen if an alpha or gamma source were used?
c) Why does the system pose little health risk to workers elsewhere in the factory?

4.15 Why are some substances radioactive?

Alpha, beta and gamma radiation are all released from inside the nucleus of atoms of radioactive substances. To understand how radiation is emitted, we must develop some idea of what an atom 'looks' like.

With the exception of hydrogen, every atom has the same basic structure of protons, neutrons and electrons shown on page 50. Further details are given in *GCSE Science Double Award Chemistry*, topic 3.8.)

The central part of the atom is called the nucleus. Although it takes up very little of the space occupied by an atom, it is very densely packed with protons and neutrons. These particles are sometimes called **nucleons** because they originate in the nucleus. Radioactivity occurs as a result of changes which take place in the nucleus.

The number of protons, neutrons and electrons in any atom can be worked out if we know the **atomic number** (the position of the element in the periodic table) and the **mass number** (or nucleon number).

mass number (A) = atomic number (Z) + number of neutrons

These numbers can be found on any copy of the periodic table.

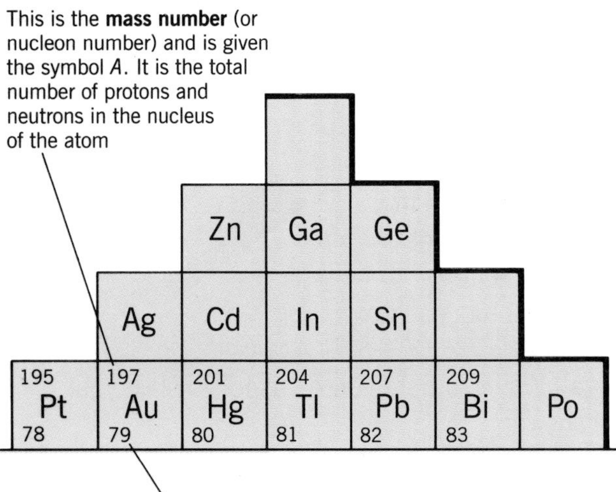

Radioactive materials

The nuclei of some atoms, particularly those with atomic numbers above 84, are very unstable and break down (decay), releasing energy and particles. These elements are the radioactive elements.

The average number of nuclei which decay in one second is called the **activity**. This is measured in units called **becquerels**. One becquerel represents an activity of one nucleus (on average) decaying each second. The activity varies from element to element.

When a radioactive element loses particles, its atomic structure must change, and a new element is formed in the process. This may itself be radioactive.

Uranium is one of the most well known radioactive elements. When the nucleus of a uranium atom breaks down an alpha particle leaves the atom. Energy is transferred from the atom by the alpha particle. In the process a new element – thorium – is formed.

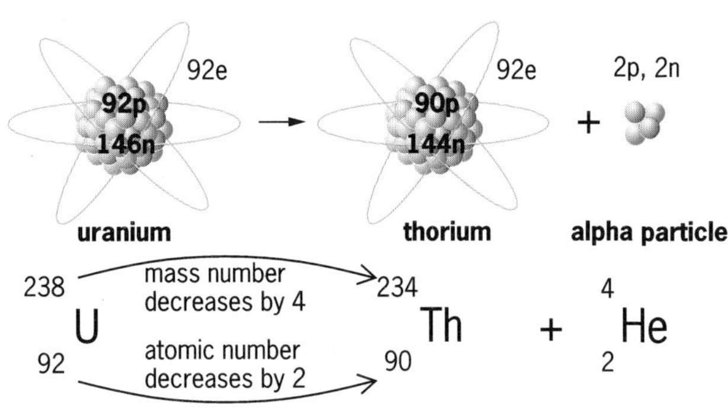

The first stage in the breakdown of uranium

Note that an alpha particle is the nucleus of a helium atom – it contains two protons and two neutrons.

In any sample of a radioactive element, the number of atoms of the original element decreases over time as the nuclei break down and form new elements. The activity therefore decreases with time. This fact can be used to estimate the age of rocks containing radioactive elements such as uranium.

Isotopes

Iodine is often used as a disinfectant. It is used in hospitals and surgeries to clean wounds or to disinfect the skin before an operation. This 'safe' iodine, found naturally in the thyroid gland in the body, is iodine-127 – the commonest form.

In 1957 at Windscale (now Sellafield), one of the first nuclear accidents released several tonnes of material containing a different form of iodine, iodine-131, into the atmosphere. Much of the iodine fell onto land close to Windscale. Farm animals ate the grass and the iodine became concentrated in their bodies. The milk obtained from the animals contained large amounts of iodine-131.

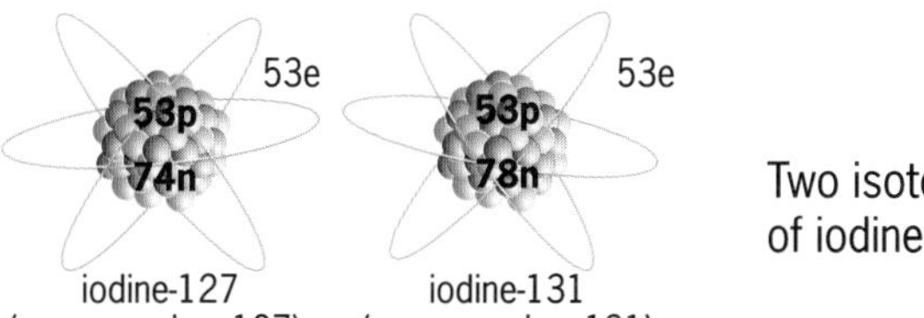

Two isotopes of iodine

Immediately farmers were banned from selling their milk, because iodine-131 is a dangerous radioactive form of iodine – excessive amounts can cause cancer of the thyroid gland.

These two forms of iodine are called **isotopes**. Isotopes are different forms of the same element which have different mass numbers but the same atomic number (and so the same position in the periodic table).

Iodine being passed through the food chain

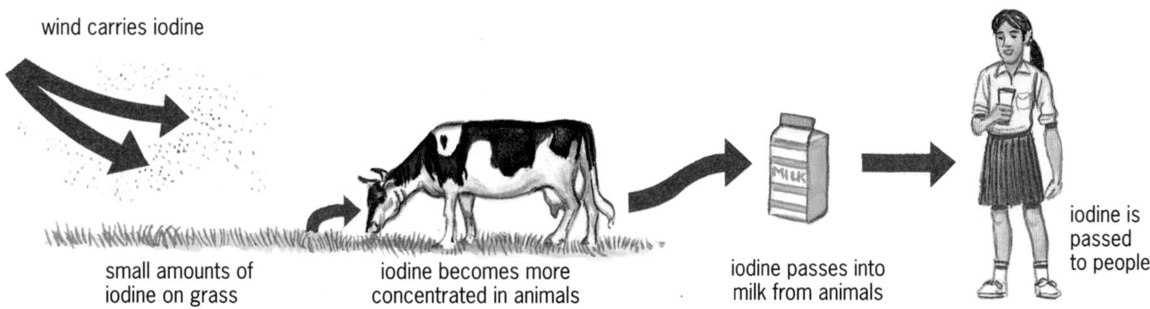

★ THINGS TO DO

1 a) Using a copy of the periodic table, make a table showing the number of protons, number of electrons and number of neutrons in one atom of the following elements:

magnesium (Mg) iron (Fe)
lead (Pb) gold (Au)
uranium (U) radon (Rn)
thorium (Th)

b) Which of the elements in your table are likely to be radioactive? Explain your answer.

2 In 1986 a Russian nuclear reactor exploded in Chernobyl releasing radioactive caesium-137 into the atmosphere. Radioactive dust fell in the English Lake District.

a) How did the radioactive dust reach Britain?

b) How would weather conditions affect the way the radioactive dust was scattered over the Earth's surface?

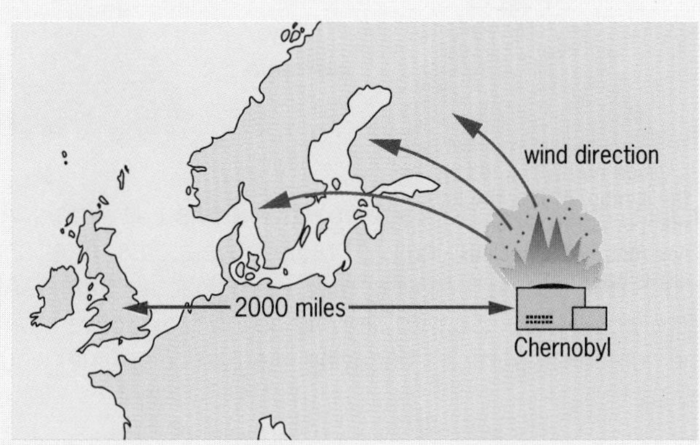

c) Most of the radioactive material which fell to the ground was absorbed by plants. The government ordered an immediate ban on the sale of animals from affected farms. Why was it necessary to do that?

d) Why was the ban still in place ten years later?

4.16 Tick tock – a radioactive clock

Radioisotopes (radioactive isotopes) are often used in hospitals as 'radiotracers' (radioactive materials which can be traced through the body). When inhaled or injected into the blood stream their progress through the organs can be traced using a special camera. Doctors can then decide how well the different organs are functioning. To ensure that the radiation is able to reach the camera, the radioisotopes are generally gamma emitters. Two common radiotracers are:

- technetium-99, which can be used to check the function of the brain, kidneys, lungs and bones,
- xenon-133, a gas which when inhaled can identify areas of the lungs which are not working as effectively as they should.

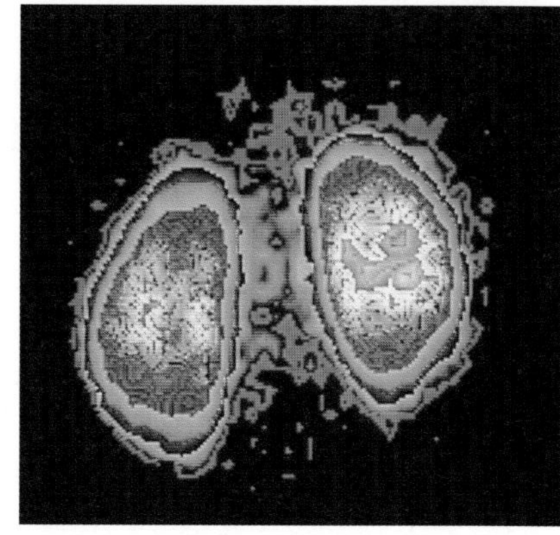

Gamma camera scan of healthy kidneys, by use of the radiotracer technetium–99

Prolonged exposure to gamma radiation can cause damage to the cells of the body, causing cancers. Radioisotopes are therefore chosen which very quickly become less radioactive – they have short 'half-lives'.

Radioactive decay

When radioactive atoms emit alpha or beta radiation they lose tiny particles of matter. This is known as 'radioactive decay'. As they decay, the original atoms change into atoms of a different element, leaving fewer of the original radioactive atoms behind. The activity of the substance decreases and hence the number of counts per minute, measured using a Geiger-Müller tube, decreases.

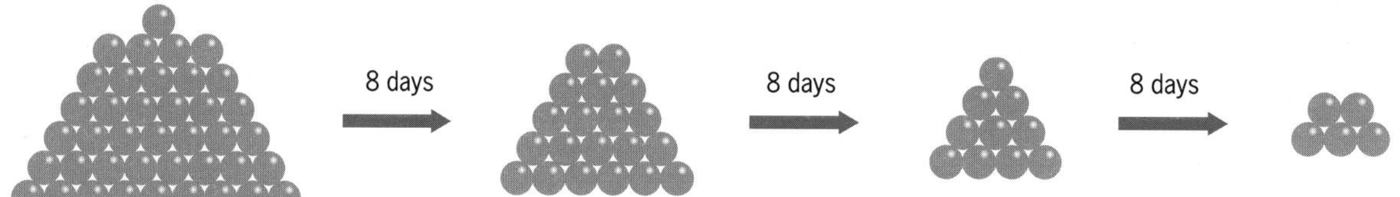

Imagine looking at just 40 radioactive iodine-131 atoms. After 8 days, 20 would have decayed, leaving only 20 radioactive atoms. After another 8 days, 10 more would have decayed, leaving only 10 radioactive atoms. After a further 8 days, 5 more would have decayed, leaving only 5 radioactive atoms. As a result the activity (the number of particles decaying in a particular time) would decrease

Half-life

The **half-life** of a radioactive substance is the time taken for half of the nuclei in any sample of the substance to decay. It follows that the half-life of a substance is the time taken for the count rate to fall to half of its original value. From the illustration above, you can see that the half-life of iodine-131 is 8 days – every 8 days the number of radioactive nuclei falls by one-half.

Although this might suggest that the substance decays in a regular manner, it does not. In fact, the decay is entirely random. At times three or four atoms may decay quickly; at other times, there may be a long delay before another atom will decay. Changes in radioactive materials are monitored over relatively long periods to take into account the random nature of decay.

Testing the half-life of a radioactive material

The half-life of some radioactive substances can be found experimentally using a Geiger-Müller tube and a scaler. The substance is placed in a position where the radiation is detected by the Geiger-Müller tube. The count rate is noted every minute, for, say, 6 minutes. Imagine obtaining these results:

Time/minutes	0	1	2	3	4	5	6
Count rate/ counts per minute	460	365	290	228	190	150	110

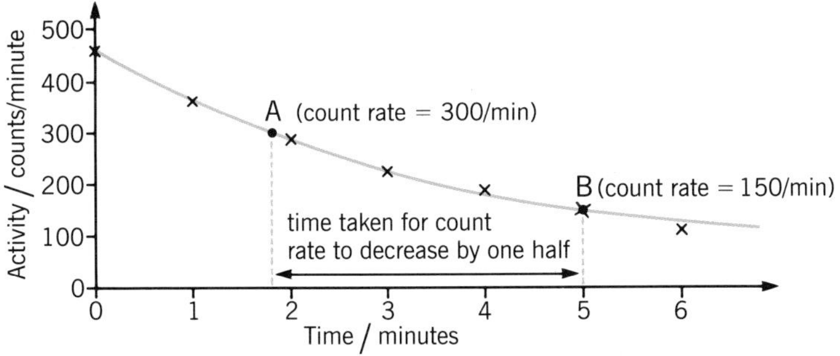

To find the half-life, any point on the graph with a suitable count rate can be taken (e.g. A). A second point is found where the number of counts per minute is exactly half of the first value chosen (B). The half-life is the time taken for the substance to decay from point A to point B. This can be read from the horizontal axis. For this substance the half-life would be 3.2 minutes.

Radioactive emissions

Radioactive emissions stem from changes which take place inside the nucleus of the atoms of radioactive elements and their compounds. Radioisotopes have very large nuclei which are unstable and break down, or decay. As they decay, radiation is emitted and a different atom, with a different number of nucleons, is formed. Some materials emit only one type of radiation. Others might emit all three types – alpha, beta and gamma.

Alpha emission

Radium is a radioactive material which emits alpha particles as it decays to form radon gas. Energy is released in the process.

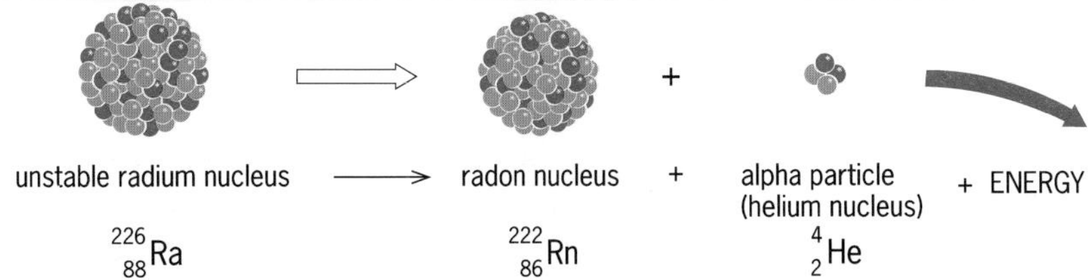

Alpha radiation is particulate. An alpha particle is identical to the nucleus of a helium atom, containing two protons and two neutrons. As a result the original atom changes into a new particle which has a nucleus containing two protons and two neutrons fewer than the original atom

Beta emission

Iodine-131 is a radioisotope which is a beta emitter. It decays to form xenon gas and a beta particle. Energy is released during the process.

$$^{131}_{53}I \rightarrow ^{131}_{54}Xe + ^{0}_{-1}e + \text{ENERGY}$$

beta particle (electron)

energy

neutron inside nucleus of $^{131}_{53}I$ → a proton is formed

Beta radiation consists of high-energy electrons. The electrons do not come from those which orbit the atom, but are produced as a neutron breaks down. As it does, a proton is formed, the beta particle (an electron) is emitted and energy is released. The original atom changes into a new particle with one extra proton in its nucleus, but one less neutron

Gamma emission

Gamma radiation is a form of electromagnetic radiation, similar to X-rays, with a very short wavelength. It is very penetrating. It is produced as the particles left in a nucleus re-organise themselves after emitting an alpha or a beta particle. Because gamma radiation is not particulate, its emission does not affect the atomic number of the atom in any way – the number of particles in the atom does not change.

Nuclear fission

Each time a change takes place inside the nucleus of an atom, energy is released. In a nuclear reactor, millions of radioactive decays occur each second, releasing huge amounts of energy. This is the principle which lies behind the production of nuclear energy.

The process whereby nuclei split up, releasing energy, is called nuclear **fission**. In a nuclear reactor the process must be controlled. If it is uncontrolled, the reaction takes place so quickly that huge amounts of energy are released in a short space of time, creating an explosive situation. That is what happens when a nuclear (or 'atomic') bomb explodes – the results are disastrous.

In the 1950s nuclear bombs were regularly tested in the atmosphere. Some of the radioactive fallout accounts for a small amount of the background radiation to which we are exposed every day

Not all radioactive materials are suitable for use in nuclear power stations. Only those with very large nuclei which split into two parts, such as uranium, can be used effectively. Fission occurs inside the fuel rods in a nuclear reactor. When the nucleus of the atom splits, it also ejects one or more neutrons at high speed. The ejected neutrons strike neighbouring nuclei, causing them to split in the same way. As they split, they release two further neutrons which strike two more nuclei. The process is a 'chain reaction' – nucleus after nucleus is split by neutrons ejected when an earlier nucleus was split.

Each time a nucleus splits, energy is released. With millions of nuclei being split every second, a nuclear reactor produces energy quickly. Eventually the rate at which nuclei are split slows down because there are fewer and fewer of the original nuclei left. The fuel rods are then removed and replaced with fresh ones.

In the core of a nuclear reactor the fission reactions are carefully controlled.

A chain reaction

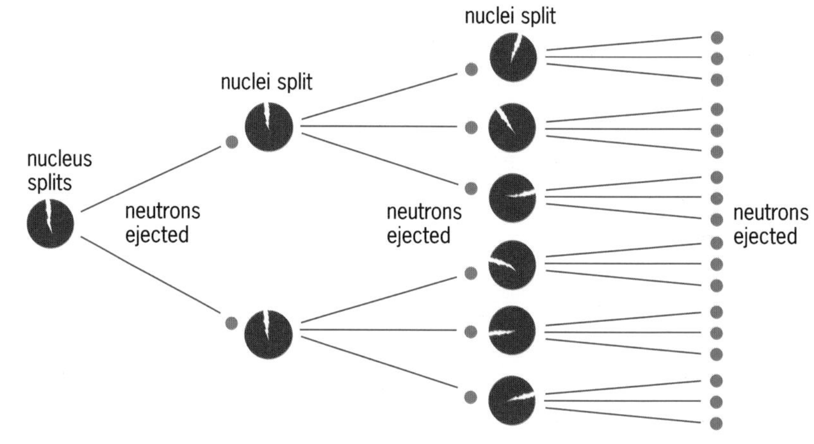

A nuclear reactor core

The fuel rods contain pellets of pure uranium-235. 1 kg of uranium-235 produces as much electricity as 60 tonnes (60 000 kg) of coal. The rods are lowered into the core of the reactor

Boron-steel control rods can be raised or lowered between the fuel rods. Boron-steel absorbs neutrons. Lowering the rods slows the reaction, as more neutrons are absorbed. Raising the control rods increases the rate of the reaction

Graphite moderator rods are placed between the fuel rods. Uranium-235 splits best when low-speed neutrons strike the nuclei. The graphite moderator slows down the high-speed neutrons

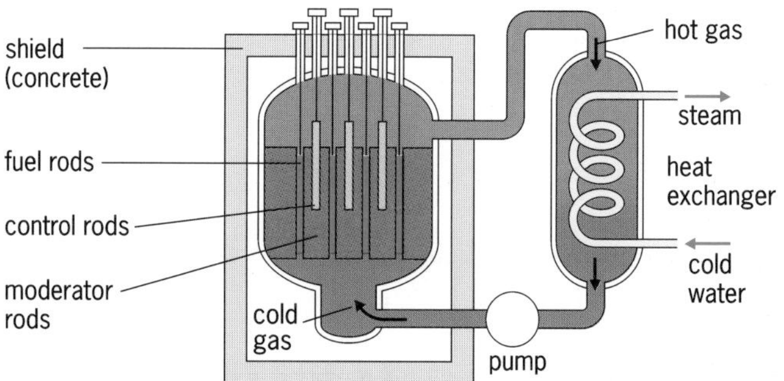

High-pressure carbon dioxide gas circulates inside the core of the reactor, absorbing the energy released by the fission process. As the gas passes over heat exchangers, it heats the water inside, changing it into high-pressure steam which drives the turbines

★ THINGS TO DO

1 The radioactive element technetium is a gamma emitter with a half-life of 8 minutes. Why is this material suitable as a medical radiotracer?

2 When photographic film has been exposed to nuclear radiation it goes black when developed. Film which has not been exposed remains clear when developed.

Workers who are regularly exposed to radioactive materials are required to wear a badge which will indicate whether they have been exposed to dangerous levels of radiation.

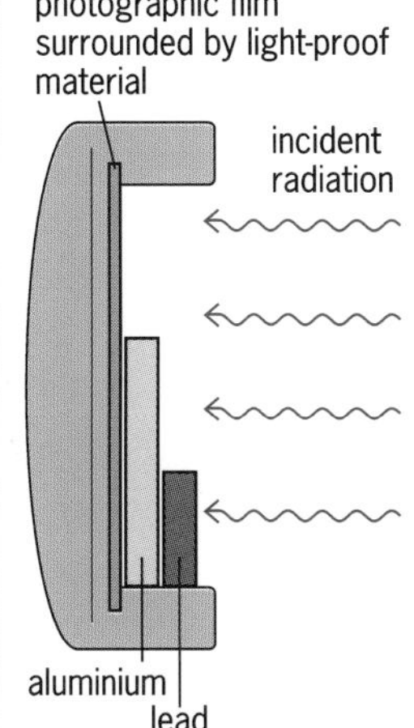

Section through a radiation-detector badge

a) How does the design of the badge illustrated help identify whether the worker has been exposed to alpha, beta or gamma radiation?
b) Draw a diagram showing how the developed film would look if the worker had been exposed to excess beta radiation.
c) Why should the badge be worn on the outside of any other clothing?

3 Copy and complete the following sentences.
a) An alpha particle consists of two . . . and two . . . It is the same as a . . . nucleus.
b) Different isotopes of the same element have the same . . . but a different . . . .
c) The half-life of an element is the time taken for . . . .
d) During a chain reaction . . . are released as the . . . of atoms split.
e) Fission is the process in which . . . .
f) Alpha radiation is absorbed by . . . .

4 Many smoke alarms contain small amounts of radioactive materials such as americium-241. The alpha particles ionise (charge) air molecules when they strike them. The ions are then attracted to the electrodes and a small current flows in the alarm. This is normal.

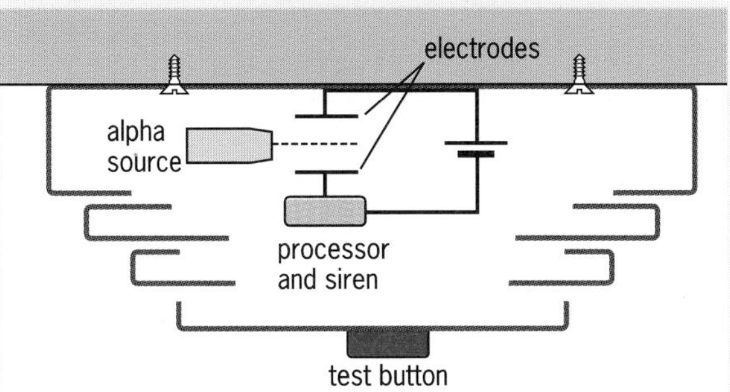

Section through a smoke alarm

If smoke particles enter the alarm fewer ions are produced so less current flows. This sets off the alarm.
a) Explain why the radioactive source is unlikely to harm anyone in the home.
b) Do you think the americium will have a short or a long half-life?
c) Why do you think fewer ions will be produced when smoke enters the alarm?
d) Why would it be unwise to use a beta or gamma source in this alarm?

5 Radioactive carbon-14 is formed in the upper atmosphere and eventually mixes with carbon dioxide lower down. Carbon dioxide is absorbed by the leaves of trees, so some of the radioactive carbon-14 is also absorbed. One gram of living wood emits 16 beta particles per minute. When the tree dies, the amount of carbon-14 begins to decay by this beta emission. The carbon-14 has a half-life of 5700 years.
a) Draw a graph showing how the number of beta emissions from one gram of wood will change over a period of 27 000 years following the death of the tree.
b) How would your graph have changed if you had only considered 0.5 grams of wood?
c) Archaeologists recently discovered the remains of a family of cave dwellers. Beside them lay remnants of wooden tools. One gram of the wood was found to be giving off 7 beta particles per minute. How old were the tools?

4.17 Shock waves

In 1995 an earthquake struck the city of Kobe in Japan, causing enormous damage and loss of life

Earthquakes are caused deep within the Earth as two adjacent tectonic plates slip across one another (see *GCSE Science Double Award Chemistry*, topic 2.4). The damage at the surface is caused by shock waves which travel through the Earth.

The structure of the Earth

We now know that the Earth is not a solid structure, but consists of a series of layers of different densities.

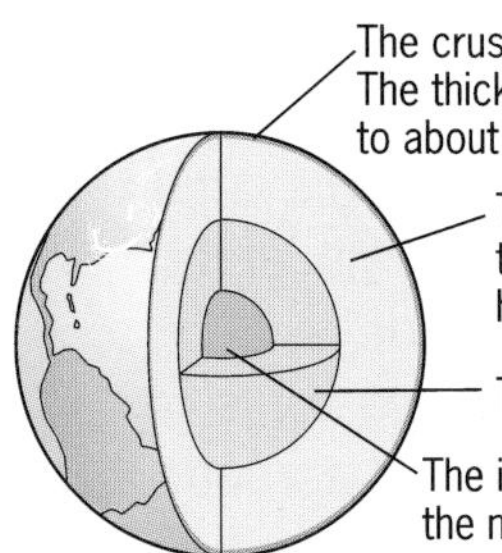
The crust is the outer layer which is solid rock. The thickness varies from only a few kilometres to about 70 km
The mantle is viscous (rather like very thick, warm toffee) and reaches about half way to the centre of the Earth
The outer core is molten rock
The inner core is solid and much denser than the mantle. The high density suggests that the core is composed largely of metals such as nickel and iron

Layers within the Earth's structure

Much of this information has been obtained by studying the shock waves (or 'seismic' waves) from earthquakes. The shock waves are recorded by instruments called seismometers in seismic stations situated all around the world.

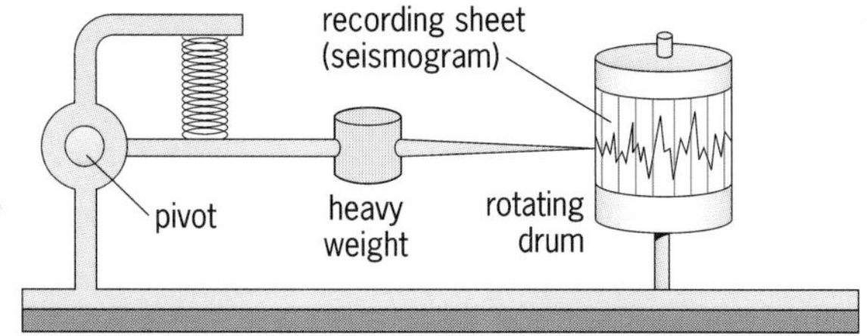
recording sheet (seismogram)
pivot
heavy weight
rotating drum

Seismometer

Types of shock wave

There are two main types of shock wave, called P and S waves, which travel through the Earth.

- P waves (primary waves) are longitudinal and can travel through solids and liquids. They travel faster through denser materials. As this type of wave reaches the surface, the rock is stretched and compressed (like the compressions and rarefactions as sound waves pass through a material). Because of this they make the ground shudder up and down.
- S waves (secondary waves) are transverse waves which cause the rock in the crust to shudder from side to side as they pass. They cannot pass through liquids. S waves are slower than P waves (P waves travel about twice as fast) and so take longer to reach the surface. When they do they cause secondary tremors.

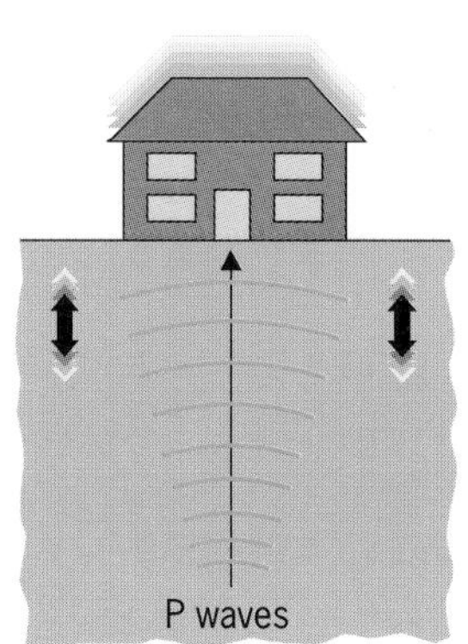
P waves

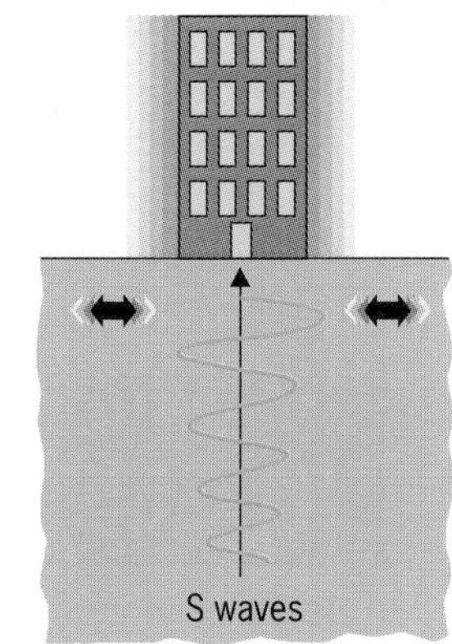
S waves

Ground tremors due to P waves (up and down) and S waves (side to side)

The time delay between receiving the P waves and the first S waves provides some idea of the distance from the focus or 'epicentre' of the earthquake (where it happens inside the Earth) to the seismic stations which detect the shock waves. If, for example, a recording station was 1000 kilometres from the epicentre, there would be about one minute between receiving the P and the S waves.

A third type of wave, L waves, can only pass through the surface rocks in the Earth's crust. They produce a rolling motion (rather like water waves) and cause most of the damage to buildings and other structures.

Inside the Earth

As both P and S waves travel through the Earth they are refracted due to differences in the density of adjacent layers. Both types of wave travel faster through denser rocks. At the boundary between layers with quite different densities the refraction may be quite noticeable. Within any one layer however, the density changes are more gradual, giving the impression that the waves are 'curving'.

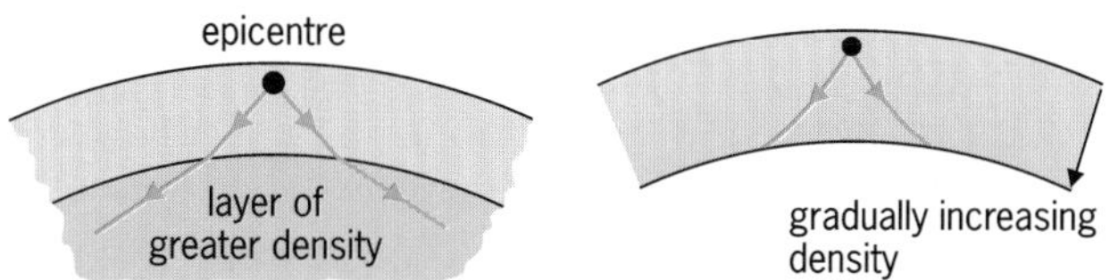

Refraction of seismic waves as they travel through material of varying density

Following an earthquake, seismic stations in an area on the opposite side of the Earth to the epicentre receive P waves but no S waves. This suggests that there must be some molten material in the inner Earth which absorbs the S waves.

Surrounding this area is a 'shadow zone' where only some very weak P waves are received. This happens because the P waves from the epicentre are refracted inwards as they enter the outer core. The S waves are absorbed by this liquid layer. The weak P waves are due to glancing reflections from the surface of the inner core.

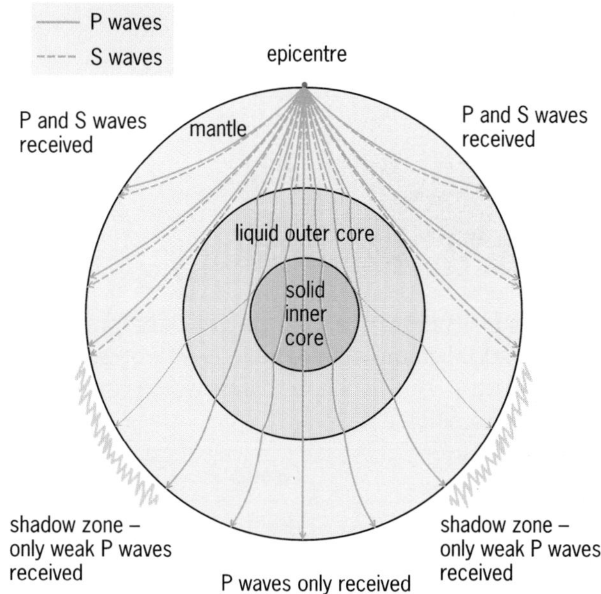

Paths of seismic waves through the Earth

★ THINGS TO DO

1 From the information above and opposite, do you think the rock deep below the surface is more or less dense than that at the surface? Explain your answer.

2 What information suggests that there must be a liquid layer close to the centre of the Earth?

3 a) Copy the seismogram shown here and mark which of the disturbances on the seismogram indicate (i) the arrival of P waves and (ii) the arrival of S waves. Explain the differences in their appearance.

b) The average speed of P waves between the focus of the earthquake and the seismic station is 14 km/s. The average speed of S waves between the two points is 6 km/s. If the time between receiving the first P waves and the first S waves was one minute, how far from the focus is the seismic station?

Seismogram recorded before, during and after an earthquake

Exam questions

1 a) The instruments in the drawings below produce sound in **two** different ways.

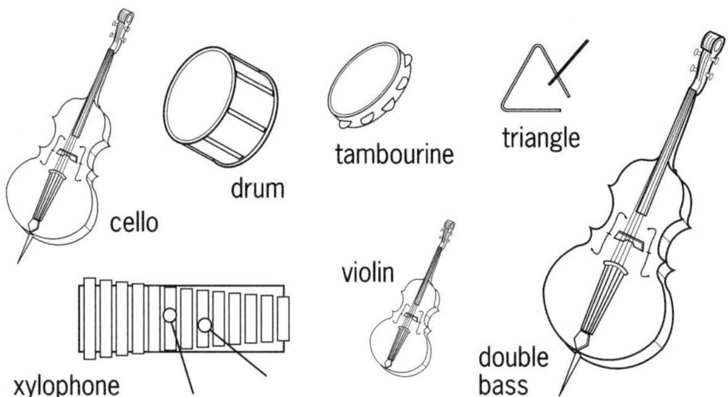

One instrument of each type has been put in the table below. Complete the table below by listing the other instruments in the drawings which produce sound in a similar way. (4)

Group 1	Group 2
violin	drum

b) i) Explain how the sound is made in:
(A) group 1 instruments; (1)
(B) group 2 instruments. (1)

c) You can make a model telephone by using plastic cartons tied to the ends of a piece of string.

i) Why does the model telephone **not** work if the string is loose? (2)

ii) Explain what would happen if the string touched another object, such as a wall. (2)

d) This diagram shows a bee. Which parts of the bee produce a buzzing sound? (1)

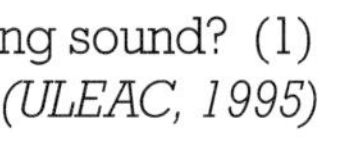

(ULEAC, 1995)

2 a) Give brief details of a common event which demonstrates that light travels faster than sound. (2)

b) i) Explain how sound is able to travel through air. (1)

ii) Why might loud background noise be considered a nuisance when you are trying to do your homework? (1)

c) i) Which of the following ranges of frequencies, in hertz, can be detected by a normal human ear?

20–200 20–2000 20-20 000 20–200 000 (1)

ii) Explain how the range of frequencies we hear changes as we get older. (1)

iii) Give **one** example of a situation where noise may damage a persons's hearing. (1)

d) The following diagram represents a sound wave travelling for 1/100th of a second.

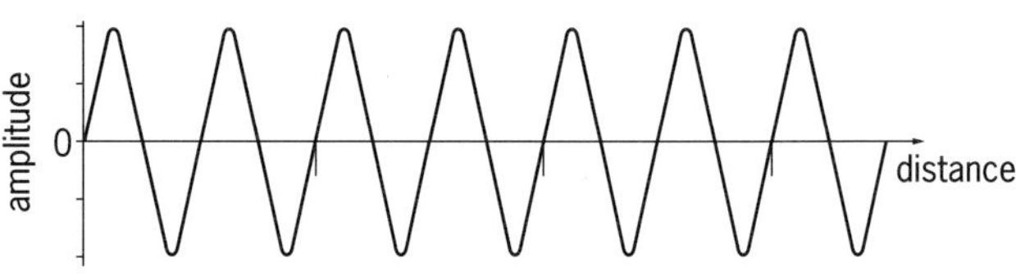

i) What is the frequency of this sound wave in hertz? (1)

ii) How would a sound change if:
1 its frequency was decreased;
2 its amplitude was increased? (2)

(ULEAC, 1995)

3 The captain of a ship can use echoes to measure the depth of the sea. This diagram shows how the captain measures the depth.

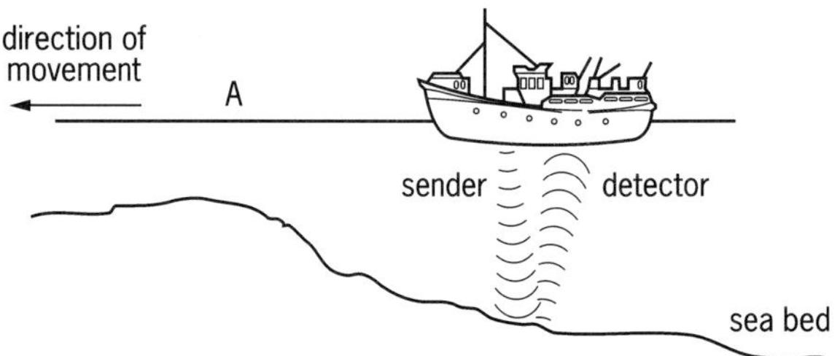

a) What device is used to detect the sound returning to the ship? (1)

b) i) In water sound travels at 1500 metres per second. The sound returns to the ship 4 seconds after it is sent.

How far down is the sea bed?

Show how you worked out your answer. (3)

ii) The ship moves to position **A**. How long will the sound take to return to the ship – more than 4 seconds, 4 seconds or less than 4 seconds?

Explain your answer. (1)

(MEG, 1995)

4 a) Jenny uses a long stretched spring to demonstrate two types of wave by moving her hand in the directions shown in the following diagrams.

Diagram A X

Diagram B Y

i) Draw what the spring would look like in each case if she kept moving her hand in the direction shown. (2)

ii) Describe the movement of the point marked X. (1)

iii) Describe the movement of the point marked Y. (1)

iv) Which diagram shows more clearly the way in which a sound wave travels through the air? (1)

b) Jenny then set up a sound demonstration.

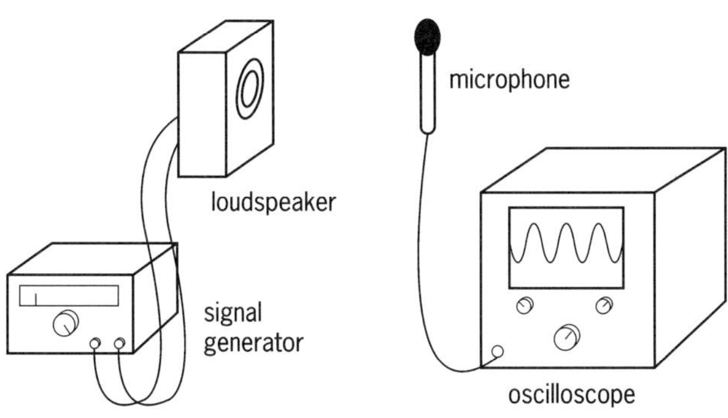

i) How will the display on the oscilloscope alter if:

(A) the frequency of the sound is increased; (1)

(B) the microphone is moved further away? (1)

ii) An energy flow diagram for this demonstration is shown below.

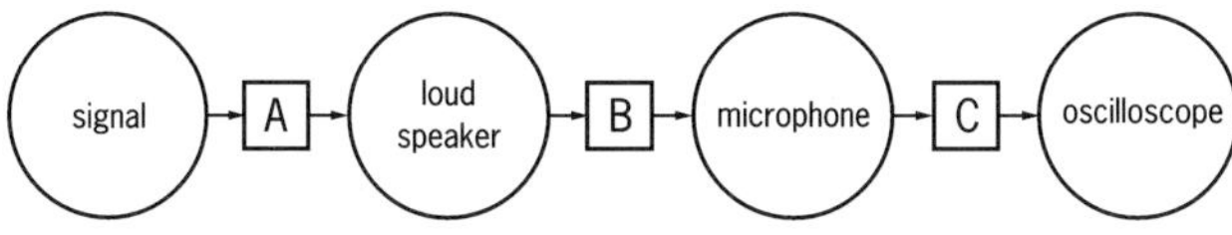

What forms of energy are represented by the boxes A, B, and C? (3)

c) Unwanted sound can be a nuisance in recording studios. It can be reduced by fixing either egg boxes or foam triangles to the walls and ceiling.

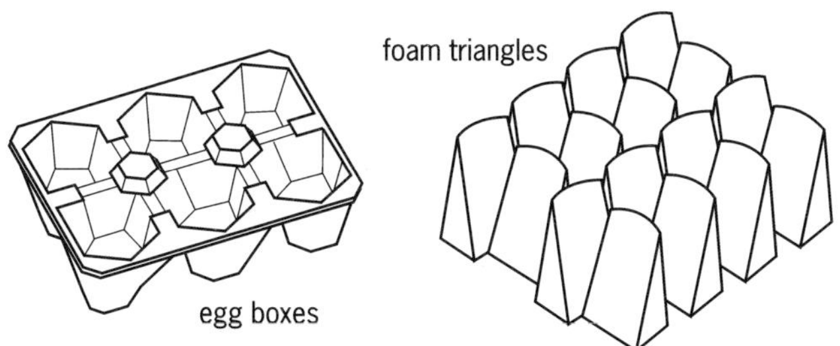

i) Explain how unwanted sound is reduced in this way. (2)

ii) Describe how sound in a room is affected when the carpet and curtains have been removed. (3)

(ULEAC, 1994)

5 a) When a ray of light travels from glass into air, some of the light is refracted and some is also reflected.

[Copy] and complete the upper diagram to show the refracted and reflected rays of light. (2)

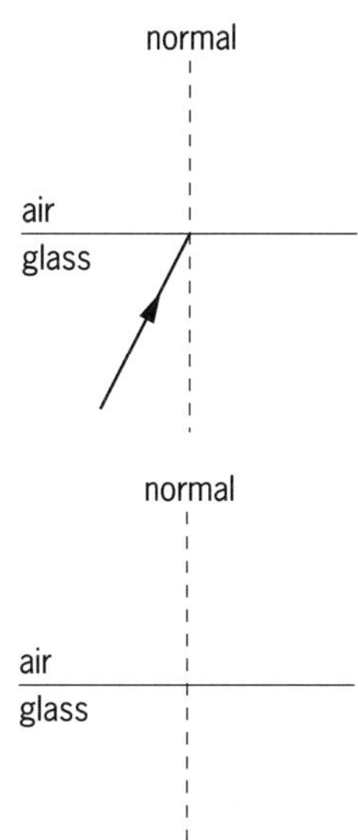

b) [Copy] the lower diagram and show on it what is meant by the critical angle. (2)

c) Under what conditions does total internal reflection occur? (1)

d) Briefly describe **one** use of total internal reflection. (2)

(WJEC, 1995)

6 a) At night a car driver was dazzled by the glare of the headlights of the vehicle behind. This is shown in diagram **1**.

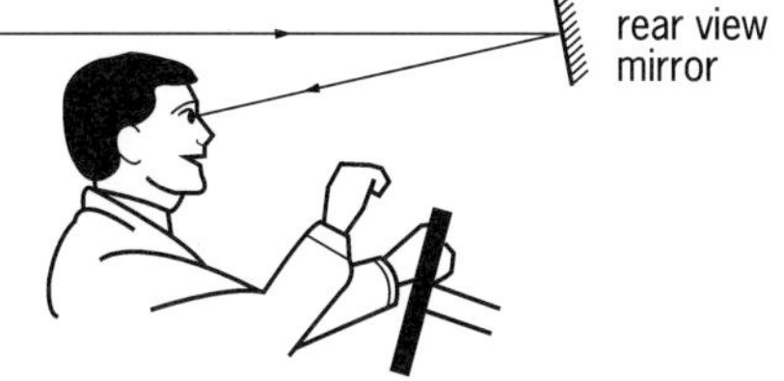

The driver tried to stop the glare of the headlights. He tilted the rear view mirror as shown in diagram **2**.

[Copy and] complete diagram **2** showing how the ray is now reflected. (1)

b) A driver looks from the road ahead to the speedometer inside the car. The shape of the lens in his eye changes. How does the shape change? (1)

c) The diagram shows two light rays hitting a glass block.

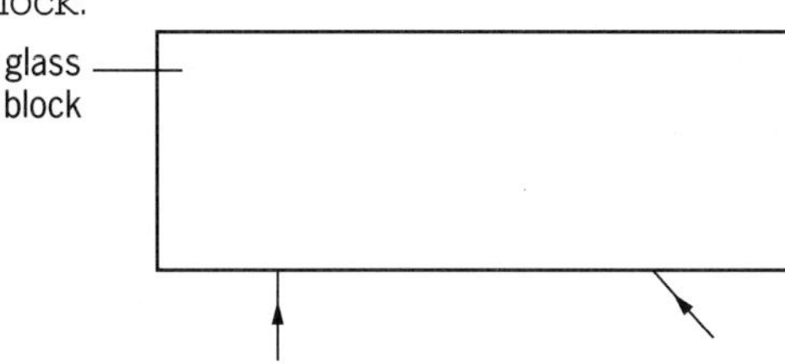

[Copy] the diagram and draw lines on it to show the paths of the **two** rays as they pass through the block **and** come out the other side. (3)

d) Optical fibres work because of total internal reflection. An endoscope is an instrument with optical fibres. Doctors can use this to see inside parts of the body.

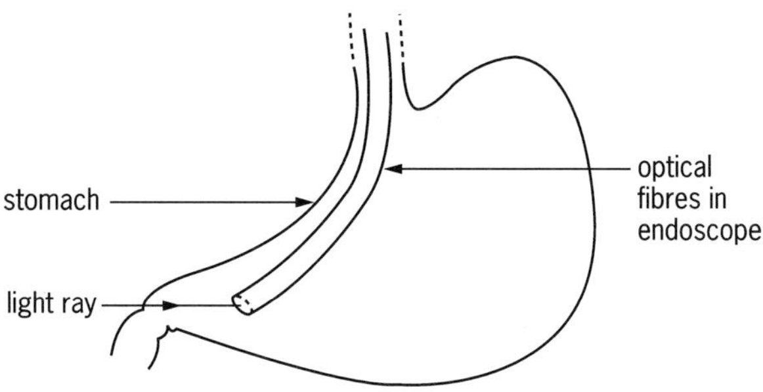

[Copy] the diagram and draw carefully on it a ray of light passing along the fibre. (2)

(SEG, 1995 (part))

7 Read the following passage carefully before answering the questions.

The electromagnetic spectrum is the name given to a family of radiations that includes infra red, visible light and ultra violet. Radio waves with wavelengths of up to 10 km and gamma rays with wavelengths of about one thousand millionth of a millimetre are at the opposite ends of the electromagnetic spectrum.

All objects are made up of electrically charged particles. When the energy of these particles is changed in some way, electromagnetic waves are produced; the greater the energy change, the shorter the wavelength of the waves.

Electromagnetic radiations are transverse waves which travel through a vacuum at a speed of 300 000 000 m/s (3×10^8 m/s).

a) Write down **one** property common to all electromagnetic radiations. (1)

b) State **one** reason why the wavelength of gamma rays is shorter than the wavelength of radio waves. (1)

c) i) Name **one** electromagnetic wave **not named** in the above passage.

ii) State **one** practical use of the electromagnetic wave you have named in **(c)**(i). (2)

d) Calculate the frequency of the radio waves transmitted on a wavelength of 1500 m. Write down the formula that you use and show your working. (3)

(WJEC, 1995)

8 a) Radioactive elements can give out three types of radiation, α (alpha), β (beta) and γ (gamma).

Below are some details about these radiations.

Radiation	α	β	γ
Thickness of metal that stops radiation	very thin metal foil	a few millimetres of metal	4 or 5 centimetres of lead
Distance radiation can travel in air	a few centimetres	a few metres	a few kilometres

From the information given in the table, suggest how you could store safely a radioactive source which emits β radiation. (1)

b) Below is a diagram showing how the thickness of kitchen foil can be tested and controlled in a factory.

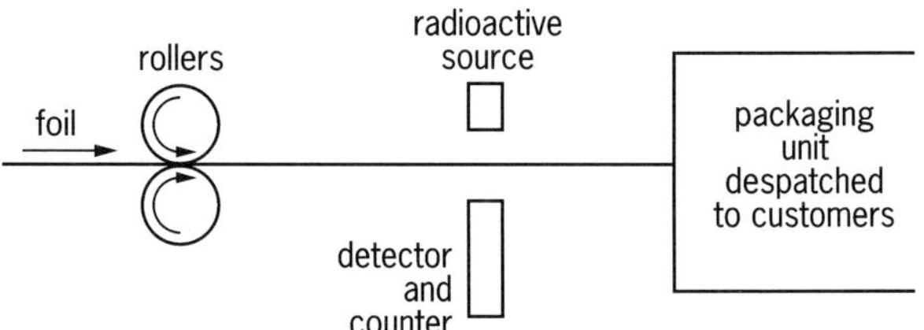

i) β particles are used in the machine. Why would α particles be unsuitable?

ii) Why could γ rays **not** be used? (2)

c) The readings detected by the counter over a period of 20 seconds are given at the foot of the page.

i) [Copy the table at the foot of the page and] complete the second line.

ii) From the information given, explain exactly what is happening to the thickness of the foil. Give reasons for your answer. (3)

d) A radioactive substance has a half-life of two years.

Date	Activity in counts per second
September 1987	3 200
September	1 600
September 1991	
	200

[Copy and] complete the table above for this substance. (3)

(WJEC)

Time in seconds	0	2	4	6	8	10	12	14	16	18	20
Count in 1 second	0	50	50	50	60	60		70	70		80
Sum of all counts	0	50	100	150	210	270	330	400	470	540	620

Glossary

Absolute zero The lowest temperature (–273 °C) that any substance can reach. At this temperature the molecules or atoms of the substance contain no heat energy.

Acceleration The rate of change of velocity of a body.

Acceleration due to gravity The acceleration of a freely falling body within a gravitational field. Close to the surface of the Earth its value is $10\,m/s^2$.

Activity The average number of nuclei of a radioactive element decaying each second.

Ampere Unit used to measure electric current.

Amplitude The maximum displacement of an oscillation from its rest position.

Atmospheric pressure The pressure exerted on a body by the atmosphere, due to the weight of the atmosphere. At the surface of the Earth atmospheric pressure is $100\,kPa/m^2$.

Atomic number The position of an element in the periodic table of the elements. The atomic number is equivalent to the number of protons in the nucleus of the atom.

Becquerel Unit of activity of a radioactive source. 1 becquerel represents an average of one nucleus decaying each second.

Centripetal force The force that acts towards the centre of the circle in which a body is moving, which keeps the body in circular motion.

Compression The state of anything that is subject to inward-acting (squashing) forces.

Conduction (thermal) The process of transferring heat through a material without any visible change in the motion of the particles of the material.

Conductors Materials that allow the ready transfer of heat by conduction, or of electricity by current flow.

Convection The process of transferring heat by the movement of the fluid (liquid or gas) through which heat is being transferred.

Convection current The continuous transfer of heat by circulation in a fluid. Convection currents are created by changes in the density of the fluid – the warmed fluid expands, and therefore has a lower density than the surrounding fluid. The less dense fluid rises through the denser, cooler fluid, carrying heat with it.

Coulomb The unit representing the amount of charge passing any point in a circuit when a current of 1 ampere flows past that point for 1 second.

Critical angle The angle of incidence at which light undergoes total internal reflection at a boundary between a dense and less dense substance.

Diffraction The spreading of waves as they pass by the edge of an obstacle or through a narrow slit.

Dispersion The phenomenon in which radiation is separated into its constituent wavelengths. Dispersion causes white light to separate into seven colours – red, orange, yellow, green, blue, indigo and violet – which collectively form the spectrum of white light.

Dynamo A device which converts mechanical energy into electrical energy.

Efficiency The ratio of the useful energy obtained from a device compared with the amount of energy put into the device to operate it.

Elastic (behaviour) The property of a material that regains its original shape after some deforming force has been removed, providing the elastic limit of the material has not been exceeded.

Elastic limit The load beyond which a material ceases to show elastic properties and exhibits plastic behaviour.

Electric charge A quantity of unbalanced (positive or negative) electricity.

Electric current The rate at which charge flows through a conductor.

Electrical energy Energy associated with the flow of charge through any part of an electric circuit.

Electrolysis A chemical change (generally decomposition of molecules in an electrolyte) that takes place when current passes through a solution.

Electromagnets Soft iron cores surrounded by coils of wire, which act as magnets when current flows through the coil.

Electromagnetic induction The generation of an induced electric current when a conductor is moved through a magnetic field. The transfer of electrical power from one circuit to another (as in the case of transformers).

Electromagnetic spectrum A continuous arrangement that displays electromagnetic waves in order of their increasing frequency or wavelength.

Electromagnetic waves Transverse waves that consist of electrical and magnetic oscillations at right angles to one another and to the direction of travel.

Equilibrium The situation in which the effects of several forces cancel another in terms of both magnitude and direction, producing zero resultant force. The state of a body at rest, or moving with constant velocity.

Fission The process whereby large unstable atomic nuclei split into two smaller nuclei, releasing energy.

Force multiplier Any machine that during operation converts a small force into a larger force.

Fossil fuels Fuels formed over millions of years by the partial decay of the remains of living things.

Frequency The rate at which some regular disturbance takes place. For a wave this represents the number of complete oscillations per second.

Friction A force caused by contact between two uneven surfaces, which resists the motion of a body.

Galaxy A group of millions of stars, held together by gravity.

Gravitational field strength The gravitational force exerted on a 1 kg mass placed within any gravitational field.

Gravitational potential energy The energy stored in a body that has been raised within the Earth's gravitational field.

Gravity An 'action at a distance' force of attraction between two bodies.

Half-life The time taken for half of the nuclei of a radioactive substance to undergo at least one disintegration (decay).

Heat Thermal energy in the process of being transferred in some way.

Hertz A unit of frequency of vibrations. 1 hertz is equivalent to one oscillation per second.

Hooke's Law Relates to the elastic behaviour of materials – the extension of a material is proportional to the applied load – providing the elastic limit is not exceeded.

Hydraulic systems Systems that transfer forces from place to place using fluids.

Insulators Materials that prevent, or significantly inhibit, the flow of heat, or electricity, through them.

Ions Particles that have excess negative or positive charge.

Ionising radiation Radiation that causes the ionisation of atoms or molecules, leaving them with excess positive or negative charge.

Isotopes Forms of the same element with the same atomic number but different mass numbers. Some elements have only one natural isotope but all have artificially created isotopes.

Joule Unit of energy. 1 joule is the work done when a force of 1 newton moves its point of application through a distance of 1 metre in the direction of the force.

Kilowatt A unit of power equal to 1000 watts, or a rate of energy transfer of 1000 joules per second.

Kilowatt-hour A unit used by electricity supply companies, representing the energy dissipated in one hour by a device with a power of 1 kilowatt.

Kinetic energy Energy associated with the movement of a body.

Longitudinal wave An energy-carrying wave in which the movement of the particles is in line with the direction in which the energy is being transferred.

Magnetic field A space in which forces would act on magnetic poles placed within it.

Mass number The number of particles (protons and neutrons) inside the nucleus of an atom.

Motor A machine that transforms electrical energy into kinetic energy, or ultimately some form of mechanical energy.

Newton The unit of force. 1 newton is the force that gives a 1 kg mass an acceleration of 1 m/s^2.

Non-renewable source A source of energy that is used up faster than it can be replaced.

Nucleon A general term used to describe a particle (proton or neutron) found in the nucleus of an atom.

Ohm The unit of electrical resistance. 1 ohm is the resistance of a sample of conducting material across which a potential difference of 1 volt causes a current of 1 ampere to flow.

Ohm's Law A relationship between the current flowing through a conductor and the potential difference across the ends of the conductor – the current through a conductor is proportional to the potential difference across the ends of that conductor, providing the temperature of the conductor is constant.

Optical fibres Very thin strands of pure optical glass through which light undergoes total internal reflection.

Parallel circuit A circuit in which the current passes through two or more paths, or loops, before rejoining.

Pascal A unit of pressure equivalent to a force of 1 newton acting on 1 m^2.

Pitch The property of a note that determines how 'high' or 'low' it sounds to the listener.

Plastic (behaviour) A property of a material that, when subjected to some distorting force, remains deformed when the distorting force is removed.

Potential difference The difference in electrical potential between two points through which a current is flowing. A potential difference of 1 volt exits between two points if 1 joule of electrical energy is changed into other forms when 1 coulomb of charge passes between the two points.

Potential energy The energy stored in a body due to its position.

Power The rate at which work is done or energy is dissipated in a device.

Pressure The force per unit area acting on a material in such a way that it is tending to change the dimensions of the material.
Primary light colours Red, blue, green. By mixing these colours of light any other colour can be produced. Combining them equally produces white light.
Projectile Any body launched sideways.

Radiation The process of transferring energy by electromagnetic waves. Also (nuclear radiation) emissions of alpha particles, beta particles and gamma rays from radioactive nuclei.
Radioactivity The physical changes (disintegration) that take place inside the nuclei of atoms of radioactive elements, and that result in the emission of (nuclear) radiation.
Reaction An equal and opposite force that arises when a force is applied to some system, such as when pillars are supported by the ground.
Refraction A phenomenon that occurs when a wave passes from one medium into another, causing a change in speed, and, possibly, direction.
Relay A device operated by a low current that may be used to control a second circuit through which a larger current flows.
Renewable source A source of energy that may be used repeatedly.
Resistance A property of materials which resist the flow of current through them to some greater or lesser degree.

Secondary colours Magenta, yellow, cyan. Produced by mixing two primary colours.
Series circuit A circuit in which all devices are connected in one continuous loop through which a common current flows.
Sound energy Energy that has been transformed into some audible form.
Sound wave A longitudinal wave that transfers sound vibrations from place to place.
Spectrum An orderly arrangement of, for example, waves, in which the frequency (or wavelength) changes progressively.
Speed The rate of change of distance with time for a moving body.
Structure A framework of rigid parts that are integrally designed to resist forces that act within the framework.
Strut Part of a structure that is resisting opposing forces that are tending to compress it.
Supernova An exploding star.

Temperature A measure of the relative hotness of bodies.
Tension The state of anything that is subject to outward-acting (stretching) forces.
Terminal velocity The maximum velocity of a freely falling body in a fluid when the opposing forces are equal in magnitude and opposite in direction.
Thermal energy Energy associated with heating effects.
Tie Part of a structure that is resisting opposing forces that place it under tension.
Total internal reflection A phenomenon that occurs when radiation travelling from a dense medium to a less dense medium strikes the boundary at an angle equal to or exceeding the critical angle for the material. The radiation is completely reflected into the denser medium.
Transformer A device that transfers the energy of an alternating current in the primary coil to a secondary coil through electromagnetic induction. Transformers may be step-up transformers, producing a higher output voltage than that which is input, or step-down transformers, which convert a higher input voltage to a lower output voltage.
Transverse wave A wave in which the oscillations are at right angles to the direction in which the wave travels.

Ultrasound Sound waves with frequencies beyond the upper limit of human hearing.

Velocity The rate of change of displacement of a moving body (in terms of both distance and direction) with time.
Voltage The value of the potential difference between two points (e.g. the terminals of a cell).
Volt The unit of potential difference. A potential difference of 1 volt exists between two points when 1 joule of work is done in transferring 1 coulomb of charge between the two points. Alternatively, a potential difference of 1 volt exists between two points when 1 ampere of current dissipates 1 watt of power on passing between the two points.

Watt Unit of power equal to a rate of energy transfer (or work done) of 1 joule per second.
Wave equation The relation *speed* = *frequency* × *wavelength* which applies to all forms of wave motion.
Wavelength The distance between two successive points on a wave that are at the same stage of oscillation, i.e. in terms of their direction and displacement from their mean position.
Weight The gravitational force acting on a body.
Work The energy transferred in any system where a force causes movement. The work done is the product of the force and the distance moved by its point of application along the line in which the force acts.

Index